A.D.

150   Ptolemy recognizes spherical shape of earth and orbits of planets, and draws maps; Hipparchus constructs first table of trigonometric rates.

250   Diophantus writes *Arithmetic,* using symbols for the variables.

825   Al-Khwarizmi (Arab) writes first algebra book and introduces Hindu numerals with place value.

1150   Bhaskara (Hindu) proposes a system of multiplication.

1200   Fibonacci (Italian) writes *Liber Quadratorum,* summarizing arithmetic and solutions of equations.

1250   Contest in Norman court for solving $x^3 + 2x^2 + 10x = 0$.

1340   Planudes (Greek monk) invents long-division algorithm.

1400   First mathematics book printed: Euclid's *Elements* (1482); Columbus majors in mathematics and science at University of Pavia; first mathematics book using "+" and "−" appears (1489). Pacioli writes first book with modern method of multiplication (1494).

1500   Copernicus and Brahe extend knowledge of astronomy.

1550   Cardan (Italian) solves cubic equations; Robert Recorde (English) writes arithmetic texts; Gregorian calendar established (1582); Stevin (Belgian) introduces decimal fractions (1585).

1600   Science explodes as result of men such as Galileo and Kepler and measuring instruments such as thermometer (1597), telescope (1609), barometer (1643), microscope (1650); Napier (English) invents logarithms (1614); Descartes (French) invents analytical geometry.

1650   Pascal (French) invents calculating machine, extends projective geometry, and studies probability; Fermat (French) extends theory of numbers.

1700   Euler (Swiss), an expert in analysis of problems, Gauss (German), one of the three top mathematicians of all time, extends many fields—especially number theory.

1800   Lobachevski (Russian), Bolyai (Hungarian), and Reimann (German) develop non-euclidean geometry; Galois (French) establishes group theory; Abel (Norwegian) proves binominal expansion; Peano (Italian) establishes postulates for natural number system; Boole (English) invents the algebra of symbolic logic.

1900   Cantor (Dane) invents the theory of sets and ways to deal with infinities; Poincaré (French) creates ideas in differential equations and function theory; Hilbert (German) establishes a new structure for geometry; Einstein (German) creates the theory of relativity; Von Neumann (Hungarian) invents the theory of games and develops computer science.

Guidelines
for
Teaching
Mathematics

DONOVAN A. JOHNSON
University of Minnesota

GERALD R. RISING
State University of New York at Buffalo

Guidelines
for
Teaching
Mathematics

Wadsworth Publishing Company, Inc.
Belmont, California

4 5 6 7 8 9 10—74 73 72 71

L. C. Cat. Card No.: 67–17698

Printed in the United States of America

preface

This book deals with the many ways and requirements of teaching mathematics. It presents the basic techniques and materials which every mathematics teacher must have and know about in order to be a successful teacher. Certainly, teaching mathematics is a complex task. For it involves not only mathematics, methods, and materials, but it involves human beings, each of whom has physical, intellectual, and emotional reactions.

When mathematics teachers are asked what their greatest difficulty is, they invariably name either motivation, individual differences, or discipline. These problems cannot be solved by textbooks. They must be faced and dealt with by the teacher alone. But when mathematics is properly taught, many of these teacher problems are resolved. Hence, in this book we emphasize a method of pedagogy which is designed to make learning and teaching mathematics a successful adventure.

As mathematics teachers, we face a multitude of decisions every day. We must decide what to teach, how to teach it, and how much emphasis to give certain ideas. We must decide what materials and activities are appropriate for students with different interests, abilities, and goals. In addition, we have to be able to evaluate the effectiveness of our own instruction.

To be a successful mathematics teacher, you must have a broad background in mathematics and you must be able to communicate your knowledge to students. You must use enlightened examples, appropriate anecdotes, and challenging activities. Your students must be drawn into the cooperative exploration of new ideas. Importantly, your students must be instilled with some of your own love of teaching, as well as of mathematics itself.

In this book, we attempt to provide a framework on which the mathematics teacher can build his teaching activities. First, we outline the directions and values of teaching through a discussion of goals and objectives and survey the current situation in relation to the school mathematics curricula. Next, we present some strategies for dealing with the content. Following this, specific techniques and examples are given for attaining the various goals of instruction. These techniques include laboratory lessons, learning games, and ways of stimulating creativity. One section is devoted to the role of different instructional materials, and another deals with specific classroom problems, such as programs for the gifted and for the slow learner. Finally, we discuss important methods of evaluating student achievement and evaluating the effectiveness of instruction.

The mathematics teacher must adapt our suggestions to his individual interests, personality, and methods. He must supplement and, at the same time, temper our point of view with his own. The teacher must always utilize additional resources—the library, the audio-visual department, local teachers and supervisors—whenever appropriate and possible.

In writing this text, we have been concerned with the balance between discussions of content and pedagogy. There are many fine books that discuss the specifics of mathematical content, but there are few that concern themselves with problems of presentation of that content. While both content and pedagogy are important, we emphasize the latter here in an attempt to fill in the gap. A glance at the text will show the reader that there is a great deal of mathematical content in these pages; here, however, the content provides the examples for pedagogical principles, rather than the basis for the presentation. Therefore, we strongly recommend that the reader supplement the study of this text with intensive study of several of the fine modern secondary school texts and teachers' manuals. Such activity will bring into sharper focus our more general discussion.

To all these demands, we add one humble request. What has gone into these pages is the result of two people drawing on their experiences and those of their many friends and co-workers. In many ways, therefore, we think of this book as a continuing discussion. We urge you to communicate to us, or to our publisher, your reactions to this book, your experience with it in the classroom, and your personal recommendations for future revisions. You may be assured that such communications will be gratefully received.

Finally, we offer our best wishes for success in the very important task you have accepted—teaching mathematics.

D. A. J.

G. R. R.

contents

Guidelines
for
Teaching
Mathematics

part one

mathematics and mathematics education today

1

introduction to the teaching of mathematics

The teaching of mathematics is a challenging, exciting adventure. It has its dangers, successes, discouragements, and delights. Its difficulties and satisfactions are derived from the subject matter, the student, and the classroom situation. The real satisfaction of teaching mathematics comes from the fact that we are teaching the subject we enjoy, to individuals who are important, in a way that we find effective.

As mathematics teachers we should be grateful for the opportunity to work in a professional field where the scope and pace of change are truly astounding. We should enjoy the opportunity to guide the learning of our future scientists and citizens. Also, we should be excited about teaching a subject that is as remarkable as mathematics is. But, at the same time, we should be disappointed with the limited learning that takes place amid the daily classroom stresses. It is the purpose of this book to offer numerous ways and means of making mathematics instruction more effective.

THE TEACHING PROCESS

Learning how to be an effective teacher is complex—even more difficult than learning mathematics, complex as that sometimes is. The flow chart below illustrates the many factors involved in the teaching of mathematical ideas. These aspects will be discussed in depth in the later chapters of this book.

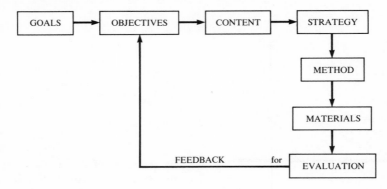

Fig. 1–1

As the chart shows, the teaching program begins with the teacher's attempt to relate the general *goals* of education (preparing for citizenship, preparing for college, advancing our society, establishing personal values) to the role of mathematics in the school. To attain these general goals, more specific *objectives* of mathematics instruction should be carefully established. These more specific objectives suggest what the learners should do (skills), know (concepts), and feel (attitudes). They direct us to the skills, concepts, and attitudes to be developed. The objectives should be stated in terms of desired student behavior, for it is the student's behavior which will finally indicate his achievement of these objectives.

The next step is selection of appropriate *content:* the specific mathematical ideas, structures, and exercises that are best suited to the attainment of the objectives. For the presentation of this content, appropriate *strategy* is selected. For example, in teaching how to calculate the square root of a number, should one use the estimation-division method or the traditional algorithm?

The *method* of instruction that is appropriate is itself a function of the strategy involved. This method in turn determines the *materials* we use as part of the instructional process.

When the instructional process is complete, the progress of the learner must be measured. The results are *evaluated* so that the instructor can determine which objectives have been attained and which need more work. On the basis of the evaluation, the next cycle can be planned.

THE POWER OF MATHEMATICS

Mathematics is a creation of the human mind, concerned primarily with ideas, processes, and reasoning. Thus, mathematics is much more than arithmetic, the science of numbers and computation; more than algebra, the language of symbols and relations; more than geometry, the study of shapes and sizes and space. It is greater than numerical trigonometry, which measures distances to stars and analyzes oscillations. It encompasses more than statistics, the science of interpreting data and graphs; more than calculus, the study of change, infinity, and limits.

Primarily, *mathematics is a way of thinking,* a way of organizing a logical proof. It can be used to determine whether or not an idea is true or at least whether it is probably true. As a way of thinking, it is used to solve all kinds of problems in the sciences, government, and industry. As a way of reasoning, it gives us insight into the power of the human mind and becomes a challenge to intellectual curiosity.

Mathematics is also a language, a language that uses carefully defined terms and concise symbolic representations, which add precision to communication. It is a language that works with ideograms, symbols for ideas, rather than phonograms, symbols for sounds. The equation $3 + 5 = 8$ means the same to a Swede, a Russian, or a Japanese, no matter how he reads it. Furthermore, because of their clarity and precision, ideograms serve as mental laborsaving devices. They enable us to perform computations, solve problems, and complete proofs that would be difficult if not impossible in any natural language. These ideograms make algorithms and manipulations accurate and efficient.

Mathematics is an organized structure of knowledge in which each proposition is deduced logically from previously proved propositions or assumptions. The structures of mathematics, somewhat like the structures of philosophy and theology, are logical structures that begin with certain undefined terms. These undefined primitive terms, such as point, line, and plane in geometry, are used to describe essential ideas. In a sense, these terms are defined by the system. Certain assumptions—called axioms, postulates, properties, or laws—are made about these ideas or operations. And, finally, these terms and assumptions are used to prove theorems. When one understands this basic organization of mathematical structures, he can more readily study new mathematical structures.

Mathematics is also the study of patterns—that is, of any kind of regularity in form or idea. Radio waves, molecular structures, orbits of celestial bodies, and the shape of a bee's cell—all have patterns that can be classified mathematically.

Mathematics is finally an art. As in any other art, beauty in mathematics consists in order and inner harmony. The mathematician tries to express a maximum number of ideas and relations with the greatest economy of means. The beauty of mathematics can be found in the process whereby a chaos of isolated facts is transformed into a logical order. The exploration of new ideas, the invention of new mathematical structures, is a challenge to the creativeness, the imagination, and the intuition of the mathematician.

What is the relationship of mathematics to the other sciences? Not only its content but also its method is different. The method of the physical sciences, such as physics, chemistry, and biology, is that of induction or experimentation. Induction is a method of reasoning from the particular to the general. A physicist, for example, may be interested in finding out the effect of tension upon a bar. To do this he experiments with large numbers of metal bars and observes the behavior of the bars.

On the other hand, a mathematician will not accept a generalization based only on observation. A mathematician requires proof based upon a logical scheme of deduction before he will accept a generalization as true. The mathematician is concerned with making generalizations that will apply to *all* cases, and since he cannot possibly observe all cases, he has to find another way out of the dilemma. Hence, he uses the method of *deductive* reasoning. From certain axioms that characterize his system, he sets out to prove that the conclusion he wants is true (or sometimes false). Once he has done this, he has confidence that his deduction is always true when the conditions fit his axiom schema. Therein lies the power of mathematics.

THE ART OF TEACHING MATHEMATICS

Teaching, as the great teacher William Lyon Phelps says in his auto-biography, is "an art so great and so difficult to master that a man or a woman can spend a long life at it, without realizing much more than his limitations and mistakes, and his distance from the ideal." Ideally, as Polya points out, the teacher's "art" requires the acting of drama, the repetitions and variations of music, the elegance of poetry, and the originality of a painting. How can a mathematics teacher acquire this art? How does he go about this task of becoming a truly creative teacher?

BACKGROUND REQUIRED OF A MATHEMATICS TEACHER

Teaching mathematics involves more than knowing and enjoying the subject. The mathematics teacher must motivate his students, he must communicate his knowledge to them, and he must guide them to discover ideas. Methods and materials serve as links between the knowledge of subject matter, principles of psychology, and actual practice in the class-room. Creative teaching requires new materials and thoughtful activities that have usually been neglected in the mathematics classroom.

Mathematics, with its abstract symbolism, its logical structures, its wide application, has unique learning problems. At one extreme, it involves learning simple skills, calculation, facts, and procedures where memory and practice are most essential. At the other extreme—the analysis of a prob-lem, the proof of a theorem, the application of a generalization, the building of a mathematical structure—it requires a high level of creative thinking. Thus, the teacher of mathematics must know when and what concepts to teach, when and why students are having difficulty, how to make concepts meaningful, when and how to practice skills, and how to stimulate productive thinking. The current emphasis on discovery, problem solving, and attitudes poses problems of adaptability and flexibility in the classroom—problems that require far greater skill than that required for the usual day-to-day lecture-recitation presentation.

Today the spirit of innovation is perhaps the outstanding characteristic of mathematics education. Revolutionary changes in school mathematics are altering traditional content, practices, classroom organization, and even basic views of learning. Thus, the mathematics teacher of today needs a background in calculus, number theory, foundations, linear algebra, non-euclidean geometry, set theory, probability, and statistics. More than this, he must be able to read mathematical literature so that he continues to learn mathematics independently and to evaluate and, when desirable, incorporate new developments. He must be up-to-date in his mathematical language, symbolism, and structures for his classroom presentations. He should find pleasure in reading mathematics books and in presenting newly discovered mathematical ideas to his students when the ideas are appropriate. (In this connection, Professor Arnold Ross of Ohio State University suggests that the beginning teacher teaches all he knows and more; the experienced teacher teaches all he knows; but the master teacher selects, from what he knows, material appropriate to his students.) Finally, the creative teacher must motivate his students, he must communicate his knowledge to them, and he must—partly through the use of instructional aids—guide them to discover ideas.

The instructional aids currently available for the mathematics teacher have multiplied tremendously in recent years. We now have programmed texts and teaching machines, computers, supplementary books and pamphlets, charts, films, filmstrips, models, overhead projectuals, games, exhibits, chalkboard devices, and construction materials such as pegboard, cardboard, plastic, balsa strips, and modeling clay. The creative teacher needs to know what materials are available and how to use these materials to enrich the learning of mathematical ideas.

Those who say that a mastery of mathematics is the only requirement for successful mathematics teaching fail to recognize that human beings are even more complex, more delicate, and more intricate than mathematics. They fail to recognize that the explosion of knowledge in psychology, curriculum development, and evaluation is relevant to the classroom situation. As a result of these new developments, the mathematics teacher must be prepared to do considerably more than just "teach his subject." He must select appropriate goals for instruction of individual units and plan a variety of lessons and units to achieve these goals. He must stimulate the learning of mathematics—by developing desirable attitudes and appreciations of mathematics and by teaching the student how to study mathematics independently. He must guide the student to discover mathematical concepts; develop ability to solve mathematical problems; and build understanding, accuracy, and efficiency in computational skills. He must evaluate the student's achievement of concepts, skills, and problem solving. In addition, he must provide a program of enrichment and acceleration for gifted students and plan an effective program for the slow learner; evaluate new curriculum proposals; procure, evaluate, and use new instructional aids; find new applications, new ideas, and new materials; and—in all of his activities—constantly evaluate his own instruction.

VARIETIES OF MATHEMATICS LESSONS

Too often, instruction in mathematics classrooms is barren and uninspiring: first of all, homework is discussed; then the teacher demonstrates a new procedure or theorem; then he assigns the next exercises—and class is dismissed. Such a procedure does little justice to the exciting content, varied instructional aids, and emphasis on student participation of mathematics today. Besides, there are many more interesting and rewarding procedures. Some of these procedures (which will be discussed in detail in subsequent chapters) are listed and discussed briefly here. These lesson types, however, are not mutually exclusive; most good lessons, in fact, contain several types.

1. *Laboratory lessons*. In these lessons pupils make measurements (often using simple equipment, such as rulers and compasses), collect data by experimentation or surveys, make drawings and models, make computation devices, and perform experiments with kits such as the Probability Kit. These can be true discovery lessons, and teachers who have used them are most enthusiastic about the results.

2. *Audio-visual presentations*. The overhead projector is a new and versatile device for which the teacher can now order a great number of commercial projectuals as well as develop equally useful homemade projectuals. There are new films such as *Sets, Crows, and Infinity; Possibly So, Pythagoras;* and *Donald in Mathemagic Land* that provide original and unique learning aids. Tape recorders and film loops provide opportunities to individualize instruction. Even the use of colored chalk can enliven presentations.

3. *Games*. Many of the commercial games available or those prepared in the classroom can promote the learning of mathematics in an interesting and entertaining way.

4. *Student-directed class discussions*. Student demonstrations, reports on enrichment topics, or even the teaching of a regular lesson can be a wholesome experience for the student demonstrator as well as the class.

5. *Discovery lessons*. The teacher can promote student discovery mainly by asking good questions and posing problems. Processes, properties, and assumptions are developed rather than crammed into the students.

6. *Small-group instruction*. Although materials aren't as plentiful for teaching mathematics as they are for the teaching of reading, it is just as appropriate to have mathematics groups as reading groups. Possibly some of the better students can help to conduct these small groups; as they do so, they will learn mathematics, they will learn to communicate, and they will get experience in a leadership role.

7. *Enrichment lessons*. There are many wonderful and exciting mathematical ideas for discussion that are not in the regular text—topics such as historical incidents, applications, space travel, game theory. We need to

present these ideas to our young people, for the mathematics classroom might be the only place where the students will encounter such topics.

8. *Communication lessons.* These are special lessons on communication and learning how to learn mathematics. They teach listening, reading, writing, and speaking correctly about mathematical ideas.

9. *Individualized instruction.* Here each student investigates an idea independently. Remedial teaching, using programmed units or guide sheets, is helpful. A laboratory or conference room adds to the effectiveness of this type of lesson.

10. *Creative learning lessons.* Writing original problems, solving problems, establishing theorems with original proofs, discovering and stating relationships in one's own language, drawing an original design are all beginning experiences in creative thinking. Communicating mathematical ideas in an original fashion—through demonstrations, proofs, exhibits, poems, or research projects—gives further opportunity for originality. The development of a new numeration system, the building of an original model, or the discovery of a new idea or a new application of mathematics—all illustrate creative work at a high level.

11. *Use of the computer.* Although computers are not generally available in schools today, in the near future they will be involved in mathematics instruction in many ways. They can be used as aids in problem solving (with students asked to prepare flow charts or write programs). They may be used as an instructional aid in learning mathematical ideas and as mediators in individualized instruction (with a computer terminal providing a lesson and a computer recording pupil responses).

All of these types of lessons have advantages and disadvantages. Particular lessons and even particular subjects lend themselves best to certain styles of presentation. For example, the need to "take apart" a diagram makes the overhead projector a useful tool for teaching congruency; stick models are especially appropriate to instruction in solid geometry; films can display trigonometry's continuous functions, which are so difficult to develop by other means. But the right choice still remains a major problem for the teacher. Industry refers to the organization of such choices as *systems development.* Systems development is the coordination of materials, personnel, and procedures to meet a given goal in the most effective way. For mathematics instruction this means that each unit, each lesson, must be programmed to use the right resource and the right teaching technique at the appropriate time.

2

the goals and objectives of mathematics education

In the construction of a new building, the architect does not design the building until he decides what effect he wishes to achieve; the builder does not select his materials until he knows what his blueprints specify; and the carpenter does not select a tool until he knows what operation he intends to perform. When the building is complete, it is considered acceptable only if it satisfies the specifications established before it was built. In a similar way we must select the mathematics program for the effect we wish to attain. We must select materials that are appropriate for the program designed, and we must use the proper tools for the activity involved. Too often in the past teachers have discussed the relative merits of a new mathematics text, an instructional aid, or a teaching method without specifying just what goals they hoped to achieve with the materials being used.

If we do not know what our goals are, how can we evaluate a learner's progress or an experimental program or a new program? Only when we know where we want to go do we have a sound basis for selecting appropriate material, content, or instructional methods. Only when we know what progress has been made in attaining these goals can we evaluate the effectiveness of our instruction.

What, then, are appropriate goals for mathematics instruction? What mathematics is needed to attain these goals? What kind of student should strive to attain these goals? Finally, what behavior indicates that a student has attained these goals? Let us discuss these questions and try to answer them.

THE SELECTION OF GOALS

In selecting appropriate goals for mathematics instruction, we must take into account not only the needs of society but also the mathematical needs of our students. Almost every committee or commission that has worked on revising the mathematics curriculum has stated certain basic mathematical needs. The following list summarizes these needs:

1. The student needs to know how mathematics contributes to his understanding of natural phenomena.

2. He needs to understand how he can use mathematical methods to investigate, interpret, and make decisions in human affairs.

3. He needs to understand how mathematics, as a science and as an art, contributes to our cultural heritage.

4. He needs to prepare for a vocation in which he utilizes mathematics as a producer and consumer of products, services, and art.

5. He needs to learn to communicate mathematical ideas correctly and clearly to others. Communication is a tool basic to all civilizations.

While it is not a specific mathematics objective, the teacher should not lose sight of the fact that the student needs to understand human relationships and to develop a personal value scale which respects the rights, needs, and achievements of others.

Mathematics instruction today must be broader and more inclusive than in the past if it is to meet the increasing demands being made on the mathematical competence of our students. The mathematics program must do more than develop the basic skills and techniques, although the broader goals of mathematics will include these skills and techniques. In other words, it must develop more than vocabulary, facts, and principles; more than the ability to analyze a problem situation; more than an understanding of the logical structure of mathematics. The mathematics program must, in addition, develop students who can use the logic of mathematics to distinguish fact from opinion, relevant from irrelevant material, and experimental results from proven theorems. This program must stimulate curiosity, so that the student will enjoy exploring new ideas and creating mathematics which is new for him even though it has been discovered by others. It must develop the reading skill, motivations, and study habits essential for independent learning of mathematics. In short, the mathematics program must produce students who know how to learn mathematics, enjoy learning mathematics, and are motivated to continue their learning.

STATEMENT OF GOALS IN BEHAVIORAL TERMS

Technically, a goal of instruction should be a statement of what the learner is to be like when he has successfully completed a learning experience. This is a description of a *pattern of behavior* which we want the learner to be able to demonstrate when he has successfully attained a goal of instruction. These behavioral statements of goals are usually called *objectives*.

When we state goals, we often use general words such as *to know, to understand, to appreciate.* More meaningful and specific are the words *to write, to identify, to solve, to state, to list, to differentiate.* These words describe what the learner does to demonstrate that he knows or understands a given idea. As we state goals, we should, then, try to indicate specifically *what the learner does* when he has achieved this goal.

If we accept the idea that mathematics instruction can attain worthy goals in relation to the needs of society and the needs of youth, what are some of these goals? The goals stated below are expressed behaviorally and arranged to form a hierarchy of performance, illustrating achievement at increasingly high levels. Each goal will be discussed at greater length in the second part of this book.

A. The student knows and understands concepts such as mathematical processes, facts, or principles (see Chapter 5).
   1. He recognizes a statement, example, or definition. *Which one of the following is a picture of a rectangle?*
   2. He recalls a fact, term, or symbol. *Draw a picture of a rectangle.*
   3. He states an idea in new terminology. *Write this open sentence in words: $A = LW$.*
   4. He differentiates between the properties of numbers, ideas, or sets. *What is the difference between a square and a rectangle?*
   5. He identifies a logical implication of the idea. *How is the area of a parallelogram related to the area of a rectangle?*
   6. He applies the knowledge to a new situation. *What is the surface area of this box?*
   7. He extends the idea to discover a new generalization. *What is the formula for the surface area of a cube?*
   8. He verifies a generalization with a proof. *How can we prove that the area of a triangle is ½bh?*
   9. He invents a new extension of the idea. *What is the formula for the area of a rectangle if the unit of area is an equilateral triangle?*

B. The student understands the logical structure of mathematics and the nature of proof (see Chapter 6).
   1. He identifies the primitive terms or basic assumptions. *What do we assume to be an element of a set?*
   2. He states definitions of basic terms. *What is a number?*
   3. He can state the basic requirements of a mathematical system. *Is the real-number system closed with respect to addition?*
   4. He can use the assumptions and definitions to prove theorems.

Prove that the product of two negative numbers is a positive number.

5. He can build a new mathematical structure based on a set of elements and binary operations. *Show that the set of rational numbers is closed under multiplication.*

C. The student performs computations with understanding, accuracy, and efficiency (see Chapter 7).

1. He is sometimes correct in his computation and probably uses crutches.
2. He performs the computation correctly by recording a memorized fact.
3. He performs the computation by using a known fact that is related to the problem.
4. He performs the computation efficiently by employing a short cut.
5. He illustrates the meaning of a computational process; for instance, he relates addition to jumps on the number line.
6. He identifies the properties of a computational process such as closure.
7. He estimates results and checks the accuracy of his computations.
8. He justifies each step of the algorithm.
9. He relates the algorithm to properties of the operation.
10. He can write a proof of the algorithm.
11. He uses the operation to establish a mathematical structure.
12. He invents a new operation and investigates its properties.

D. The student has the ability to solve problems (see Chapter 8).

1. He identifies the question to be answered in the problem situation.
2. He selects relevant information needed to solve the problem.
3. He relates the problem to analogous situations which supply clues or solutions.
4. He draws a flow diagram of the relationships and processes involved.
5. He finds the answer to the question of the problem.
6. He generalizes the solution to other problems.
7. He applies his knowledge of mathematical concepts and processes to everyday situations.
8. He uses ideas about measurement in a construction project such as building a model.
9. He uses a mathematical tool to solve a problem; for instance, he uses a proportion to prepare a chemical solution.
10. He identifies the role of mathematics in a news statement about, for instance, the probability of an accident.

11. He states a generalization (such as Euler's formula for the edges, vertices, and surfaces of polyhedra) about the pattern in a set of data.

E. The student develops attitudes and appreciations which lead to curiosity, initiative, confidence, and interests (see Chapter 9).

1. He enjoys learning mathematical ideas.
2. He shows confidence in and respect for mathematics courses, the teacher, and current class activities.
3. He spends time completing optional assignments outside of class time.
4. He discusses mathematical ideas outside the classroom.
5. He is curious about new mathematical ideas to the extent that he explores ideas independently.
6. He identifies the role of statistics in guiding discoveries in government, industry, and science.
7. He discusses the role of the computer in changing our society.
8. He recognizes the applications of mathematics in science.
9. He knows how mathematics has contributed to historical events.

F. The student learns how to develop proper methods of learning mathematics and communicating mathematics, and also develops study habits essential for independent progress (see Chapter 10).

1. He listens carefully to class discussions.
2. He has a vocabulary of necessary mathematical terms and symbols.
3. He uses correct terms when he participates in class discussions.
4. He reads mathematical material with understanding.
5. He writes an organized solution to a problem.
6. He writes precise definitions and identifies conditions.
7. He completes his assignments correctly and on time.
8. He has facility in using his text as a source of information and knows how to find information outside his text.
9. He plans his time, materials, and place for study.
10. He asks questions of himself and others when difficulties cannot be resolved independently.

In addition to specific statements about the terminal behavior expected of the learner, we need to state the *conditions* under which the learner will demonstrate his mastery. Consider the statement "to be able to recognize the graph of an equation." Although this statement does name a terminal act, there are still some shortcomings in the statement. What kinds of graphs will the learner be expected to recognize? Is it important that the graph have certain qualities such as a labeled scale? Will the learner be given the equation to graph or will he be expected to identify the proper equation from the graph? Therefore, instead of simply saying "to be able to graph an equation," we can improve our communication by saying: "Given a linear equation with two variables, the learner must be able to find a set of ordered pairs of the solution set, label a set of axes, plot the points located by the ordered pairs, and draw the required line." When making specific statements about conditions, we should also consider what problems, materials, and time will be available to the learner. May he use a book, a slide rule, a table of logarithms, and a formula? Under what conditions is he expected to perform—on a test, in the science class, on his homework?

After we have described what we want the learner to be able to do, we should indicate how well we want him to do it. Hence, we need to state the *criterion* of acceptable performance. If we can specify a minimum acceptable performance for each goal, we will have a basis for determining whether or not a program is successful.

One criterion may be a *time limit*. We may specify, for instance, "The learner must be able to perform 30 additions in 5 minutes." Or we may want him to demonstrate his understanding of each step: "The learner must be able to justify each step in a long-division operation." Another specification may be the minimum number of *correct responses* in a given situation: "The learner must correctly identify the solution sets of at least 15 out of 20 linear equations." A more important specification—more than asking for a response that requires only paper and pencil—is that the learner should be able to apply what he has learned to new situations.

The goals and procedures outlined above set the tone for your course, give the student a sense of direction, and provide him with the knowledge of what is expected of him and what the future holds for him. In this way learning mathematics becomes for him a worthwhile activity.

LEARNING EXERCISES

1. Formulate an answer to the student who asks, "Why do I need to study geometry?"
2. Trace the history of objectives for mathematics instruction.
3. State a principle which you expect to teach. State behavorial objectives for this principle. Determine the level of mastery for each of these objectives. State conditions and criteria for evaluating your students' responses.
4. What do you think should be the mathematical competence of "the educated man"?
5. What do you think should be the mathematical competence of the bottom 25 percent of the high school seniors?
6. State the goals of a mathematics course. State behavorial objectives for each goal.
7. State the goals for a study of this text. State behavorial objectives for each goal.
8. What major events during the past ten years have been largely dependent on mathematical ideas?

3

the new school mathematics

Man was early confronted with four questions that led to the beginning of mathematics: (1) How many are there? (2) When did it happen? (3) Where did it occur? (4) How much of it is there? The first question required a number or counting system; the second, a notion of time; the third, a method of mapping; and the fourth, devices and units of measure. These are still basic questions that are asked and must be answered by mathematics. However, mathematics has been extended far beyond these questions. Today it is answering questions such as (1) Why is this true? (2) How likely is this to happen? (3) What is the best decision? (4) Is this possible? To answer these questions mathematics has been extended to fields such as symbolic logic, probability, game theory, and computer programming.

FACTORS CAUSING A CHANGE IN SCHOOL MATHEMATICS

1. *New mathematics have been created.* Mathematics is a dynamic, exploding field of knowledge, and its exponential growth is evident in the quantity as well as the quality of recent mathematics. As an example of the increased rate of development of

mathematics, it is fascinating to note that during the past decade as much new mathematics was developed as was developed in all previous history!

2. *New uses for mathematics have been discovered.* As new mathematical ideas have been created, mathematics has proved of further use to the sciences, the humanities, and even to the arts. Psychologists are using mathematics to build learning models; social sciences are using probability and game theory to study politics, crime, and economics; even linguists are using mathematical analysis to study language and literature. One of the most dramatic examples of applied mathematics is in the creation and development of the electronic computer (see Chapter 19 for a discussion of its use in the school). Computers are now used to control space ships, plot political strategy, compose music, and instruct students.

3. *Our scientific society needs greater numbers of persons with high mathematical competence.* More mathematics must be taught to more students, so that these students will be able to transfer their mathematical knowledge to a variety of situations. In addition, more than ever before, basic education must provide for the continuation of learning after the person has left school.

4. *New knowledge about how children learn mathematical ideas has been discovered in recent years.* In order to attain society's new demands for mathematical competence, research has provided new information on the process of learning. We know that students can learn complex mathematical ideas quickly when they are given the opportunity to participate in appropriate learning activities, and that young children can comprehend complex ideas if these ideas are communicated in meaningful, original ways. Our new concept of the learning processes stresses the importance of understanding, with a special emphasis on building understanding through individual discovery. Numerous teaching aids have been prepared to facilitate and increase discovery activities.

5. *Increased financial support of experimental projects by private foundations and the federal government has stimulated innovations.* Financial support has made it possible to organize writing teams, test new materials, and provide the profession with information concerning the new curricula. Federal support through the National Science Foundation, the National Defense Education Act, the Elementary and Secondary Education Act, and many others has been the most powerful vector promoting change.

6. *Probably one of the greatest factors in creating a need for new mathematics was the lack of success of traditional content and method.* Students attained a low level of competence in skills and had little understanding of what they were doing. Not only that, but they usually came out of mathematics classes with a dislike for mathematics. When mathematics becomes a grind and a distasteful activity lacking intellectual flavor, then retention and application are minimal. Our new knowledge of principles of learning has shown us the importance of *understanding*. Since one of the ways of building understanding is through *individual discovery,* this is the type of learning emphasized.

SOME ASPECTS OF THE NEW SCHOOL MATHEMATICS

The new topics in today's school mathematics include numeration systems, sets, mathematical structures, vectors, matrices, linear programming, probability, statistics, symbolic logic, non-euclidean geometry, transformations, and computer programming. Most of these topics originated during the past hundred years. Others represent extensions of old fields with new ideas and new applications. For example, the binary numeration system was invented by Leibnitz in the seventeenth century. Little attention was given to this "impractical" idea until the invention of the electronic computer, which requires binary numerals for its operation. Galileo had used the idea of a one-to-one correspondence, but George Cantor applied this tool in the development of set theory and the study of infinity.

Probably the most significant aspect of the past century has been the attention given to mathematical structures. Through the development of non-euclidean geometries, by Lobachevski and Bolyai about 1830, mathematicians could accept assumptions that were independent of physical representation. The mathematician was now free to use his imagination in creating new "arithmetics," "algebras," and "geometries." These new structures might be concerned with a finite or an infinite number of elements. George Boole (1815–1864) established a symbolism for logical deductions, and this Boolean algebra provided the necessary tools for programming logic into circuits in the computer. David Hilbert (1862–1943) established a new foundation for the structure of euclidean geometry which had itself been used as a model structure for centuries. Giuseppe Peano (1858–1932) stated basic assumptions for arithmetic and built a new structure for the counting number system.

Group theory, originated by Galois, has been called the supreme structure of mathematical abstraction. A mathematical group is the basic structure for many of the branches and topics of mathematics such as number systems, transformations, vectors, matrices, and sets.

One of the major new fields of mathematics of this generation is the theory of games, developed by John von Neumann (1903–1957). This theory treats laws of strategy not only in games but in business, government, and international affairs. Today another field of great activity is computer programming. Using numerical analysis, probability and game theory, symbolic logic and binary numerals, the computer is building a new world of automation, prosperity, and leisure.

The most obvious mark of new mathematics programs is the inclusion of new topics such as those enumerated above. As an illustration of how a new topic unifies and clarifies mathematics, consider the topic of sets. A set is described as a collection of objects, ideas, or symbols. Sets are used to give meaning to the idea of number and operations such as addition. Sets are used to designate the roots of equations, to describe geometric figures, to define basic operations.

An angle is defined as a set of points. Likewise, a graph is a set of points. The integers are a subset of the rational numbers. Probability is described in terms of sets of events, and functions are defined as sets of ordered pairs. Even deductions are illustrated by the intersections of sets. And set-builder notation such as $\{(x,y): x^2 + y^2 = r^2\}$ becomes a means of defining terms such as a circle.

THE NEW CONTENT OF SECONDARY SCHOOL MATHEMATICS

As a result of the introduction of new content, some secondary-school courses have changed drastically. The seventh- and eighth-grade course is no longer devoted merely to applications of arithmetic. These courses now include numeration systems, sets, plane and space geometry, equations, finite systems, number systems, and probability as well as new treatments of whole numbers, fractions, decimals, percent, measurement, and graphing. Ninth-grade algebra continues to include the classical topics of algebra (directed numbers, graphs of equations, systems of equations, factoring, quadratics, and radicals) but also introduces proof, emphasizes number systems, and includes inequalities.

Tenth-grade geometry, no longer merely plane geometry, contains coordinate geometry and solid geometry. However, geometry continues to be the most criticized course in secondary mathematics. Because all mathematics courses now emphasize proof and mathematical systems, geometry has lost its significance as a course on the logic and structure of mathematics. Critics are suggesting a complete revision of the content of geometry. They are suggesting that vectors, transformations, projective geometry, combinatorial topology, convex sets, non-euclidean geometry, and coordinate geometry all be part of the new content.

The eleventh-grade mathematics course tends to be a fusion of intermediate algebra including logarithms and complex numbers with numerical trigonometry. The emphasis is now on functions and structure.

The twelfth grade continues to be a dilemma. Some advocate that it be devoted to the study of calculus; others support analytical geometry. The Commission on Mathematics suggests a semester on probability and statistics, while others propose that it be largely concerned with linear algebra. Other recommendations include a topics course, including brief exposures to number theory, history of mathematics, or limits with short monographs rather than a full text providing the basic source.

With all these additions to the secondary school program, adjustments have to be made. To provide sufficient time for the new areas, some topics have been eliminated and others reduced drastically. The applicational topics (insurance, installment buying, stocks and bonds, taxation, banking, consumer problems) have been largely eliminated. These social applications are curtailed as mathematical topics for several reasons. Since the mathematics involved in these topics is minimal, they are better dealt with in connection with the social and commercial aspects treated in social science and business courses. Furthermore, in these changing times and with the advent of the electronic computer the specific applications of today may be unimportant in the future. The number of drill problems of arithmetic and algebra has also been reduced, as has the number of proofs of geometry and the computational aspects of logarithms and trigonometry.

In addition to the elimination or reduction of topics, traditional topics are now covered in less time, and some topics are introduced earlier in the curriculum. For example, the number line, equations, and geometric figures are treated extensively in the elementary school; and many concepts traditionally taught in the ninth and tenth grades are now introduced in the seventh and eighth grades. Hence, modern senior high school courses already include most of the ideas of traditional college algebra and analytical geometry. Many colleges now offer calculus as a first-semester freshman course, and some high school graduates are given advanced placement as a result of high school studies. The Cambridge Conference goes so far as to suggest that in another generation what is now the first three years of college mathematics will be taught in high school, thus repeating the downward spiral that saw all of college mathematics of a hundred years ago moved to the high school.

THE NEW EMPHASIS

Another hallmark of the new school mathematics is the new language and symbols. Computation is discussed in terms of the concepts of "operation" or "mapping," which involves the "distributive property," "identity element," "closure," and "inverses." Equations are called "open sentences" with "truth sets" of "ordered pairs." In addition, new symbols such as $\cup$, $\cap$, $\not>$, $\Longrightarrow$, and ϵ are common. It is the intent of this new language and symbolism to add precision and clarity to mathematical concepts.

An illustration of the new precision in symbolism is the following (used in one program):

$\overline{AB}$ the symbol for a segment

AB the symbol for the measure of length of a segment

$\overrightarrow{AB}$ the symbol for a ray

$\overleftrightarrow{AB}$ the symbol for a line

Another aspect of the new mathematics programs is the emphasis on understanding the *why* of mathematical operations. We formerly used tricks or shortcuts such as "borrowing," "moving the decimal point," "transposing," or "canceling." Now basic techniques are designed to provide this basic understanding. The new programs emphasize basic procedures such as regrouping, writing different numerals for the same number, or writing equivalent equations. This new approach shows a student how a process works by teaching him some basic laws that are used throughout mathematics. For example, the distributive law not only explains how to multiply: $8 \times 37 = 8(30 + 7) = 240 + 56 = 296$; it is also useful in factoring: $5ax + 15ax^2 = 5ax(1 + 3x)$.

Another important point of emphasis in the new programs is the structure of mathematics, the framework that supports all mathematical activity. This emphasis on structure is related to current learning theory. Psychologists today say that we learn most effectively when we see the structure of the topic, problem, or subject being studied because the structure of a subject helps us remember it and enables us to apply our knowledge to new situations. Hence, understanding the structure of mathematics and mathematical laws and procedures appears to be the most appropriate foundation for continued study and application of mathematics.

The final point, and perhaps most important, is the new spirit of mathematics in these new programs. Mathematics is presented as an elegant invention of the human mind. New content emphasizes the power, the unity, and the uniqueness of mathematics. Mathematics then becomes a field with aesthetic qualities similar to those of art, music, or literature. This emphasis is reflected in the variety of mathematics books and pamphlets now available which are suitable for independent, recreational reading.

The rapid development and adoption of the new school mathematics programs demonstrates the remarkable production that can result when competent people work together with adequate financial support. Most of the experimental projects in mathematics have involved the cooperative efforts of mathematicians, educators, psychologists, and school teachers supported by federal or foundation grants. Early participation in these new programs was an exciting experience for teachers and students. This enthusiasm was contagious, and other teachers and schools were encouraged to participate. In fact, some schools adopted new programs without having a staff prepared to teach the new content; and some programs were accepted without anyone's asking where they would lead or for what students they were designed. Possibly as a result, the programs have received criticism as well as adulation.

CRITICISMS OF THE NEW PROGRAMS

The major criticisms made of the new programs are the following:
1. The applications of mathematics are largely ignored.
2. The limited attention to practice results in inadequate computational skill.
3. The rigor, precision, and symbolism are too great for a large proportion of secondary-school students.
4. The content outlined for each grade is too extensive to be adequately presented in the time available.
5. The general objectives of education for citizenship in our democracy are ignored.
6. There are no adequate courses for the low-ability, non-college-bound, or culturally deprived students.
7. The emphasis on logic and structure has reduced the mastery of basic concepts and operations.

8. The formality of the presentation has resulted in a loss of interest on the part of many students.

9. The new programs are not effective as preparation for college mathematics.

To meet these criticisms, it would be helpful to have evidence based on research. Although considerable experimentation has been done with these new programs, no definitive results are available. The evaluations are largely value judgments of individuals based on limited experience or inconclusive evidence based on testing instruments that themselves usually favor the traditional programs. Without satisfactory evidence it is to be expected that critics will have a field day.

Much of the current criticism of the so-called "new math" is due to a lack of understanding on the part of the public and even the teachers themselves. The public does not know what the new programs are or what they seek to do. Some people assume, for example, that lack of skill in computation is due to the "new math" rather than recognizing that students of traditional mathematics also lacked computational skill.[1] Similarly, the teachers do not always use good judgment in their handling of new programs. They assume that the new topics will entirely replace important traditional topics. For example, some teachers spend a great amount of time on numeration systems—even insisting that students show competence in computing in a base other than ten; these teachers do not recognize the purpose of numeration systems—namely, to help students understand numerals and operations rather than to develop skill in computing with new numerals.

CURRENT TRENDS IN SCHOOL MATHEMATICS

The "revolution" in school mathematics is continuing as mathematicians, educators, and teachers work on new programs. Present developments suggest that school mathematics is continuing to change in these directions:

1. New topics will be introduced at all levels.

2. Topics will continue to be introduced at earlier grade levels.

3. Some topics will be eliminated and others reduced to make room for new topics.

4. The language and symbolism will become more precise and more sophisticated.

5. The emphasis on discovery, intuition, and participation of the learner will lead to the development of new instructional aids.

[1] In 1931 Schorling, studying over 200,000 students in grades 5–12, found that only 20 percent of the twelfth-grade students could compute 2.1 percent of 60. In 1937 Taylor studied more than 2000 freshmen in teachers' colleges and found that more than half could not divide 175 by .35. In 1942 Admiral Nimitz reported that 68 percent of 4200 freshmen at 27 United States universities and colleges were unable to pass the arithmetical-reasoning portion of the examination for entering the Naval Reserve Officers' Training Corps. In 1943 Brueckner, conducting a national survey, found that the arithmetical competence throughout the country was even worse than the Nimitz report indicated.

6. The need for evaluating new programs will stimulate research and the development of new measuring instruments.

7. Programs for the slow learner and the culturally deprived will have major emphasis as a result of criticisms and federal support.

8. The new programs will demand a level of teacher competence in mathematics which will result in higher standards in teacher education and certification.

9. The time and attention devoted to drill and manipulative exercises will be drastically reduced.

10. This last point suggests a major item that needs emphasis. *Very little of the classical, traditional mathematics is being discarded.* Number concepts, computation, measurement, algebra, geometry, trigonometry, and analytical geometry will be included in the programs of the immediate future. These topics are still of fundamental importance for advanced study and for everyday applications. They have been enriched by new insights. They should not be neglected even though new topics appear and new emphasis is the fashion of the day. What is valuable about the new school mathematics is not that it is new but rather that it offers an opportunity for students to learn mathematics more effectively, more pleasantly, and more meaningfully than has been possible before.

LEARNING EXERCISES

1. Investigate what is currently being done by groups such as the School Mathematics Study Group, the National Council of Teachers of Mathematics, and the Mathematical Association of America to revise school mathematics.

2. Compare a new mathematics textbook with one whose copyright date is ten years earlier. What changes have taken place in content? What changes have taken place in vocabulary and symbolism?

3. What events in the last ten years have had a major influence on school mathematics?

4. Name eight persons who have been leaders in developing new school mathematics during the past ten years.

5. Survey the literature of popular magazines to determine the tenor of present day comments on school mathematics.

6. What major innovations in school mathematics have been developed within your state?

7. Investigate the changes in school mathematics during the past ten years in a foreign country.

8. What provisions contained in recent legislation, state or national, have implications for school mathematics?

9. Select an experimental program. Compare it with a traditional program in terms of content, language, and emphasis.

4

strategies for teaching mathematical concepts

In teaching a new concept the teacher must decide what content will attain the objective of the study, then select the proper strategy for teaching the concept. This selection of strategy must precede selection of the method of instruction because it determines the method; also, strategy follows the selection of objective and content because they help to determine the strategy.

The strategy for teaching a given mathematical concept is the procedure, the algorithm, used to deal with the concept. The strategy selected by the teacher may begin from a number of bases; for example, in teaching numeration systems, we are faced with a number of questions:

Should we use a historical approach and begin with a discussion of ancient numeration systems?

Should we use a specific base such as five for a new numeration system or should several systems be considered simultaneously?

If we do use a single base, which one should logically be considered first?

Should we use the arabic digits for the new system or should a new set of symbols be created?

Should we use subscripts to identify the base or is some other means, such as color, more appropriate?

Should we treat an operation such as addition with one number base or compare results for several bases?

Should we develop complicated algorithms, such as division and square root, in the new base system?

Should we change non-decimal numerals directly to another base without recourse to base ten?

Should we include rational numbers in our study?

Should we consider problems of negative bases?

Should a finite modular system be related to the corresponding numeration system?

After answering these questions, the teacher selects the procedure which is the most efficient and most pleasant to attain the objectives of the study.

The strategy selected depends on the topic, the class, the objectives, and the procedures known to the teacher. It is often appropriate to use a different strategy, a new approach, when the topic is taught a second time or when it is reviewed. When alternate strategies are utilized, they add life to a topic and generate the same kind of interest that study of an entirely new topic produces.

New strategies have a therapeutic effect on the teacher. They break the routine aspects of teaching—especially when the same subject has been taught several times or when several sections of the same subject are taught in the same year. The new approach makes the teacher's role a little more exciting and offers him a bit more challenge. All teachers should develop a repertoire of alternate strategies.

Strategies should be reviewed and a particular one selected at the time unit plans are developed, because the strategy for teaching determines the over-all classroom presentation and the materials to be used.

CRITERIA FOR SELECTING STRATEGIES

There are several strategies available for teaching most mathematical topics. The following sections will suggest many strategies that can be used. Once the possible strategies are determined, the teacher must select the one most suitable to his particular situation.

Here are some guidelines for selecting a strategy:

1. *The strategy should be mathematically correct.* If alternative proofs of a theorem are possible, the one selected must be based on definitions, axioms, and proved theorems previously developed in the classroom.

2. *The strategy should have meaning for the class.* The mathematics should not be too sophisticated, that is, "over the heads" of students. Usually it should be possible to illustrate the concepts of an algorithm in terms of what they have learned previously. In developing the structure of the rational numbers, for example, the teacher will want to be sure that the class knows what an identity is, what closure means, and what an inverse does.

3. *The strategy should meet the demands for a proper teaching procedure.* It should be possible to formulate the process by means of concrete

visual representations, to lead to the abstract representations, and to end with generalizations. The strategy should rely on a minimum of new concepts, specified conditions, and new procedures. Thus, a secondary school teacher would hesitate to develop the real numbers on the basis of sequence limits because it would involve him in additional complex problems.

4. *The strategy should provide a satisfying experience,* so that students will be willing to exert the energy required to master the new technique. If factoring a set of algebraic phrases becomes a meaningless manipulation, it would be better not to have given the assignment.

5. *That strategy is best which has the greatest application to future use of the concept.* Thus, mathematicians recommend that dealing with the logarithm as a function is more valuable in advanced mathematics than dealing with logs as computational tools, a use essentially displaced by calculating equipment. The teacher should recognize that while a particular strategy may appear to be better on the basis of one or more points, it might be poor on others. For example, in the treatment of logs, the definition of the logarithm as the area under a curve, while more satisfactory mathematically, may be too sophisticated for some students (see following discussion).

STRATEGIES FOR TEACHING SOME BASIC CONCEPTS

The following are examples of alternate strategies for teaching some basic concepts. The first example, taken from elementary school mathematics, is offered to give some insights into a problem at a more basic level. Awareness of the alternatives and the choices made by elementary teachers will be increasingly important to the secondary school teacher as new programs with varied approaches develop in the elementary school.

THE DEFINITION OF ADDITION

One of the first strategies the elementary school teacher must select is for the treatment of addition. What does addition mean? How is the transfer best made from concrete objects to the symbolic representation? How is the meaning of carrying (regrouping) made clear? How must the concept be modified as rational numbers, negative integers, and real numbers are introduced?

The usual introduction to addition begins with *combinations* of sets of objects:

$$A, B, C \text{ and } D, E \text{ combined are } A, B, C, D, E.$$

Recording the number of objects in each group or set, we have

$$3 + 2 = 5$$

Some teachers now deal with this situation in the symbolism and operations of sets:

$$K = \{A, B, C\}$$
$$M = \{D, E\}$$
$$N(K) = 3$$
$$N(M) = 2$$
$$\{A, B, C\} \cup \{D, E\} = \{A, B, C, D, E\}$$
$$N(K) + N(M) = N(K \cup M)$$

A sum is the number of elements in the union of two disjoint sets. Note the high level of sophistication of this treatment, both in terms of symbols and vocabulary.

Another strategy involves the developing of number concepts in terms of the number line—addition is illustrated by jumps on the number line.

For example, $3 + 4 = 7$ is visualized as follows:

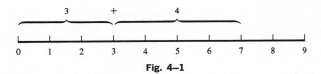

Fig. 4–1

At a higher level, the addition operation is considered a mapping or a two-to-one correspondence.

The number-line representation has the advantage of giving the relationships of numbers, the order, the "distance" apart; therefore, it is useful in developing the properties of addition. It also lends itself without essential modification to the introduction of rational and real numbers, negative numbers, and graphing. Especially on the basis of graphing, which makes it useful at higher grade levels, the number-line representation seems the most appropriate strategy for discussing number concepts and operations.

LONG DIVISION

The algorithm for long division is typically "estimate a quotient, multiply, subtract, bring down, divide," and so on. It works but has little meaning to the student. Compare the ease and meaning of the process on the right with that on the left:

```
        25
    23)584       23)584
       46           230 10
      ----          ---
      124           354
      115           230 10
      ----          ---
        9           124
                    115  5
                    ----
                      9 25
```

The strategy on the left could have more meaning if it were introduced as follows:

$$\begin{array}{r} \underline{20 + 5} \\ 23\overline{)584} \\ \underline{460} = (20 \times 23) \\ \overline{124} \\ \underline{115} = (5 \times 23) \\ 9 \end{array}$$

Actually, the end result should be the ability to use the algorithm on the left. But this use should follow the development on the right, which focuses on the meaning of division as a process of repeated subtraction.

DIVISION BY A RATIONAL NUMBER

Division by a so-called fraction has rarely been made meaningful. The usual treatment is to "invert the divisor and multiply." What strategy will add meaning to this operation?

One easy strategy is to change the fractions to fractions with common denominators. Thus, $3/4 \div 2/3$ becomes $9/12 \div 8/12$. If the denominators are considered to be names for types of units, the problem becomes one of dividing nine of those units by eight of them, giving the quotient $9/8$. This example may be justified by reference to the number line, numbers involving feet and inches, or pie cut-outs.

Another more complex strategy is to relate the division problem to the definition of division:

$$\text{If } a \div b = c, \text{ then } a = c \times b$$

In terms of rational numbers:

$$\text{If } \frac{m}{n} \div \frac{r}{s} = c, \text{ then } \frac{m}{n} = c \times \frac{r}{s}$$

$$\text{Then } \left(\frac{m}{n}\right) \times \frac{s}{r} = \left(c \times \frac{r}{s}\right) \times \frac{s}{r} \text{ or } \frac{m}{n} \times \frac{s}{r} = c$$

$$\text{Thus } \frac{m}{n} \div \frac{r}{s} = \frac{m}{n} \times \frac{s}{r}$$

Still another strategy utilizes a property of one, the identity element for multiplication: $a \cdot 1 = a$ for any a. The division problem

$$\frac{m}{n} \div \frac{r}{s} \text{ is rewritten } \frac{\dfrac{m}{n}}{\dfrac{r}{s}}$$

Using the identity element we have (since $x/x = 1$ for $x \neq 0$):

$$\frac{\dfrac{m}{n}}{\dfrac{r}{s}} \cdot 1 = \frac{\dfrac{m}{n}}{\dfrac{r}{s}} \cdot \frac{\dfrac{s}{r}}{\dfrac{s}{r}} = \frac{\dfrac{m}{n} \cdot \dfrac{s}{r}}{1} = \frac{m}{n} \cdot \frac{s}{r}$$

This technique leads to alternate approaches for specific examples:

$$\frac{5}{6} \div \frac{2}{3} = \frac{\frac{5}{6} \cdot \frac{3}{2}}{\frac{2}{3} \cdot \frac{3}{2}} = \frac{15}{12} = \frac{5}{4}, \text{ or}$$

$$\frac{5}{6} \div \frac{2}{3} = \frac{\frac{5}{6} \cdot 6}{\frac{2}{3} \cdot 6} = \frac{5}{4}$$

In the second case the choice of 6/6 for one instead of (3/2)/(3/2) simplifies the computation.

PERCENT AND PERCENTAGE

The computation of percents and percentage has always been trouble-some—partly because of the confusion of the similar terms "percent" and "percentage," partly because different numerals (e.g., 75%, .75, and 3/4) are used for the same percent with no distinction made between the rate and the numeral. But the main source of difficulty is the failure to recognize the difference between a percent and a rational number.

A percent is a rate. It is also a ratio. But it is *not* a numeral for a rational number. Here is an example showing the kind of paradox that arises when a ratio and fraction are interchanged. Given two rational numbers 3/4 and 5/8, the sum 3/4 + 5/8 = 6/8 + 5/8 = 11/8. But if 3/4 and 5/8 are ratios, then we may say 3/4 + 5/8 = 8/12. To show why this is true, consider 3/4 as representing the rate "Our team won 3 out of 4 games in football." Then 5/8 may represent the rate "Our team won 5 out of 8 games in basketball." For both sports this statement follows: "Our teams won 8 out of 12 games this year." In other words, 3/4 + 5/8 = 8/12 when 3/4 and 5/8 represent rates or ratios.

Of course, there are many different numerals to represent rates just as there are different numerals for rational numbers. Thus 3 out of 4 is equivalent to the rate 6 out of 8 or 15 out of 20. 3/4 is one member of a set of equivalent rates or

$$\frac{3}{4} \ \epsilon \ \left\{ \frac{3}{4}, \frac{6}{8}, \frac{9}{12}, \frac{12}{16}, \frac{15}{20}, \cdots , \cdots , \frac{75}{100}, \cdots \right\}$$

Consequently, 3/4, 75/100, .75, and 75% are four numerals for the same rate.

Various means are used to distinguish the rate 3/4 from the rational number 3/4. One program uses $\frac{3}{4}$ and 3/4. Another refers to a rate as a rate pair, and thus rate $\frac{3}{4}$ is represented by (3,4). This may be confusing to some students since (3,4) is also the notation for the coordinates of a point on the Cartesian plane.

Percents are usually used to solve three types of exercises such as the following:

1. What is 6% of 84?
2. What percent is 12 out of 60?
3. Seven is 9% of what number?

One past strategy was to classify a problem into one of these three categories. Then, the following rules were used to complete the exercises.

Case I.   Change the percent to a decimal and multiply.
Case II. Divide the whole by the part and change the decimal to a percent.
Case III. Change the percent to a decimal and divide the part of the whole by this decimal.

These rate rules for Cases I, II, and III were meaningless. Percents above 100 were especially difficult in using these rules.

Another strategy has been to solve all percent problems by the use of the formula $br = p$ (base × rate = percentage). Then by the substitution of the values given for two variables, the resulting equation can always be solved for the third variable. The main difficulty here is that the student too often cannot distinguish between b and p, the base and the percentage.

A third strategy uses a proportion for all rate problems. Since rates are ratios, it seems reasonable to use a proportion which is an expression of equality for two ratios. Then a percent is always a ratio in which the comparison base is 100. Then 75% is the ratio 75 to 100 or 75/100. All percentage problems now consist in finding two numerals for the same rate. Usually the problem is simplified because one of the numerals concerned has 100 as its comparison base.

This is how this strategy solves the three exercises above:

1. What is 6% of 84? 6 of 100 equals what of 84? Or

$$\frac{6}{100} = \frac{x}{84}$$

2. What percent is 12 out of 60? What of 100 is 12 of 60? Or

$$\frac{x}{100} = \frac{12}{60}$$

3. Seven is 9% of what number? 7 of what number equals 9 of 100? Or

$$\frac{7}{x} = \frac{9}{100}$$

To find the truth sets for each proportion, the student uses the equality of cross-products and equivalent equations. Thus, in exercise 3:

$$700 = 9x \text{ or } x = \frac{700}{9}$$

Of these three strategies, the last seems the most appropriate. It solves all situations by the same method, namely, a proportion. It avoids the confusion of percent and percentage. It is mathematically correct in finding two equivalent rates. But, above all, it is a strategy that makes sense because it is based on the meaning of a percent.

SQUARE ROOT

The square root of a number has several bases for exploration. At the intuitive level, it can be illustrated as the length of the side of a square whose area is given. Thus, if 25 is the measure of the area of a square, the measure of each side is 5. Then the square root of 25 is 5.

At a higher level the square root of a number is illustrated as one of the two equal factors of a number. This is satisfactory for perfect squares such as 36 but is not appropriate for numbers such as 17. Since factors are usually restricted to counting numbers, a difficulty might arise, for 17 does not have two equal factors that are counting numbers. The student might then conclude erroneously that there is no square root of 17.

This matter of equal factors is related to the use of exponents. For example, 7×7 is represented as 7^2 and called "seven squared" or the second power of 7. Then, finding the square root of a non-negative number is the inverse of squaring a non-negative number. Then $\sqrt{49} = \sqrt{7^2}$ or $\sqrt{49} = 7$.

The approximate value of the square root of numbers that are not perfect squares can be found by a measurement approach. This approach is based on the Pythagorean formula for the right triangle, $a^2 + b^2 = c^2$ or $c = \sqrt{a^2 + b^2}$.

The strategy here is based on drawings on graph paper:

1. Draw an isosceles right triangle with each leg one unit long. Then the hypotenuse represents $c = \sqrt{1^2 + 1^2}$ or $c = \sqrt{2}$. The actual value of $\sqrt{2}$ can be determined by measuring the length of c with a separate strip of the graph paper.
2. Using the $\sqrt{2}$ as a length of one side and 1 as the length of the second side, draw another right triangle. The hypotenuse of this triangle represents $\sqrt{3}$. Continuing in the same way, the square roots of the integers may be determined. When constructed together, they form a spiral array.

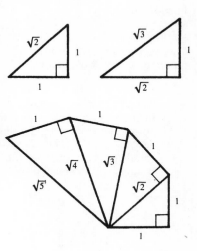

Fig. 4–2

Since the square roots of so many numbers are irrational numbers, the algorithm for the computation of a square root is troublesome for students. The usual strategy is to use the algorithm based on the square of a polynomial. It is widely accepted only because it "works" in finding a square root correct to any desired degree of accuracy. Here is how it applies to $\sqrt{746}$

$$
\begin{array}{r}
2\ 7.3 \\
\sqrt{746.00} \\
4 \\
\hline
40\,|\,346 \\
47\,|\,329 \\
\hline
540\,|\,1700 \\
543\,|\,1629 \\
\hline
71
\end{array}
$$

When students ask why this method works, it is helpful to show them a geometric and algebraic justification based on the square. It can be visualized somewhat as follows:

Given: A square whose area is 746 square units. What is the length of each side?

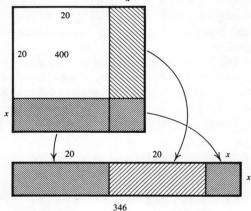

Part of this given square is a square 20 by 20. Then $(20 + x)^2 = 746$.

The remaining area can be represented by this rectangle:

Fig. 4–3

Since $(20 + x)^2 = 746$, $400 + 40x + x^2 = 746$, or $x(40 + x) = 346$, then x can be estimated by dividing 346 (the area of the rectangle) by 40, an approximation to the length of the rectangle ("double the first digit and add zero"). This suggests 8, but when 8 is added to 40 to get the total length of the rectangle, the product 48×8 is more than 346. Hence, x is approximately equal to 7.

The remaining area can be represented by y in the equation $(2 \cdot 27 + y) y = 17$ or by the rectangle.

Fig. 4–4

Consequently, dividing 17 by 54 gives an approximation for y, namely .3. This process can be repeated as often as necessary.

To be consistent with measurement theory, the square root should have the same accuracy as the given number. In this case it means the square root should have 3 significant figures.

The algorithm above is, of course, based on the square of a binomial $(a + b)^2 = a^2 + 2ab + b^2$. As such, it is a good extension of products of binomials. To be meaningful and be remembered, this basis should be carefully established.

A second strategy for computing square root is the estimation-division method. To get the square root of 746, estimate the answer and then divide. Suppose we begin by estimating the square root as being 25 (since $20^2 = 400$ and $30^2 = 900$).

1. Divide by estimated root $746 \div 25 = 29.84$.
2. Find the average of divisor and quotient

$$\frac{25 + 29.84}{2} = 27.42$$

3. Divide the square by this new estimate
$$746 \div 27.42 = 27.206$$

4. Find the average of divisor and quotient

$$\frac{27.42 + 27.206}{2} = 27.31$$

In this strategy, note that no totally new algorithm needs to be learned. Here we use division and averaging. It is based on the idea that the arithmetic mean of two numbers is an approximation to the geometric mean, that is, $\frac{x + y}{2} \approx \sqrt{xy}$. Where $xy = N$, N is the number whose square root is to be determined. This last method, the one in most common use in today's texts, is as mathematically correct as the first and at the same time seems easier to remember. Answering some of the many questions left open by the algorithm is, however, not easy. To see this, examine some of the algebra involved.

Choose the first estimate
$$x_1 > \sqrt{n} > 0$$

Let the error in this first estimate be e_1, so that
$$x_1 = \sqrt{n} + e_1, \, e_1 \geq 0$$

The second estimate is found by averaging as described above:
$$x_2 = \frac{1}{2}\left(\frac{n}{x_1} + x_1\right) = \frac{n}{2x_1} + \frac{x_1}{2}$$

Let e_2 be the error in this second approximation
$$x_2 = \sqrt{n} + e_2$$

Then

$$e_2 = x_2 - \sqrt{n} = \left(\frac{n}{2x_1} + \frac{x_1}{2}\right) - \sqrt{n} = \frac{n - 2x_1\sqrt{n} + x_1^2}{2x} = \frac{(\sqrt{n} - x_1)^2}{2x_1} > 0$$

Thus:

$$(1) \quad x_2 = \sqrt{n} + e_2 > \sqrt{n}$$

At the same time $x_1 > \sqrt{n}$ implies the following chain of reasoning:

$$x_1^2 > n; \ x_1 > \frac{n}{x_1}; \ 2x_1 > \frac{n}{x_1} + x_1; \ x_1 > \frac{1}{2}\left(\frac{n}{x_1} + x_1\right) = x_2$$

So:

$$(2) \quad x_1 > x_2$$

Statements (1) and (2) place x_2 between x_1 and $\sqrt{n}$, thus making it a better approximation.

This complicated justification still leaves unresolved two more difficult questions: how much better is the approximation, and does the sequence $x_1, x_2, x_3, \ldots$ converge to $\sqrt{n}$.

Note that the teacher is left in a real quandary by these alternate strategies. Each poses real problems if understanding is a basic objective. Because of these difficulties some teachers do not teach any algorithm and direct their students to tables, logarithmic solutions, or graphs. Others, especially those with calculators available, use direct trial (by squaring) to approximate roots.

MULTIPLICATION OF DIRECTED NUMBERS

One of the most frequent, and unanswered, questions in an algebra class is "Why does a negative times a negative give a positive product?" To add meaning to this process, a variety of strategies such as the following are used:

1. Relate the multiplication process to trips on the number line. This will relate the multiplication process to the visualization of multiplication used in elementary school arithmetic. The new element introduced here is the idea of positive and negative directions, positive and negative time, and positive and negative distance.

   Suppose that John lives on an east-west highway. Consider the highway as a number line with John's home at the origin. Using positive coordinates to locate points east of John's home and negative coordinates for points west, consider distances to the east of John's home positive and distances west negative. Therefore, the direction of travel is positive when toward the east and negative toward the west. Future time is called positive and past time is negative, with the present being zero. (Note how many conditions must be established for this "intuitive" development of products of integers.)

   Then $(^+50)\ (^+3) = {}^+150$ since travel toward the east at 50 mph for three hours in the future results in arriving at 150 miles east of John's house.

How then would the following be interpreted?

$$(^-50)\ (^+3) = {}^-150$$
$$(^+50)\ (^-3) = {}^-150$$

Finally $(^-50)\ (^-3) = {}^+150$ means that a truck traveling 50 mph west was 150 miles east of John's home three hours ago.

2. Gains and losses on the football field provide a similar travel situation.
3. Income and expenses resulting in being "in the red" or "in the black" give another application.
4. The UICSM uses the ingenious method of a motion picture projector which runs forward $(+)$ or backward $(-)$. Then a motion picture of a pump filling $(+)$ or draining $(-)$ a tank will result in an increase in water in the tank $(+)$ or a decrease $(-)$. The reversed projector $(-)$ of a pump draining the tank $(-)$ results in the tank being filled $(+)$.
5. A different strategy uses patterns for predicting the product:

a. $^+3 \cdot {}^+2 = {}^+6$	b. $^-3 \cdot {}^+2 = {}^-6$
$^+3 \cdot {}^+1 = {}^+3$	$^-3 \cdot {}^+1 = {}^-3$
$^+3 \cdot 0 = 0$	$^-3 \cdot 0 = 0$
$^+3 \cdot {}^-1 = ?$	$^-3 \cdot {}^-1 = ?$
$^+3 \cdot {}^-2 = ?$	$^-3 \cdot {}^-2 = ?$

6. At a higher level, a deductive approach is possible.

a. $^+3 \cdot 0 = 0$	a. property of zero
b. $^+3\ (^+3 + {}^-3) = 0$	b. substitution of $(^+3 + {}^-3)$ for 0
c. $(^+3)(^+3) + (^+3)(^-3) = 0$	c. distributive property
d. $^+9 + (^+3)(^-3) = 0$	d. substitution of $^+9$ for $(^+3)(^+3)$
e. $(^+3)(^-3) = {}^-9$	e. since $(^+3)(^-3)$ must be the additive inverse of $^+9$ in d.

The general forms are similar.

a. $^-a \cdot 0 = 0$
b. $^-a\ [b + (^-b)] = 0$
c. $^-ab + {}^-a(^-b) = 0$
d. $(^-a)\ (^-b) = -(^-ab)$
e. $(^-a)(^-b) = ab$

It is likely that the total strategy for teaching the product of two negative numbers will start with a number line example, include the pattern of results and end with the deductive presentation.

SPACE GEOMETRY

Space or solid geometry is now an integrated part of tenth grade geometry. But there are different strategies for integrating plane and space geometry.

1. Begin with a point and next consider lines as sets of points. Then a plane is a set of points or a set of lines. Finally space becomes a set of points, a set of lines, or a set of planes. This strategy is usually based on a development using coordinate geometry. The number line locates points on a line, two perpendicular lines provide coordinates on a plane, and three mutually perpendicular lines provide the coordinates for space geometry.

2. The second strategy consists of extending plane geometry concepts to the analogous concepts in space geometry.

Plane geometry	*Space geometry*
lines	planes
parallel lines	parallel planes
plane angles	polyhedral angles
polygons	polyhedra
circles	spheres

3. The third strategy treats plane geometry first and space geometry last. Often, inadequate time for the entire course means very little space geometry is included.

A basic requirement for success in space geometry, no matter what strategy is employed, is to allow ample time for intuitive development. One of the greatest difficulties is visualizing the relationships in three-dimensional space by two-dimensional drawings. Learning principles of orthographic projection, making models, and using blackboard stencils to get proper perspective help develop the perception of space.

CONIC SECTIONS

The conic sections may be taught from three approaches: locus, algebra, and space geometry. The first avenue stresses the construction of the conics in the plane by recourse to the locus defining statements:

> *Ellipse:* A point the sum of whose distances from two fixed points is constant. (*Circle* is a special case of this, the two points coincident.)
>
> *Hyperbola:* A point the absolute value of the difference of whose distances from two fixed points is constant.
>
> *Parabola:* A point whose distances from a fixed point and a fixed line are equal.

The conic sections may also be approached by folding wax paper. Fold a line to represent the directrix and locate a point to represent the focus of a parabola. Make multiple folds so that the directrix is superimposed on the focus. The creases will form the envelope of a parabola. Relating the locus definition to the creases will give the mathematical analysis of the result.

In a similar way, an ellipse can be formed by using a circle and a point within the circle on wax paper. Folding many creases so that the circle is superimposed on the point will give the envelope of an ellipse. Again the locus definition is used for the mathematical explanation. If a point is selected outside the circle, creases formed by superimposing this point on the circle will give the envelope of an hyperbola.

Another avenue defines the conic figures in terms of algebraic statements from which graphs are constructed. (Rotations and translations are considered separately.)

Ellipse

$$\frac{x^2}{a^2} + \frac{y^2}{b^2} = 1$$

(Circle is a special case of this, $a = \pm b$.)

Hyperbola

$$\frac{x^2}{a^2} - \frac{y^2}{b^2} = 1 \text{ (or } -1\text{)}$$

Parabola

$$y = ax^2 \text{ or } x = ay^2$$

The third avenue defines the conics on the cone itself

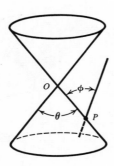

Fig. 4–5

Through a point P on an element of the right circular cone a plane is passed as on Fig. 4–5. The figures which are the intersection of the plane and the cone depend on the relation between θ and ϕ.

Ellipse

$$m(\angle\theta) < m(\angle\phi) < \pi$$

Circle is a special case of this:

$$m(\angle\phi) = \frac{\pi + m(\angle\theta)}{2}$$

Hyperbola

$$0 < m(\angle\phi) < m(\angle\theta)$$

Parabola

$$m(\angle\phi) = m(\angle\theta)$$

Here is an example of a topic which may be approached from many directions, and often is in the classroom. Unfortunately, the real value of the multiple strategy approach is lost here because students are seldom shown the interrelation between the approaches. The interrelationship is not hard to establish and in fact offers some insight into the unity of mathematics.

To show the locus-space geometry connection reference is made to Dandelin's cone. To prove that the elliptical section of the cone through P in Figure 4–6 satisfies the locus definition, two spheres (like scoops of ice cream) are inserted in the cone in such a way that they are tangent to the plane of the ellipse at F and F' respectively. An element of the cone is drawn through P tangent to the spheres at G and G'. For any position of P

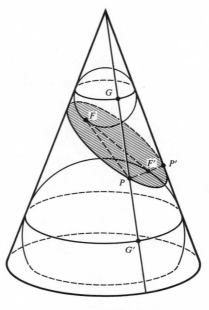

Fig. 4–6

the line GG' is constant. But $PG = PF$ and $PG' = PF'$ since two tangents to a sphere from an external point are equal. Since $GG' = GP + PG' = FP + PF'$, this latter sum is also constant and the connection is made.

To establish the locus-algebra connection, place the ellipse symmetric to the origin. Let the fixed points (foci) be at $F_1(f,0)$ and $F_2(-f,0)$ and let

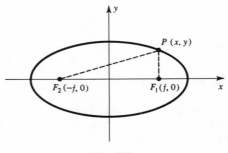

Fig. 4–7

the constant distance F_2PF_1 be $2a$. Assign the coordinates (x,y) to the locus point P. The formula for distance between two points provides the following equation:

$$\sqrt{(x+f)^2 + y^2} + \sqrt{(x-f)^2 + y^2} = 2a$$

Eliminating the radicals in this equation and simplifying gives

$$\frac{x^2}{a^2} + \frac{y^2}{a^2 - f^2} = 1$$

Fig. 4–8a shows why the constant distance $2a$ was chosen. When P is on the

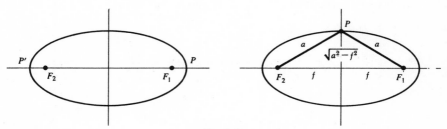

Fig. 4–8

y-axis, $F_2P + PF_1 = pp' = 2a$. By symmetry, then, P is the point (a,o); $P'(-a,o)$.

Fig. 4–8b suggests the substitution $\sqrt{a^2 - f^2} = b$. This substitution completes the derivation of the algebraic equation

$$\frac{x^2}{a^2} + \frac{y^2}{b^2} = 1$$

Since the arguments are transitive, the connection between the three definitions is established. Similar arguments may be made for hyperbolas and parabolas and are suggested as exercises for strong mathematics students.

SUM AND PRODUCT OF ROOTS OF A QUADRATIC

The standard derivation of the formulae for sums and products of roots of a quadratic equation is by reference to the quadratic formula:

$$x_1 = \frac{-b + \sqrt{b^2 - 4ac}}{2a}$$

$$x_2 = \frac{-b - \sqrt{b^2 - 4ac}}{2a}$$

$$x_1 + x_2 = \frac{-2b}{2a} = -\frac{b}{a}$$

$$x_1 x_2 = \frac{b^2 - (b^2 - 4ac)}{4a^2} = \frac{4ac}{4a^2} = \frac{c}{a}$$

Alternate derivations may be used when other topics are being studied. The method of equating coefficients may be used. This theorem states that in the equation:

$$a_n x^n + a_{n-1} x^{n-1} + \cdots + a_1 x + a_0 = b_n x^n + b_{n-1} x^{n-1} + \cdots + b_1 x + b_0$$

when $m > n$ values of x make the statement true, then

$$a_n = b_n, a_{n-1} = b_{n-1}, \ldots a_1 = b_1, a_0 = b_0.$$

To form a quadratic with roots x_1 and x_2 we set $(x - x_1)(x - x_2) = 0$. We may also set $ax^2 + bx + c = 0$ and write this in the form $x^2 + \dfrac{b}{a}x + \dfrac{c}{a} = 0$. Equating the two we have an equation true for all substitutions of x (not just x_1 and x_2):

$$(x - x_1)(x - x_2) = x^2 + \frac{b}{a}x + \frac{c}{a}$$

This may be written:

$$x^2 - (x_1 + x_2)x + x_1 x_2 = x^2 + \frac{b}{a}x + \frac{c}{a}$$

Applying the theorem, we have

$$-(x_1 + x_2) = \frac{b}{a} \text{ or } x_1 + x_2 = -\frac{b}{a}$$

$$x_1 x_2 = \frac{c}{a}$$

Another derivation (of the same formula) depends on symmetry properties of the parabola and the formula for the axis of symmetry. In Fig. 4–9 the

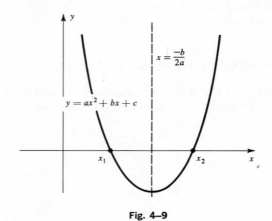

Fig. 4–9

equation of the axis of symmetry of the graph $ax^2 + bx + c = y$ is $x = -b/2a$. Symmetry indicates that this is midway between (or the average of) the roots x_1 and x_2. Apply the formula for finding the mean:

$$\frac{x_1 + x_2}{2} = \frac{-b}{2a} \text{ or } x_1 + x_2 = \frac{-b}{a}$$

ANALYTIC VERSUS SYNTHETIC PROOF

Integrating coordinate geometry into the tenth grade geometry course is now widely accepted. One of the reasons for this acceptance is that analytic proofs based on a coordinate system are considered easier and more useful than synthetic proofs. Here is a simple example:

Theorem
The diagonals of a parallelogram bisect each other.

Synthetic Proof
Given: Parallelogram *ABCD* with diagonals *BD* and *AC* intersecting at *M*.
Proof:
$\triangle AMB \cong \triangle CMD$

Analytic Proof
Given: Parallelogram *ABCD* with vertices as follows: $A(0, 0)$, $B(b, 0)$, $D(a, c)$, $C(a + b, c)$
Proof:
Midpoint of
$\overline{AC}$ is $\left(\dfrac{a + b}{2}, \dfrac{c}{2}\right)$
Midpoint of
$\overline{BD}$ is $\left(\dfrac{a + b}{2}, \dfrac{c}{2}\right)$

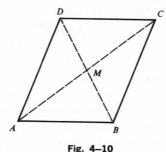

Fig. 4–10

Similar proofs are possible for many of the theorems of geometry.
Whether one method is easier or more meaningful than another has not been established.

STRATEGIES FOR SPECIFIC TOPICS

For almost every topic taught in school mathematics, the teacher faces the problem of selecting the best or selecting several presentation strategies. Here are some further examples in addition to those discussed above:

    1. Equations.
        a. Perform actual operations on each member of the equation.
        b. Write equivalent equations based on properties of equalities.

c. Write a two-column proof justifying each step.

d. Use shortcuts such as "transposing" terms or "canceling" terms (not recommended by the authors unless careful groundwork is laid and the processes completely justified!).

2. Factoring.

a. Find products by means of the distributive property. Reverse the process to find factors.

b. Relate the terms of a product to the areas of a rectangle. Factoring then becomes a process of finding dimensions of rectangles with given areas.

c. Classify products into given categories and then apply the appropriate rule for writing the factors.

d. Guess one factor, test it, and find another by division. Use parity (odd-even) relations for sums and products to lead to possible factors.

3. Congruence.

a. Assume that triangles are congruent according to three given conditions.

b. Assume one basic congruence theorem and then prove the others on the basis of this congruence assumption.

c. Construct triangles according to given conditions. Compare them by superposition. Prove the congruence theorems by the traditional superposition proofs.

d. Consider congruence as a special case of similarity.

e. Follow Euclid's treatment of congruence.

4. Logarithms.

a. Define logarithms as exponents and operate as with exponents.

b. Change numerals to scientific notation. Use the results of computation with scientific notation to identify characteristic and mantissa.

c. Define logarithms as the area under a curve, specifically

$$\log n = k \int_1^n \frac{dx}{x}$$

where k determines the base of the particular log system. Develop the properties of logs by recourse to the geometric analog.

5. Measurement.

a. Estimate measures. Use English or metric units but do not convert from one to another. Rather, develop a mastery of the relative size of all units in each system.

b. Establish new, arbitrary units of measure. Use these units to make measurements and convert from one unit to another.

c. Learn the metric system with emphasis on the meaning of prefixes. Memorize key conversion factors for metric to English and learn to convert measures from one system to another.

d. Study measurement with emphasis on the approximate nature of measures and the necessary computational rules. Know the difference between precision and accuracy and learn to apply these ideas to computations with measures.

6. Trigonometric functions.

a. Define them in terms of right triangles. Build a table of functions by drawing right triangles, measuring the sides, computing ratios.

b. Define the functions in terms of a rectangular coordinate system.

c. Define the functions in terms of rational numbers and infinite sequences.

d. Develop the functions as line values on the circle.

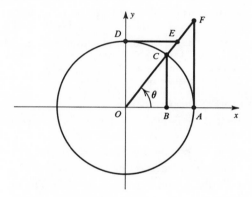

Fig. 4–11

$$BC = \sin \phi \qquad\qquad OE = \csc \phi$$
$$OB = \cos \phi \qquad\qquad OF = \sec \phi$$
$$AF = \tan \phi \qquad\qquad DE = \operatorname{ctn} \phi$$

e. Define the functions in terms of a wrapping function.

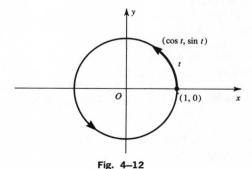

Fig. 4–12

On Fig. 4–12, t is the distance measured counterclockwise on the unit circle from the point $(1, 0)$. (Tangent is defined to be $\sin t/\cos t$.)

    f. Develop the functions from a vector approach.

7. Quadratic functions.

    a. A strictly algebraic treatment designed to provide techniques for solving quadratic equations by factoring, completing the square, and applying the quadratic formula.

    b. A graphical study based on point by point construction of the graph $y = ax^2 + bx + c$.

    c. A strategy based on the idea of a function machine $x \rightarrow ax^2 + bx + c$.

    d. A study of properties of the quadratic equation such as sum and product of roots and properties of the discriminant.

    e. A structural study of the graph of quadratics $y = x^2$, $y = ax^2$, $y = x^2 + p$, $y = (x - q)^2$ and finally $y = a(x - q)^2 + p$.

    f. A study based on an application such as a freely falling body: $s = \frac{1}{2}gt^2 + v_o t + s_o$, where s is the height, t time, v_o initial velocity, s_o initial height and $g = 32$ (ft/sec/sec) the constant of acceleration due to gravity.

8. Systems of linear equations.

    a. Find the common solution as the intersection set of two truth sets.

    b. Find the common solution by graphing.

    c. Find the intersection of truth sets by substitution.

    d. Find the common solution by determinants.

    e. Find the solutions by a computer program.

SOURCES OF TEACHING STRATEGIES

Many teachers are limited by their experience and background, and feel that they are not creative enough to use alternate routes to content development. Such teachers often feel that they should "play it safe" and follow the textbook presentation completely. But these same teachers often change textbooks and teach new courses. They change to the method of presentation of the new book readily enough. They could just as well examine and occasionally try new (or even old) approaches within the framework of the current program.

Where do ideas come from? We have already suggested one excellent source: other textbooks for the same course. Some additional sources include:

1. Texts and teachers' manuals for experimental programs, like those for SMSG.
2. Journals, especially European, that stress classroom presentations,

like *Mathematics Teaching* (English), and *Praxis der Mathematik* (German).
3. Reference books like Kasner and Newman's *Mathematics and the Imagination*.
4. Other teachers.
5. Professional meetings.

Mathematics is a versatile science. Possible procedures, proofs, and methods of solving problems are legion. In teaching mathematics we select the most elegant algorithm or proof that has real meaning in terms of both content and pedagogical aims for our students.

LEARNING EXERCISES

1. Select a given mathematical topic. Find the different strategies for teaching it. What strategy is most suitable for your class?
2. Illustrate different proofs of the Pythagorean theorem. Which proof is the most suitable as the first proof for a tenth grade geometry class? Why?
3. Examine a modern mathematics textbook and a textbook of a generation ago. How do these texts differ in the strategies used?
4. Write the synthetic and analytic proofs of theorems in geometry. Discuss the relative advantages or disadvantages of the different proofs.
5. Write a lesson plan for teaching division by a rational number. Use a strategy different from that discussed in this text that has meaning and is mathematically correct.

part two

attaining
the specific objectives
of mathematics
teaching

5

learning
mathematical
concepts
through
discovery

How are mathematical concepts learned? What goes on in the mind of of the student as he attempts to unravel new ideas? How should ideas be presented to the student so that a concept is learned quickly and correctly? If we understand the process whereby mathematical concepts are learned, then we can plan proper learning experiences.

Concepts are defined in many different ways. We will define a mathematical concept to be a mental construct. A concept is a mental abstraction of common properties of a set of experiences or phenomena. The elements of these sets may involve objects (set concepts), actions (operational concepts), comparisons (relational concepts), or organizations (structural concepts). The basic types of mathematical concepts are illustrated by these examples:

Set concepts: A number is the common property of equivalent sets.

Operational concepts: Addition is the common property of the union of disjoint sets.

Relational concepts: Equality is the common property of the number of elements of equivalent sets.

Structural concepts: Closure is the common property of a mathematical group.

In the case of the set concept, for

Fig. 5–1

example, the concept "three" is abstracted from the common properties of many sets as in Fig. 5–1. The mental construct is similar to the idea of color, also the common property of many sets. Note that in each case the concept is essentially abstracted from the object or objects themselves.

NECESSARY CONDITIONS FOR LEARNING MATHEMATICAL CONCEPTS

If concepts are to be learned, certain necessary conditions must be present. The learner must be ready, willing, and able to learn. Then, he needs guidance, resources, and time for the learning. Thus, the following conditions are essential in building new mathematical concepts:

1. The learner must have the necessary information, skills, and experiences so that he is *ready* to learn a new concept. Only when he has the background necessary to perceive common properties, relationships, patterns, and structure of ideas will he be able to generalize. For example, algebraic fractions cannot be considered if the learner has a meager understanding of rational numbers, the meaning of common denominator, the impossibility of division by zero, and the identity element for multiplication.

2. The learner must have been motivated to the extent that he is *willing* to participate in learning activities. The learner learns what he is doing, seeing, feeling, or thinking. Hence, learning is possible only if the learner himself responds to the learning situation. And he will respond only when he thinks that a response is desirable. Instead of asking a student to learn the associative law for addition for a future test, we would do better to ask him to look for a shortcut in the solution of the following exercises:

$$37 \ + \ 52 \ + 48$$
$$234 \ + 987 \ + 13$$
$$7\tfrac{1}{3} + \ 3\tfrac{3}{4} + \ 5\tfrac{4}{7}$$

3. The learner must have the necessary capability so that he is *able* to participate in the learning activities. Learning mathematical concepts is an intellectual process that involves activities such as manipulating, visualizing, listening, reading, computing, writing, thinking, verbalizing, abstracting, generalizing, and symbolizing. This means that concepts to be learned must be selected within the range of the learner's ability to do these things if he is to make progress. We should not expect a slow learner to compute cube root when he has not been able to learn how to compute square roots. We should not expect the student to learn to solve quadratic equations if he can't solve linear equations.

4. The learner must be given some *guidance* so that motivation is preserved and learning is efficient. Learning by trial and error or by haphazard reflection may discourage him so that he never reaches the goal. Ideas should be presented to him so that he can perceive common elements. Thus, learning how to subtract a directed number is facilitated if the student is helped to compare the directed distances between points on the number line and the results of adding opposites:

Subtraction as the directed distance between two points on the number line

$(+3) - (+7) = -4$

$+3 \longleftarrow +7$

$(-5) - (-9) = +4$

$-9 \longrightarrow -5$

Subtraction as the sum of opposites

$(+3) - (+7) = (+3) + (-7) = -4$

$(-5) - (-9) = (-5) + (+9) = +4$

5. The learner must be provided with appropriate *materials* (e.g., a text, a model, a film, or a tape) with which to work. For example, to learn how to add in a new number base, the student could make an addition slide rule to help him build an addition table.

6. The learner must be given adequate *time* to participate in learning activities. To discover a concept independently is time consuming. Learning is a growth process leading gradually to responses at an increasingly mature level. To master a concept, then, requires varied experiences, applications, and uses—all time-consuming activity. Too many teachers move on to new ideas before this absorption can take place. When teaching a basic concept such as ratio and proportion, a teacher should take time to develop mastery and use the concept in a variety of situations so that the student will apply it as needed in the chemistry class, social science class, the shop, or the home.

THE CLASSROOM LEARNING SITUATION

The way in which the student is responding to a learning situation can be illustrated by the chart in Fig. 5–2.

The goal of classroom activities is to learn mathematics. But the learner is reacting to a variety of disturbing stimuli in the classroom. He responds by doing what seems at the moment most desirable or most necessary for him. Most of these activities are not directed toward the learning goal. The barrier which separates him from the goal is ignorance or lack of skill. He cannot answer the question or solve the problem at hand. If the barrier is insurmountable—that is, if the learner has insufficient ability, background, or motivation—the goal is never attained, the learner is frustrated, and responses are likely to turn toward other goals—antisocial goals, such as disrupting the class.

It is the teacher's role (1) to establish the desirability of the learning goals described in Chapter 2, (2) to provide means of overcoming the barrier, and (3) to make the learner aware of the path that led to his

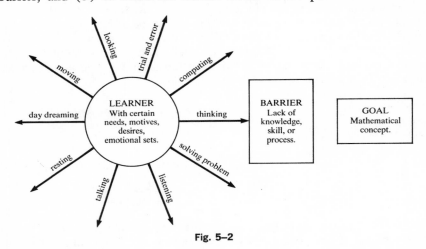

Fig. 5–2

success so that he will use it again. This path is established by making him aware of relationships, organization, structure, and applications. The path becomes narrow and difficult if it is established merely by drill and practice; it becomes broad and easy when such questions as how and why are answered. With this latter approach supplemented by time, experience, and reflection, concepts take on greater meaning and become useful in attaining other concepts. Thus, equations take on more meaning when related to inequalities and when used to solve problems based on formulas. At the same time, they make the attainment of goals related to inequalities and problem solving easier to achieve. Intuition and constructive thinking lead to deduction and analytic thinking.

HOW MATHEMATICAL CONCEPTS ARE FORMED

The typical sequence for learning a mathematical concept progresses from perception to abstraction to integration to deduction, as outlined in the flow chart of Fig. 5–3. Concepts of the simplest order, such as addition, are formed as the result of repeated sensory or motor experiences. Concepts of higher order, such as functions, are formed when experiences and previously learned concepts are related through reflective thought. In short, we learn mathematical concepts in the following way: (1) We sort objects, events, or ideas into classes or categories. (2) We become aware of relationships within the classes or categories involved. (3) We find a pattern which suggests relationships or structure. (4) We formulate a conclusion which seems to describe the pattern of events or ideas involved. (5) We establish the generalization by a deductive proof.

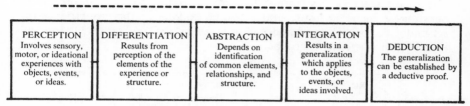

| PERCEPTION Involves sensory, motor, or ideational experiences with objects, events, or ideas. | DIFFERENTIATION Results from perception of the elements of the experience or structure. | ABSTRACTION Depends on identification of common elements, relationships, and structure. | INTEGRATION Results in a generalization which applies to the objects, events, or ideas involved. | DEDUCTION The generalization can be established by a deductive proof. |

Fig. 5–3.   Concept Formation Flow Chart.

Let us apply the flow chart of concept formation by seeing how a specific concept is formed: addition of a positive and a negative number. We first assure ourselves that the learner has the necessary background information about positive and negative numbers as coordinates of points on a number line and an understanding of absolute value. If he has mastered these ideas he is *ready* to learn the addition concept.

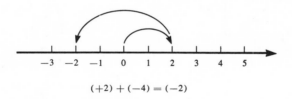

$$(+2) + (-4) = (-2)$$

Fig. 5–4

Experience: The first stage in learning a concept is the sensory experience with concrete objects or visual representations. The manipulative sensory stage for the addition of integers consists of illustrations of these sums in terms of "jumps" on a number line. The learner readily relates this process to his experience with the number line in adding two counting numbers.

Differentiation: These experiences are then compared and related to find the role of each process or each result. Examples worked by reference to the number line are recorded and the results examined carefully for a pattern of data suggesting a possible generalization. Thus, $^{+}5 + {}^{-}2 = {}^{+}3$, $^{-}2 + {}^{+}5 = +3$, and $^{-}5 + {}^{+}2 = -3$ suggests the relationship of the sum to the addends.

Abstraction: The first idea abstracted is usually that there is some kind of a subtraction involved in performing the operation. However, the learner is often able to find the sum of a positive and a negative number before he is able to verbalize the generalization. (Before he generalizes, the student often makes applications such as finding the truth set for $x + 7 = 2$.)

Integration: The learner finally relates the results of his additions to the use of absolute values and states a generalization: the sum of a positive and a negative number is the difference of the absolute values directed toward the larger addend. After considerable practice and guidance he is able to establish the generalization by a deductive proof. Then he determines how what he has learned fits with what has gone before and what questions it opens for future study. And he explores all the properties of the set under the operation of addition to establish the mathematical structure involved, in this case, a group.

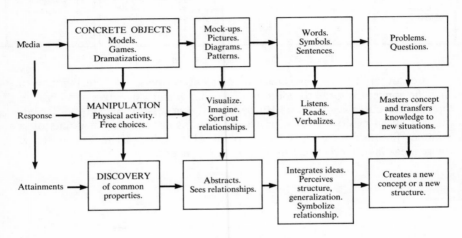

Fig. 5–5.   Model of Learning.

Notice the number of steps and varied responses made before one reaches the deduction stage. Too often, when presenting mathematical concepts, teachers begin with the generalization or even the deductive proof of the concept. Instead they should learn and use the relationships of the media, the response, and the thought processes in learning a mathematical structure as illustrated by the model of Fig. 5–5.

THE ROLE AND SEQUENCE OF DIFFERENT MEDIA FOR THINKING

Each of the different media used for learning concepts plays a particular role, the sequence usually running from concrete to visual to symbol—as indicated in Fig. 5–5.

1. Concrete objects and models provide sensory experiences from which discoveries can be made. An odometer removed from an old car provides a concrete basis for an understanding of decimal relationships.

2. Games and dramatizations provide for interaction and lend informality to learning. Tossing dice, one black for positive numbers and one

red for negative numbers, gives informal drill in adding a positive and a negative number.

3. Mockups, pictures, diagrams, and patterns give the learner an opportunity to visualize and think. This is the way a house plan directs the thinking of the builder. Visualization makes it possible for the student to *see* relationships rather than simply to hear about ideas from the teacher. For this reason the number line is especially useful for learning how to operate with directed numbers.

4. Words, symbols, and sentences are the tools for thinking and communicating. With these tools it is possible to relate new concepts to experiences, ideas, or structures which are already known. With these tools a new concept can be discussed, questions can be raised, and independent reading undertaken. When we can verbalize a generalization, when we can defend a cause-and-effect relationship, when we can describe a structure, and when we can organize a course of action, then we are operating above the plane of rote memorization and mechanical manipulation of symbols. As a child matures, he should also become more reliant on reflection and less dependent on immediate perception in learning new concepts and in building structures with these concepts. Thus, the need for using concrete objects or visual representations is lessened in the upper grades of secondary school mathematics.

5. Finally, questions are raised and problems posed which require the concept to be transferred to a new situation. These probing questions and challenging problems require the learner to combine concepts to form a new concept or a new structure. When a concept is truly mastered by a talented student, he is able to use it to create an original structure. After learning how to add and multiply directed numbers, the student may be able to invent a new numeration system in which the base is a negative number—thus applying his knowledge at a creative level.

DISCOVERING A CONCEPT WITH A GAME

The process of concept formation can be illustrated by the following classroom sequence, which actually took place in a ninth-grade algebra class. A student brought to the class a game called "Jump It," which her uncle "had solved mathematically." The teacher took advantage of this unexpected opportunity to have his class use their knowledge about systems of linear equations and quadratic equations to discover a new generalization.

The game consists of a board with a row of nine holes, as shown in Fig. 5–6. Four black pegs are placed in the four holes at one end, and four white pegs are placed in four holes at the other end. There is an empty hole in the middle.

The object of the game is to exchange the positions of the black and white pegs. A peg may be moved from one hole to another empty hole. A peg may be moved from one hole to the next one or by "jumping" over at most one peg.[1]

---

[1] Gerald Rising, "Some Comments on a Simple Puzzle," *The Mathematics Teacher* (April 1956), 267–269.

1. The learner *confronts* a situation, a question, an idea, or a structure to be explored. The teacher asks Jane, who brought the game, to explain the rules to the class.

2. The learner *accepts* the exploration of the new situation or idea as being worthwhile. The class is challenged by the uncle's "solution" to the puzzle, and students are eager to try the game.

3. The learner *reacts* to the learning situation by participating in discovery activities. He needs to see, hear, speak, think, write, or do something about the problem presented. Students make replicas of the original game with paper counters and try it themselves. *When they are able to solve the puzzle, they are urged to find a minimal solution using the least number of moves.*

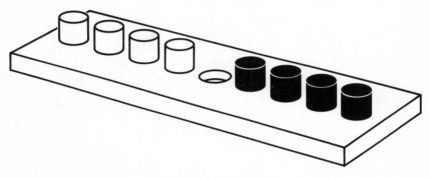

Fig. 5–6.   Jump-It.

4. The learner may use *trial and error* in his search for patterns or relationships from which to abstract a generalization. Most students start with an unorganized attack on the problem, making several false starts and having to begin again. Eventually, they develop a more deliberate strategy. They reduce the puzzle to three holes and two pegs, then five holes and four pegs, then seven holes and six pegs. As they watch the pattern of successful moves, they get a clue to the solution with eight pegs and nine holes.

5. The learner *associates* his previous experiences, memories, skills, or knowledge with the elements of the new situation. Several students relate the game to checkers, while others associate it with related peg games. One student suggests that the game could be played with cards. Another suggests that two sets of different coins could be used.

6. The learner *needs an awareness of his progress* to attain accuracy or reject errors in a generalization. Soon all students have completed the puzzle at least once; they check each other, and several students have what they believe to be the minimal solution.

7. The learner is able to *differentiate* between the properties of the objects, events, data, or ideas involved. Students are urged to focus on the numerical aspects of the puzzle (rather than the moves required to

complete the solution), the *number* of pegs and the *number* of moves in the minimal solution.

8. The learner is able to *abstract* the common elements of the situation involved. Bill suggests recording the number of pegs and the number of moves to discover a relationship. The class constructs a table relating these variables.

9. The learner becomes *aware* of the generalization or structure—the concept involved. Sam suggests that the table is exactly like the ones for which the class had to construct equations.

10. The learner is able to *express* the generalization visually, verbally, or symbolically. The class develops the formula relating the variables by the techniques introduced earlier, arriving at the equation $N = n \ (n + 2)$. (See point 13 below.)

11. The learner is able to use the generalization in a new situation. The teacher poses several questions to ensure understanding: "How many moves would it take to complete the puzzle with ten counters?" "How many counters would there be if the completion of the puzzle required more than thirty-five moves?"

12. The learner attains *insight into the implications* of his generalization. The class discusses the generality of the results. The students first consider whether or not the results may be extrapolated; then they test one or two predictions.

13. The learner develops an *understanding* of the explicitness, completeness, precision, and logic of the generalization. The students examine the limits of the generalization (in this case, to positive integers) and begin to examine the way it is developed. They focus on the increase in moves when additional pieces are added. First and second differences are obtained to determine whether the solution is linear or quadratic. The data give this set of ordered pairs:

Number of Black pegs (x)	Minimum Number of moves (y)	First Difference	Second Difference
1	3		
		5	
2	8		2
		7	
3	15		2
		9	
4	24		2
		11	
5	33		

Since second differences are constant, the relation is quadratic, or of the form $y = ax^2 + bx + c$.

Since $x = 1$ and $y = 3$, then $3 = a + b + c$.
Since $x = 2$ and $y = 8$, then $8 = 4a + 2b + c$.
Since $x = 3$ and $y = 15$, then $15 = 9a + 3b + c$.
Then $a = 1$, $b = 2$, and $c = 0$.

Thus, the general formula for this game is $y = x^2 + 2x$ or $x(x + 2)$.

14. The learner is able to justify the generalization by a *deductive proof;* he then develops a proof by *mathematical induction.*

15. The learner uses the generalization to *discover or create* a broader concept of which the original generalization is a part. Several students set out to analyze additional games of the same type (Tower of Hanoi, etc.), referring to Hoyle as a principal resource; others attempt to generalize the games to two dimensions.

BASIC PRINCIPLES FOR TEACHING CONCEPTS

The way in which concepts are formed suggest the following:

1. *Concepts cannot be given to the learner.* He must construct them out of his own experiences and thoughts. Therefore, effective teaching consists in providing learning experiences for every student.

2. *Concepts are formed as part of a growth process.* Wider implications and deeper meanings develop from a variety of experiences; therefore, mathematical maturity is nourished by a spiral approach.

3. *Any concept becomes more meaningful and more useful when it is related to the total structure of which it is a part.* Therefore, the mathematical concepts learned each day should be woven into the mathematical structure involved in that day's lesson.

4. *Concepts are best developed by varied experiences rather than by repetitive presentations.* Therefore, problem solving, discovery activities, and a varied routine are more effective than monotonous repetition in learning mathematics.

5. *The level at which a concept should be introduced in a given lesson depends on the readiness, motivation, and ability of the learner.* Therefore, provision must be made for individual differences and motivation in each day's lesson.

6. *Concepts are more likely to be formed when the learner actively operates on his environment and restructures his own thinking than when he simply carries out instructions in a teacher-directed situation.* Therefore, the mathematics lesson usually should not be a lecture by the teacher but a group activity in probing an idea.

7. *Action, manipulation, and imagery precede verbalizing, and verbalizing precedes writing.* The learner should try things out to see what happens. He should manipulate objects, words, and symbols. He should pose his own questions and seek his own answers. He must feel free to ask questions, to make mistakes, to use crutches as he searches for the generalization to be stated.

THE SPIRAL APPROACH TO LEARNING

A method of teaching which develops a concept from the intuitive level to the analytic level, from exploration to mastery, by spacing instruction is called spiral teaching. It is often emphasized in connection with modern mathematical pedagogy.

In the diagram below, the solid line represents the sequential curriculum, the topic by topic study of mathematics, while the dotted line represents contact with a given concept. The over-all vertical ascent indicates an increasingly higher level of maturity and sophistication on the part of the learner as he meets a concept in a new setting at a higher level.

Spiral instruction involves the teaching of a given topic with its related concepts at several widely separated times, with each new exposure to the topic including both new approaches and a higher level of sophistication. Thus, spiral teaching is not at all the same as mere repetition. The spiral approach requires careful planning by both the curriculum developer and the classroom teacher.

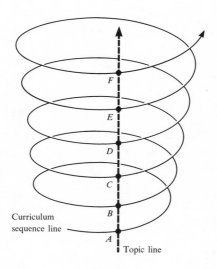

Fig. 5–7

The spiral approach may be illustrated by the concept of graphical representation. In the elementary school, pupils read graphs of statistical data and construct bar graphs and distributive graphs (A on Fig. 5–7). Later, students plot graphs of points on the number line to represent the truth sets of equations and inequalities (B). Soon two dimensional graphs are drawn for linear equations with two variables (C). At a more mature level the intercepts, slopes, and intersections are made meaningful (D). Later these graphs are related to quadratic equations and to periodic and exponential functions (E). At a very mature level graphs are used to discuss continuity, limits, and probability (F).

What concepts does the learner have to know in order to learn the next concept? As illustrated in the flow chart of sub-concepts of Fig. 5–8, each successive step in the hierarchy of the concept depends on other simple subconcepts. The student must have mastered all the concepts at lower levels of the chart in order to understand fully the higher level concepts. Failure to master an idea at any point in the chart makes the understanding

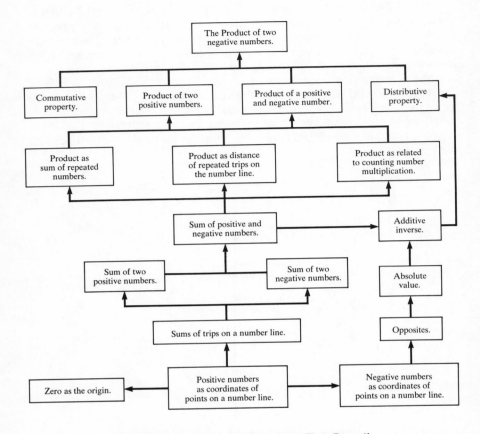

Fig. 5–8.   Flow Chart of Subconcepts That Form the Basis for Multiplications of Negative Numbers.

of higher entries questionable at best. To learn a new concept then requires the recall of all the supporting subconcepts.

DISCOVERY TEACHING

Discovery teaching is instruction which focuses attention on the student. This is not a new pedagogical technique: one of its first advocates was Socrates, and good teachers have been using this method for generations. However, it is not an easy technique because it must be continuously adapted to the students' responses, questions, and experiences and therefore cannot be structured in advance. Moreover, in applying this method the teacher himself may "discover" ideas that are new to him and questions that he cannot answer. It is patience-trying and time-consuming, but teachers who use it never want to go back to an uninspiring and ineffective pattern of recitation-lecture.

HOW DISCOVERY PROMOTES LEARNING

The basic objectives in using the discovery method are to present mathematics so that it makes sense, so that it has significance to the learner, and so that it can be a pleasant experience.

When the teacher illustrates the similarity of polygons having the same shape but different dimensions, he is using a concrete representation to stand for an idea. By this method the student is learning through his reactions and responses to experience.

Since our individual perceptions depend on our past experiences, interest, emotions, and imagination, the teacher cannot control the perceptions of his students and he cannot "give" meaning to the learner. The teacher's role is to guide the learner to connect new ideas to his storehouse of past experiences and memories. In teaching the elementary ideas about vectors, the teacher may make many references to travel in order to stimulate the sense of the topic's relatedness to everyday situations. Then these ideas can be connected to the number line, ordered pairs, and translations on the coordinate plane.

Guesses, conjectures, trial-and-error experiments are used in the discovery method to search for ideas and to relate these new ideas to previous concepts. Thus, the number line quickly relates negative numbers to the corresponding positive numbers, and trips on the number line represent additions.

When the student's reactions are verbal or written, he needs the give and take of discussion to clarify his ideas and to guide him toward fruitful investigations. Only when he has attained a high level of mastery of mathematical vocabulary should he be required to state mathematical ideas in correct language.

Discovering an idea independently gives a sense of confidence, which strongly motivates continued explorations. Finding the pattern of results in folding and unfolding a hexaflexagon has stimulated many reluctant learners to try every possible sequence of folds.

Since we remember about one fifth of what we hear, one half of what we see, and three fourths of what we do, discovery activities (by stressing our most retentive senses) promote a flexible, investigating, creative response to solving problems, and this flexible approach is essential for the transfer and application of knowledge to new situations. Discovery fosters desirable attitudes, for it encourages curiosity for further learning. Discovery is one of the best means of building attitudes of appreciation, enjoyment, and loyalty.

In planning a discovery lesson the teacher outlines a series of questions, problems, or laboratory exercises. The lesson might begin with an introduction, so that the student has a clear idea what he is to explore, what facts he has at his disposal, and what methods seem appropriate.

After the teacher poses a problem, he stimulates the thinking of the students by asking open-ended questions. Student responses should be encouraged by such statements as "That's almost right" or "That's a good idea" or "Keep talking" or even the brief "I see" or "Oh?" Comments such as these reduce the students' fear of being wrong or being embarrassed by the rejection of a poor suggestion. The skillful teacher will use half-formed ideas as stepping stones to correct ideas. It is the teacher's role to keep the investigation going at a challenging rate and in useful directions, for even a correct statement does not always mean that the student understands the idea. The teacher must ask questions which force the student to test his answers, find contradictions, identify special cases, or state a generalization. His role is *not* that of a prosecuting attorney eliciting "yes" or "no" answers. His role is that of guiding the student up a stairway of ideas to the generalization at the top. He guides thinking by helping students to block their own blind alleys and to concentrate on productive avenues.

To illustrate this teaching style here are some questions teachers use in discovery lessons:

"Give me another example."
"Do you believe that, Bill?"
"Will that work with fractions too?"
"How do you know that?"
"Are you sure? Let's test a zero."
"Can anyone find a case for which John's rule doesn't work?"
"Why do you and June disagree?"
"Well, what do you think?"
"How many agree? . . . Can we decide on the basis of this vote? . . . Alice, can you convince this majority that they're wrong?"
"That seems to work. Will it always?"
"Have we forgotten any cases?"
"What do you mean by that?"
"Say that another way."
"How can we simplify this?"
"Can you make a rule that a sixth grader could follow?"

The reader should note that these questions have several aspects in common:

1. They say to the student, "Keep thinking!"
2. They are encouraging.
3. They are equally applicable to right and wrong answers.
4. They treat each student as a partner in the learning process.
5. They encourage interaction between students.

A DISCOVERY LESSON

Let us consider a specific discovery lesson to see the interaction of student and teacher:

Teacher. We have learned how to find solution sets for equalities. Today we will consider another important relationship—inequalities. First, let's see if we can't devise some informal rules for operating with them. I've written $x > y$ on the board as our basic relationship. Next let's consider statements of the form $x + a$ and $y + a$ which relate addition to our inequalities. Can we say anything about these expressions?

Dorothy. $x + a > y + a$.

T. Oh?

D. Because it's like $x = y$. We add the same thing to both sides.

T. I see.

Bill. That doesn't necessarily work.

Lon. But it does this time. If I take $5 > 4$ (*at this point the teacher offers chalk and Lon writes his mathematical statement on the board*) and add 2 to each side, I get $7 > 6$, a correct statement.

T. Do you agree, Jane?

Jane. Yes.

T. Do you think it will always work?

J. Yes.

T. Why?

J. It just seems that way.

T. Oh?

J. If one thing is bigger than another and you increase them the same amount, the bigger stays bigger.

T. That's good Jane. Can anyone say this another way?

D. Yes. It's like piles of flour on a table. If you add the same amount to each pile, the smaller piles can't get larger than the large piles.

T. Can anyone think of a case where this wouldn't hold true?

D. What if a is negative?

T. Aha!

D. It still works. Subtracting 2 from each side of $5 > 4$ gives $3 > 2$.

T. Can anyone suggest an example when we might run into trouble?

L. How about subtracting 6 from each side?

T. Okay.

L. You get $-1 > -2$. Still okay.

T. (*after a pause*). I guess I'll agree to this until we need to write a more formal proof. Can anyone state this as a theorem?

Konrad. If one thing is greater than a second, the same thing added to each will leave the first greater.

T. Maybe symbols would clarify that.

L. If $x > y$, then $x + a > y + a$. (*Given chalk, he writes this on the board.*)

T. Fine. We'll return to prove that later. Now how about products such as ax and ay?

K. $ax > ay$

T. I see. Everyone agree? (*Writes "If $x > y$, then $ax > ay$" on the board.*) How about some examples?

L. If $5 > 4$, $10 > 8$.

T. How did he get that, Jim?

Jim. Doubled.

T. Okay. How about fractions?

D. If $5 > 4$, $2\frac{1}{2} > 2$. Still okay dividing.

T. Always?

D. Yes. It's like the piles of flour.

T. I see, but I don't know that you've convinced me.

Henry. Hey, it doesn't work.

T. Well, Henry has a counter example. Before he tells us, can anyone else find one? (*Walks over to Henry's desk to see what he has written.*)

J. $0 = 0$.

T. How does that apply here?

J. Multiply each side by 0.

T. Can you add to my statement to exclude this (*pointing to board*)?

P. Just put "when $a \neq 0$" (*writes with offered chalk*).

T. I don't think that that was your case, Henry.

H. If you multiply by -2 you get -10 and -8. -10 is smaller instead of larger.

T. Now what? Do we discard everything?

D. Change $a \neq 0$ to $a > 0$.

T. (*frowning*). Anyone agree?

L. Yes. If you keep them positive, it's okay.

T. What about starting with $5 > -2$?

L. Still okay. They stay on opposite sides of zero.

T. I'm satisfied then, but we've still got Henry to contend with.

H. How about "If $x > y$ and $a < 0$, $ax < ay$"?

T. Let's test some cases before we decide.

And so the lesson progresses with the active involvement of the students and the teacher.

One method of promoting discovery is to present a lesson in silence. George Polya, a master of discovery teaching, likes to teach the Pythagorean theorem without words, using these diagrams.

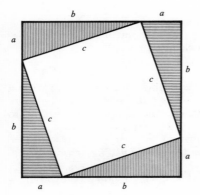 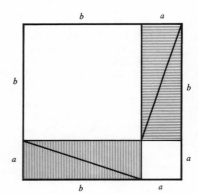

Fig. 5–9

Polya works on this lesson by drawing the above diagrams on the chalkboard and by having students write statements on the chalkboard. Although neither teacher nor student talks, the relationship $a^2 + b^2 = c^2$ is quickly established.[2]

Of course, it is quite difficult to have more than one student discover an idea. As soon as the first student sees the pattern, he tells the teacher and, at the same time, the rest of the class. To avoid this, the teacher should not

[2] The film *Let Us Teach Guessing* (16 mm., color, 2 reels, Modern Learning Aids) is a delightful illustration of how Polya gets his class to discover a generalization through dialogue.

ask for either the solution to the problem or the method of solution, but instead for the answer to a related problem. This question ensures that the student has mastered the technique and, at the same time, allows others to discover the technique for themselves. Another advantage of this method is that other students may produce different and viable methods of solution. Too often, we fix a single pattern when many patterns are possible.

Consider a simple illustration. The game Nim is played by two persons, each in turn removing one, two, or three counters from a pile. The winner is the player who takes the last counter. This game has as a pattern of winning (W) and losing (L) (related to the number of remaining counters):

$$1\ \ 2\ 3\ 4\ \ 5\ \ 6\ 7\ 8\ \ .\ .\ .$$
$$W\ \ L\ L\ L\ \ W\ \ L\ L\ L\ \ .\ .\ .$$

Students are first asked to continue the fairly obvious pattern. Then they record the numerical pattern of winning counters: 1, 5, 9, . . . and extend that. Given an opportunity to record the rule they followed to get new numbers in this sequence, they may offer all of the following:

1. Every other odd number starting with one.
2. Start with one, keep adding four.
3. Start with one, skip three numbers, say the next, skip three, say the next.
4. Numbers that leave a remainder of one when divided by four.
5. One more than the four-times table.
6. $4n + 1$, for $n = 0, 1, 2, . . .$

Here are some specific ways in which a teacher may stimulate learning through discovery:

1. *Pose a question, problem, idea, procedure, example for investigation.* Then be sure the student has a clear idea of what he is to explore and how he should go about exploring it.

2. *Stimulate the thinking of the students by dialogue.* Guide their thinking by asking questions, giving occasional hints, forcing them to relate to known ideas, and requiring reasons. Ask questions which demand student participation.

3. *Plan investigations, exercises, or activities that produce patterns.* These patterns may involve numbers, measurements, answers, designs, graphs, number pairs. The patterns are then examined for a generalization that will generate the pattern.

4. *Arrange laboratory periods in which measurements are made, data are collected, equipment is used, models are constructed, charts are drawn, or computations are performed.* The results are then examined for a generalization such as a formula.

5. *Provide reading, research, or investigations where ideas are explored independently.* Many students discover new concepts directly by reading and thinking about higher relationships rather than by a concrete or intuitive approach.

6. *Use test items which measure a student's ability to discover new*

ideas. This will emphasize to the student the need for learning how to discover ideas.

EXAMPLES OF IDEAS TO BE DISCOVERED

Almost any topic or lesson in mathematics can be developed through discovery activities. However, to help you get started, the following specific ideas can be used to develop class dialogue.

1. The difference between the prime numbers 5 and 2 is 3. Why do no other prime numbers have this property?
2. What is a short cut for squaring numbers ending in 5? Why does it work?
3. What are some unusual properties of 1 and 0?
4. What do we know about odd integers?
5. When is the square of a number less than the number?
6. In how many ways can a sandwich be cut into two equal parts?
7. If $ad = bc$, then $a/b = c/d$. When is this not true?
8. When is $a/b + c/d = (a + c)/(b + d)$?
9. Why is $1.9999\underline{\qquad} = 2$?
10. Why are all regular hexagons similar?
11. What is the distance between two skew lines?
12. What are the properties of the rational numbers of the form $0 < a/b < 1$?
13. What kinds of numbers can be used for a base of a numeration system?
14. How do we know that there is an infinite number of millions?

Here are some topics to be investigated by examining patterns:

1. What is the maximum number of pieces of pie if a round pie is divided by seven cuts?
2. What is the formula for the relationship between the number of vertices, edges and regions of a closed network (Euler's formula)?
3. How is the slope and intercept of a line related to the equation of the line?
4. What relationships exist among the numbers of Pascal's triangle?
5. What is the pattern for multiples of 9? 8? Do these patterns occur in another numeration system?

Here are some questions to investigate through laboratory activities:

1. How is the perimeter of a right triangle related to its area?
2. If the rays of an angle intercept arcs on a circle, how are the intercepted arcs of the circle related to the measure of the angle formed by the rays?
3. What is the number of subsets of a set?
4. What are different ways of illustrating the Pythagorean theorem?
5. What geometric relations can be discovered by paper folding?
6. How can the formulas for the areas of geometric figures be related to the area of a rectangle?

7. What equality properties apply to inequalities?
8. Show that the sum of the first n odd integers is n^2.

CAUTIONS FOR THE DISCOVERY LESSON

Since there are many pitfalls in using the discovery method, some cautions should be kept in mind.

1. *Be sure that correct generalizations are the end result.* Wrong discoveries are difficult to correct. Errors in associations result in chaotic chains of mistaken inferences and deductions; and, of course, failure to discover the generalization is discouraging and confusing.

2. *Maintain a high level of intellectual curiosity even though it may not always be directed toward the idea you wish to attain.* Curiosity is often satisfied by incorrect or partial information; so do not expect curiosity alone to generate the disciplined attention and motivation needed to master difficult ideas. Without judicious guidance and logical restraints, discovery activities may lead to "dense fogs of frustrating perplexity." If a student does not perceive a possible route for his thoughts to follow, discovery activities merely lead to a dead end.

3. *Do not expect everybody to discover every generalization.* Even the high-ability student may lack the curiosity or flexibility to discover ideas. Each student will vary in the time needed to investigate an idea, and the entire class cannot be held back until the slowest discoverer has arrived.

4. *Do not plan to discover all the ideas of your course.* Discovery of some ideas is too inefficient. Sometimes students do not need an intuitive, empirical, discovery approach in order to understand an idea. Not all learning fits into the discovery pattern.

5. *Expect discoveries to take time.* Even though discovery learning is time consuming, the improved meaning and the increased retention that usually result indicate that it is efficient.

6. *Do not expect the generalization to be verbalized as soon as it is discovered.* Unverbalized awareness of the generalization should be the first stage in learning. When the generalization is first verbalized, expect the statement to lack precision and completeness. Words often get in the way. Even though they are extremely important for communication, they can actually obstruct the discovery process.

7. *Avoid overstructuring experiences.* Permit much individual initiative and originality in exploring ideas. Keep a balance between freedom and direction, reflection and knowledge, uncertainty and memory, creativeness and conformity, exploration and generalization.

8. *Avoid jumping to conclusions on the basis of too few samples.* The exploration should be an example of how a rational person explores ideas and problems.

9. *Do not be negative, critical, or unreceptive to unusual or off-beat questions or suggestions.* However, incorrect responses must not be accepted as true; and disruptive, non-essential explorations must be eliminated. Students should know that their status is not threatened by incorrect answers.

10. *Keep the student aware of the progress he is making.* He should expect difficulties, frustrations, failures. If possible, have crucial ideas "discovered" repeatedly or by different methods.

11. *Finally, each student must recognize why his discoveries are significant and how the ideas are incorporated in the structure involved.* This consolidation of the new insight is as important as the discovery itself.

LEARNING EXERCISES

1. Select a mathematical concept. Outline the experiences that should be provided in order for the learning of the concept to develop from a concrete stage to the creative level.

2. Examine a school mathematics curriculum and identify the spiral presentation of a given topic.

3. Select a mathematical topic taught in a given course. Identify the major mathematical ideas that are needed for readiness to study this topic.

4. Review a research study by Jean Piaget on how children learn basic mathematical concepts.

5. Examine the presentation of a given concept in three different textbooks. Outline and compare the steps they use in developing the concept.

6. Make and administer a pretest for a unit to determine the readiness of a given class for that unit.

7. Draw a flow chart for the sequence of topics to be developed in the study of directed numbers.

8. Present the game *Nim* to a class. Direct the discovery of the solution by a dialogue with the students.

9. Use discovery to find the answers to these questions: (a) How many open or closed regions are formed by five intersecting lines in a given plane? (b) How many open or closed spaces are formed by five intersecting planes?

10. Plan a discovery lesson on permutations leading to a formula based on factorials ($n!$).

11. Direct a class discovery of the binomial expansion by finding powers of binomials.

12. Examine a textbook and find a section which uses discovery as a method of developing a generalization.

13. Find ways in which discovery teaching is used in other fields, such as science, social studies, and English.

6

the structure and logic of mathematics

One of the primary aims of mathematics instruction has always been to teach logic and proof. However, in secondary mathematics courses—except for tenth-grade geometry—very little emphasis was formerly given to proof and deduction. Now all school mathematics emphasizes logic and structure. Even symbolic logic and truth tables are taught as early as the junior high school. In the new school mathematics, students are expected to prove theorems of algebra as well as those of geometry.

The emphasis on the structure of mathematics is now begun in the elementary school, where the commutative, associative, and distributive properties of operations are investigated. In the very early grades, the properties of 0 and 1 are used as the basis for rationalizing certain algorithms; and relationships between operations and their inverses are used to find truth sets. In junior high school mathematics sets, operations, and properties are used to illustrate the mathematical structure of a group: the counting numbers, the integers, the rational numbers, and the real numbers—each is seen as a set of numbers with certain properties for the operations of addition and multiplication; and finite number systems (modular systems) and finite geometries are used to build finite mathematical systems. In senior high school mathematics, fields of mathematics such as geometry are examined as complete mathematical structures; in the process, the nature of proof and the proofs of theorems are studied intensively.

Why do the new mathematics courses place so much emphasis on the structure of mathematics? For several reasons:

When one learns the structure of mathematics, he should have an easier time learning new topics or even new branches of mathematics. Attention to the structure of a subject adds "wholeness" to the learning; and learning in terms of wholes is more effective than attention diverted to isolated elements. Thus, attention to structure is particularly appropriate for continued study or independent learning in the future.

When certain basic properties (e.g., the distributive property) are known, they can be used to explain a variety of new situations. The principle $a(b + c) = ab + ac$ can furnish a rationale for a factoring problem, $3x + 6y = 3(x + 2y)$; for addition of fractions, $2/a + 3/a = 5/a$; even a simple multiplication problem, $3 \times 21 = 63$ is seen as $3(20 + 1)$.

When one discovers the structure of mathematics, he should gain interest in the study of mathematics. Mathematics is a unique, elegant creation of the human mind. Its uniqueness is related to its deductive structure. Consequently, many insightful students, when properly guided, enjoy viewing mathematics as a powerful deductive science.

When one masters the structure of mathematics, he should be able to transfer his knowledge to new problems. Experiences in creating new mathematical structures should build a flexible, insightful approach to problems. Knowing basic procedures should improve skill in analyzing a new situation. Emphasis on the reason for a result such as $(-3)(-4) = + 12$ should indicate a way of rationalizing other operations.

When one understands the structure of a subject, he should improve his retention of ideas. We are more likely to remember a few big ideas than a multitude of independent facts. Thus, the identity element for multiplication, $a \cdot 1 = 1 \cdot a = a$, can provide one with a basis for reconstructing many individual algorithms. Among the questions resolved by use of this one axiom are the following:

$$\frac{a}{b} = \frac{?}{bc}$$

$$\left(\frac{a}{b} = \frac{a}{b} \cdot 1 = \frac{a}{b} \cdot \frac{c}{c} = \frac{ac}{bc}\right)$$

$$\frac{32.79}{6.3} = ?$$

$$\left(\frac{32.79}{6.3} = \frac{32.79}{6.3} \cdot \frac{10}{10} = \frac{327.9}{63}\right)$$

$$\frac{2}{3} \div \frac{5}{6} = ?$$

$$\left(\frac{2}{3} \div \frac{5}{6} = \frac{2/3}{5/6} = \frac{2/3}{5/6} \cdot 1 = \frac{2/3}{5/6} \cdot \frac{6}{6} = \frac{4}{5}\right)$$

When one learns certain structures, he may be able to invent new structures and thus exercise creative talent. A challenging experience for any person is the opportunity to invent a new operation, write new symbols, select a set of elements, and then use these to build a new mathematical system. Teachers often find it a wholesome experience to have students develop and prove theorems which are original for them. For example, suppose $a * b$ means $ab + b$. For the set of counting members is the operation commutative or associative? Is there an identity element? If not, is there a way to circumvent this problem? Is the set of counting numbers closed with respect of this operation?

THE STRUCTURE OF MATHEMATICS

Mathematics is frequently described as a structure consisting of a collection of mathematical systems (or topics), each of which has the typical structure of a deductive science. What is the structure of a deductive system? A deductive system begins by selecting some undefined terms, called *primitive terms*. These terms are needed to supply basic words for communication. Thus, in geometry we use the term "point" as an undefined term in all statements involving points. The use of the word "undefined" here is true only in the strict sense, since the undefined terms like "point" and "line" are actually defined in context by the definitions of other terms, by the facts that are proved about them, and by their relationships. Thus, axioms like "Two points determine one line," "Two distinct lines intersect in at most one point," and "Three non-collinear points determine a plane" characterize or in a very real sense define these "undefined" terms. These primitive terms are then used to state precise definitions of new terms.

Next, certain basic assumptions, called *axioms,* are stated. These axioms are usually chosen because they seem to agree with our experience. They are the statements that provide basic relationships between the fundamental elements of the system. Finally, certain theorems are stated and are proved by a sequence of statements. Each of these statements is justified by a definition, an axiom, or a previously proved theorem. Let us apply this procedure to one of the basic mathematical systems, the theory of *sets*. In this system the only undefined terms are "set" and "element." With these terms the operations of union and intersection of sets are defined. Then it is assumed that these operations have properties such as commutativity and associativity. Next, theorems about sets are proved by means of these undefined terms, definitions, and assumptions.

In order to prove a statement by logical reasoning, the following sequence may be used:

If I get a job, then I will earn money.
If I earn money, then I can buy a bicycle.
If I can buy a bicycle, then I can go to the football game.
Hence, if I get a job, then I can go to the football game.

For beginning experiences, this format may be used:

If $\Box + 5 = 9$, then $\Box = 9 - 5$.
If $\Box = 9 - 5$, then $\Box = 4$.
Therefore, if $\Box + 5 = 9$, then $\Box = 4$.

Notice that these statements are in an "if-then" form, that one statement leads to another. Here is an example of how this reasoning is used in algebra:

Statement	*Reason*
1. If $3x + 7 = 19$, then $3x = 12$.	1. Subtraction property of equality.
2. If $3x = 12$, then $x = 4$.	2. Division property of equality.
3. Hence, if $3x + 7 = 19$, then $x = 4$.	3. Transitive property of implication (statements 1 and 2).

This, then, is the form of proof used in mathematics—from the informal proof in arithmetic to the long elaborate proof of a theorem in advanced mathematics.

GROUPS, RINGS, AND FIELDS

The new school mathematics is concerned with mathematical systems called groups, rings, and fields. These systems are concerned with certain sets, operations, and properties of numbers.

Let us consider a simple mathematical structure called a *group*. To illustrate the nature of a group we will use the set of rational numbers represented by fractions and an operation such as multiplication. What are the properties of the rational numbers as related to multiplication?

Are the rational numbers closed with respect to multiplication? Yes. Every product of two rational numbers is another unique rational number. For example:

$$2/3 \times 1/5 = 2/15, \text{ and } 7/4 \times 3/3 = 21/12$$

Does the associative property apply to the multiplication of rational numbers? Yes. For example:

$$(2/3 \times 4/5) \times 7/9 = 2/3 \times (4/5 \times 7/9)$$

Does the set of rational numbers have an identity element for multiplication? Is there a number, n, such that $a/b \times n = a/b$? Yes. It is 1. For example:

$$3/4 \times 1 = 3/4, \text{ and } a/b \times 1 = a/b.$$

Does every rational number have an inverse with respect to multiplication? Is there a number, n, such that $a/b \times n = 1$? Yes. Since $a/b \times b/a = ab/ba = ab/ab = 1$, the multiplicative inverse of a/b is b/a. We say that b/a is the reciprocal of a/b. Thus, for $3/4$ the reciprocal is $4/3$, and $3/4 \times 4/3 = 1$.

Although we have not proved that these properties always hold true (an example does not, of course, constitute a proof), we can easily prove that they do by noting similar properties of the integers. Thus, if we wish to prove that the rational numbers are closed with respect to multiplication, we note that in the product $a/b \times c/d = ac/bd$, both ac and bd are integers because of the closure property of integers. This means that ac/bd represents a rational number and completes the proof. Other properties are proved by similar means.

We now have the six requirements for a mathematical group:

Requirements	*Example*
1. A set of elements.	1. The set of rational numbers.
2. An operation.	2. Multiplication.
3. The set of elements is closed with respect to the operation.	3. The product of any two rational numbers is another rational number.
4. The operation is associative.	4. The grouping of the rational numbers in multiplication does not change the product.
5. There is an identity element for the operation.	5. The identity element for multiplication is 1: $a/b \times 1 = a/b$.
6. There is an inverse, with respect to the operations, for each non-zero element of the set.	6. The multiplicative inverse for each rational number is its reciprocal.

In a similar way other sets of numbers (such as the counting numbers, the integers, and the real numbers) are examined with respect to addition and multiplication to see whether they are examples of mathematical groups.

When a set of numbers involves two operations, such as addition and multiplication, we may have mathematical systems called rings or fields. The requirements of rings and fields are summarized and related to groups in the table below:

TABLE 6–1

Property	Operation	Group	Ring	Field
Closure	$+$	G_1	R	F
Closure	$\times$	G_2	R	F
Associative	$+$	G_1	R	F
Associative	$\times$	G_2	R	F
Identity element	$+$	G_1	R	F
Identity element	$\times$	G_2		F
Inverse	$+$	G_1	R	F
Inverse (non-zero elements)	$\times$	G_2		F
Commutative	$+$		R	F
Commutative	$\times$			F (except skew fields)
Distributive	$(\times)$ over $(+)$		R	F

If we examine the properties of the set of rational numbers or real numbers or complex numbers (in each case excluding zero for multiplicative inverses) with respect to addition and multiplication, we have examples of fields.

FINITE MATHEMATICAL STRUCTURES

A good way to study mathematical structures is to select a finite set of elements and then select operations to apply to these elements. The results of the operations are examined to determine whether or not this finite system is a group, a ring, or a field.

As an example of a finite mathematical structure, consider the set {0, 1, 2, 3, 4}. Instead of a number line, this set is best illustrated by an integral number circle on which a finite number of elements are used.

Fig. 6–1

Let us select the operation "addition," which we will consider a clockwise counting—beginning with zero. We will use the symbol $\oplus$ instead of + to show this circular "addition." We call this finite system a "modular arithmetic" or a "mod-5" system. Our regular clock is a good illustration of a modular arithmetic. On our clock $8 + 7 = 3$ rather than 15. Similarly, for our mod-5 system we get these results: $2 \oplus 2 = 4$, and $3 \oplus 3 = 1$.

For reference purposes we make an "addition" table for all the possible addition combinations.

TABLE 6–2.   ADDITION TABLE (MOD-5).

$\oplus$	0	1	2	3	4
0	0	1	2	3	4
1	1	2	3	4	0
2	2	3	4	0	1
3	3	4	0	1	2
4	4	0	1	2	3

Is our mod-5 system closed with respect to $\oplus$? Yes. Every result in our table is another element of the set {0, 1, 2, 3, 4}.

Is our mod-5 system associative with respect to $\oplus$? Does $(2 \oplus 3) \oplus 4 = 2 \oplus (3 \oplus 4)$? Yes. Thus, we assume that the associative property applies to all "additions" in this system. How many checks would have to be made?

Is there an identity element for the operation $\oplus$? If $3 \oplus n = 3$ and $4 \oplus n = 4$, what is n? It is 0. Hence, our identity element for "addition" is 0.

Is there an additive inverse for every element of our set? Is there a number, n, such that $x \oplus n = 0$? If we examine our addition table, we find that $1 \oplus 4 = 0$, $2 \oplus 3 = 0$, $3 \oplus 2 = 0$, $4 \oplus 1 = 0$, and $0 \oplus 0 = 0$. Hence, every element of our set has an additive inverse.

As we check the characteristics of this finite system, we find that it satisfies all the characteristics of a group.

If we establish another operation, $\otimes$, we can then determine whether this set, with the operations $\oplus$ and $\otimes$, is a ring or a field. The operation $\otimes$ can be illustrated by the example $2 \otimes 3 = 2 \oplus 2 \oplus 2$. Now determine whether or not the mod-5 system is a ring or a field.

HOW TO ORGANIZE LOGIC AND STRUCTURE

There are several ways in which the logic and structure of mathematics can be organized for instruction:

1. *As a separate course or unit,* in which principles of reasoning, finite structures, venn diagrams, symbolic logic, truth tables, and the structure of mathematics are presented as a complete, unified topic.

2. *As a complete structure for one subject or field of mathematics* (e.g., high school geometry).

3. *As a part of every mathematics course.* Then the emphasis on structure becomes a unifying idea, and the proofs become means of teaching problem solving as well as logical reasoning. Frequently this treatment becomes too rigorous and formal for many students.

No matter what organization is used, the teacher must realize that the logic and structure of an abstract subject such as mathematics must be presented in a well-organized program. This program, like any other, must evaluate what students know and build carefully on this knowledge. It must introduce ideas in a framework understandable and interesting to students and must use all available techniques of reinforcement.

HOW TO TEACH LOGIC AND STRUCTURE

Reasoning and logical inference are complex mental processes. We need to use every means at our disposal for assuring success and maintaining interest in the process. There are many ways to do this:

1. *Relate the chain of if-then statements to the logic used in daily decisions.* Start with simple, concrete situations and lead to logical conclusions by questions and answers. Implications can be used to illustrate answers to any number of questions such as "Why do you study mathematics?" "If I learn mathematics, then I can become an engineer." "Why do you want to buy a new coat?" "If I buy a new coat, then I will look more attractive. If I look more attractive, then Bill may ask me to the party."

Before the formal structure of mathematics can be understood, the student must have available to him a reservoir of experiences and concepts to which operations such as those of logic are applied. Only within the framework of experiences of this type does the structure and logic make sense to the student. Thus he must be aided to relate the formal ideas to concepts and experiences already familiar to him, whether these concepts and experiences come from arithmetic and algebra or the out-of-school informal and (to him) nonmathematical world.

2. *Illustrate the reasoning process visually by Venn diagrams or Euler circles.* Why do girls study mathematics? Because:

    a. All girls (G) are intelligent (I).
    b. All intelligent persons study mathematics (M).
    c. Therefore, girls study mathematics.

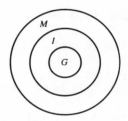

Fig. 6–2

The diagram shows that all girls are a subset of persons who study mathematics.

3. *Complete proofs in algebra and number theory—proofs that are simple and verify experimental results.* The product of two even numbers is always another even number. By working out many multiplications, we find that this statement seems to be true. But when we represent the even numbers as $2a$ and $2b$, with a and b integers, the product is $2a \cdot 2b = 2 \cdot 2 \cdot a \cdot b = 2(2ab)$. Since $2ab$ is an integer, $2(2ab)$ is of the form $2n$ for an integer, $n;$ and $2a \cdot 2b$ is therefore an even number.

The Pythagorean theorem is another illustration of a theorem that can be "discovered" by drawing and measurement. We can extend this procedure by finding the pattern of the triples of measures of sides of right triangles. Later an algebraic proof is given, and finally several geometric proofs are possible.

4. *As much as possible, avoid proving statements that are trivial or meaningless to students.* It is difficult to motivate students to learn proofs of statements that are obvious. Only when such statements have meaning and importance to students—as when they are provided in answer to a student question or when they are absolutely necessary to further development—should they be introduced.

5. *Avoid the proof of too many theorems.* We can't take the time to prove every theorem. We prove enough to learn the method of proof and to see the structure of a topic. In particular, theorems with complicated proofs that occur early in geometry are usually better postulated, their proofs

delayed until students are better equipped to understand them. For example, students can learn techniques of proof when they use the congruence theorems to write simple proofs of congruency. Once the technique of proof is mastered, the better students may reexamine the proofs of the more difficult congruency theorems themselves.

6. *Never require the memorization of proofs.* Proofs, like problems, are useful primarily as exercises in reasoning. Many teachers reason incorrectly that memorization of proofs leads to later understanding. Quite the contrary, there is reason to believe that memorizing the steps in a proof actually blocks understanding. It is certainly better that the student's energy be expended on learning the technique of proof.

7. *Give students confidence by providing them with opportunities to write short simple proofs* before progressing systematically to more difficult proofs. A student cannot prove that the medians of a triangle are concurrent if he cannot prove triangles congruent. At other times, a teacher can "soften" proofs by providing some of the steps of the proof and leaving blanks for the student to supply reasons or statements. Beginning work with proofs can be made easier if the teacher asks *groups* of students to combine their ideas to find a complete proof.

8. *See to it that students know and understand the cornerstones of proof: the axioms, postulates, and definitions.* Failure to master these basic tools makes later work virtually impossible. Systematic review of them should be a continuing part of the classroom program.

9. *Illustrate proofs through the use of symbolic logic.* Some people believe that the use of symbols makes proof difficult. But consider the role of symbols in algebra. Until Diophantus introduced the use of a symbol for the variable in an open sentence, little progress was made in developing algebra. Until that time, problems were solved by means of written statements; and an elegant solution was one that could be stated in rhyme. Now we solve these problems by writing equations. When symbols are used for variables in an equation, even young children can find the solution set. Thus, $3\square + 5 = 29$ is now a fourth-grade problem. Only two centuries ago it was a problem for college mathematics. Similarly, symbols such as p, q, and r can be used to represent statements in proofs, just as x, y, and z are used to represent variables in equations. Experimental teaching has found that sixth graders and slow ninth graders can use this type of symbolism correctly and with enthusiasm.

10. *Apply logic to the solution of puzzles and paradoxes.* There are a great many interesting situations described in books on puzzles and fallacies. Many of these furnish problems to be solved by the use of logical reasoning. Frequently, students can make up situations to be submitted for solution by the class. These so-called "brain busters" are stimulating especially to the higher-ability student.

11. *After studying logic and proof by means of truth tables or venn diagrams, relate the proof to an electric circuit.* Simple demonstration boards consisting of circuits with switches in series or parallel illustrate the truth values of compound statements. These circuits are dramatic demonstrations of truth tables and lead to a consideration of the logic circuits of electronic computers.

A simple card device for testing syllogisms is described by Martin Gardner in the March 1952 issue of *Scientific American.* Other simple logic machines and kits for building logic circuits are available at low cost.

12. *Give students opportunities to write proofs in various forms.* Actually, students might learn proof more readily by writing five different proofs of a given theorem than by proving five different theorems. Proofs can be done in these different ways:

    a. double-column "T" form
    b. paragraph form
    c. diagrammatic format
    d. flow chart
    e. symbolic-logic sequence

Paragraph proofs and diagrammatic proofs are useful as alternate vehicles for demonstration. These alternate forms help students see that there is no single acceptable style for proof, and they relate more directly to forms of proof used in debate and legal reasoning. A paragraph proof in particular allows greater latitude and encourages extra explanation. Consider the following example:

Theorem
Between every two rational numbers there is at least one rational.

Proof
We will show that the average of the two rationals lies between them. If A and B are any two rationals, we must show $A < C < B$. Let $C = \frac{1}{2}(A + B)$, a rational number by the properties of closure for addition and multiplication for rationals. To show $A < \frac{1}{2}(A + B)$, we choose $A < B$. By adding A to each side of this inequality, we have $2A < A + B$. Multiplying by $\frac{1}{2}$ gives $A < \frac{1}{2}(A + B)$. Both of these steps are a result of axioms of order (addition and multiplication). By a symmetric argument, it may be shown that $\frac{1}{2}(A + B) < B$. Thus, the rational number $C = \frac{1}{2}(A + B)$ lies between A and B.

On the other hand, a diagrammatic proof forces students to examine in greater detail the elements of their proof. Because reasons for statements would necessarily confuse a diagrammatic proof, they are usually omitted; however, students should be required to produce these reasons on demand. Here is an example of a diagrammatic proof:

Given
    $\overleftrightarrow{AC}$ a straight line
    $DC = BC$
    $m \angle DCE = m \angle BCE$
Prove
    $AD = AB$

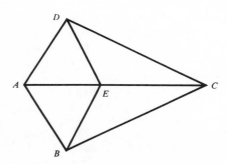

Fig. 6–3

$$\left.\begin{array}{l} \overline{DC} \cong \overline{BC} \\ m \angle DCE = m \angle BCE \\ \overline{EC} \cong \overline{EC} \end{array}\right\} \rightarrow \triangle DEC \cong \triangle BEC \rightarrow \angle DEC \cong \angle BEC$$

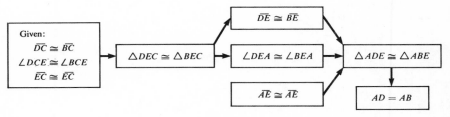

A simple flow chart of this proof might be the following:

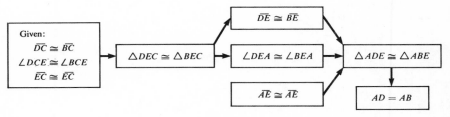

Fig. 6–4

In symbolic logic we use the following symbols:

$p = $ "$\overline{DC} \cong \overline{BC}$"	$t = $ "$\overline{DE} \cong \overline{BE}$"
$q = $ "$\angle DCE \cong \angle BCE$"	$u = $ "$\angle DEA \cong \angle BEA$"
$r = $ "$\overline{EC} \cong \overline{EC}$"	$v = $ "$\overline{AE} \cong \overline{AE}$"
$s = $ "$\triangle DEC \cong \triangle BEC$"	$w = $ "$\triangle ADE \cong \triangle ABE$"
	$x = $ "$AD = AB$"

$$(p \wedge q) \wedge r \Rightarrow s$$
$$s \Rightarrow t \wedge u$$
$$t \wedge u \wedge v \Rightarrow w$$
$$w \Rightarrow x$$

By the transitive property of implications, $(p \wedge q) \wedge r \Rightarrow x$.

13. *Help students to develop analytic as well as synthetic proofs and urge them to use combinations of the two approaches in working out a proof.* Students who have written synthetic proofs (the standard form) usually think of analytic proofs as "backward" proofs. Consider the proof of the last example in synthetic form. (Reasons are omitted but may be required.)

1. $AD \cong AB$ because $\triangle ADE \cong \triangle ABE$ (2).
2. $\triangle ADE \cong \triangle ABE$ because $\underline{AE} \cong \underline{AE}, \underline{DE} \cong \underline{BE}$ (5) and $\angle \underline{DEA} \cong \underline{\angle BEA}$ (3).
3. $\angle DEA \cong \angle BEA$ because they are *supplements* of (4) $\angle \underline{DEC} \cong \underline{\angle BEC}$ (5).
4. They are supplements of these angles because $\overleftrightarrow{AC}$ is a straight line.

5. $DE = BE$ and $\angle DEC \cong \angle BEC$ because $\triangle \underline{DEC} \cong \triangle \underline{BEC}$ (6).

6. $\triangle DEC \cong \triangle BEC$ because $DC = BC$, $EC = EC$, and $\angle DCE \cong \angle BCE$.

(Note that in this proof a technique that is also useful in synthetic proofs is used. In each step an idea that must be established is underlined; when it has been established, the number or numbers of the steps which provide this basis are written in parentheses after the phrase.)

Once they have seen an analytic proof, students may better understand the task confronting them by means of an analogy to a battlefield problem.

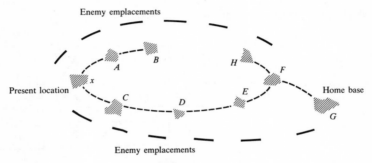

Fig. 6–5

They are a platoon separated from their base by a valley surrounded by enemy emplacements. They can observe the entire valley from their present position. Their problem is to return to their base. There are several routes they may choose. One approach to the problem would be to rush out to the nearest safe place and from there reconnoitre to find another spot ahead. This is what many students do in writing proofs. They often find themselves in positions like B and cannot go forward safely. (Many students make an unsuccessful "dash for it" from here, leaving gaps in their proofs.) A better technique is to *chart a course* by observing: "I can get from X to A to B but no farther, or I can get from X to C to D to E to F to G. Since the latter is a complete route, I will follow it." Or "I can get to G from F and F from H, but that is a dead end. I could get to G from F, F from E, E from D, D from C, C from $X;$ so I will follow that route in reverse." The first of these techniques illustrates the synthetic; the second, the analytic approach to organizing the proof. Once the mental map is drawn, the proof can be written in either form.

A combination of these two methods is usually the preferred procedure. This method, that of "narrowing the gap," is as useful in problem solving as in working out proofs. Working forward from what is given and backward from what is to be proved (by the synthetic and analytic means already pointed out) usually isolates the key difficulty in the proof and makes this difficulty easier to attack. A typical example of this procedure is the solution of identities in trigonometry.

14. *Be sure to provide plenty of experience with indirect proof,* a very

important form of proof often applied—and misapplied—in modern society. Too often, teachers use indirect proof for only one or two theorems and fail to give students any real understanding of the techniques involved.

The kind of indirect proof used in geometry takes the following form:

    1. One of the following (say, A, B, C) is true.
    2. All but one (say, A and B) are false.
    3. The remaining one (in this case C) is necessarily true.

Students usually see this method applied only to the following theorem:

> If two lines are cut by a transversal to form equal alternate interior angles, the lines are parallel. (1) In this proof there are two alternatives: the lines are parallel, or they are not parallel. (2) That they are not parallel is disproved. (3) The remaining case must then be true: They are parallel.

A number of other theorems, however, can be proved by this technique, in particular theorems involving inequalities. Consider the proof of the following theorem:

> If one angle of a triangle is greater than the second, the side opposite the larger angle is greater than the side opposite the smaller. If the converse of this theorem has already been proved, this theorem is easily established by indirect reasoning: (1) Three cases are apparent: the sides are equal, the side opposite the larger is smaller, or the side opposite the smaller side is larger. (2) The first of these cannot apply because equal sides would force the angles to be equal. The second contradicts the converse. (3) The remaining possibility is established, and the proof is complete.

The logic used in discharging the unwanted cases is of the form:

$$p \rightarrow q$$
$$\underline{q \text{ false}}$$
$$p \text{ false}$$

This form of proof is often called *reductio ad absurdum*. It should not be confused with:

$$p \rightarrow q$$
$$\underline{p \text{ false}}$$

In this case no conclusion is possible, since q is either false or true (as may be seen later in the truth table for implications). For example, consider the false statement $2 = 3$. By adding,

$$
\begin{array}{ccc}
2 = 3 & & 2 = 3 \\
& \text{and} & \\
\underline{2 = 3} & & \underline{3 = 2} \\
4 = 6 & & 5 = 5
\end{array}
$$

It is rather easy to locate examples of indirect reasoning in newspaper, radio, and television advertising. Students delight in locating sources of misleading statements: in the form of the implication, in failure to list all the possible cases to be examined, or in failure to discharge all alternatives satisfactorily.

15. *Especially at the junior high school level, lay the groundwork for the later, more formal study of logic by encouraging bright students to play logic games* such as WFF 'N PROOF. The materials are designed to be autotelic—that is, self-teaching—games. Two or more bright students can work almost completely independently, learning the sequence of games and thus a great deal about logical operations and relations.

16. *Use good logic yourself and demand its use by your students*—not only in formal proofs but in statements and activities. Set a high standard of thoughtful and consistent reasoning in your dealings and relations with students.

A TOPIC AS A COMPLETE MATHEMATICAL SYSTEM

One way to emphasize structure is to organize each topic as a structured unit. Here is how this may be done with a unit on area.

Undefined terms: None are needed because area is treated as a complete topic with a host of already accepted terms.

Definitions
1. A polygonal region is the union of a polygon and its interior.
2. The area of any polygonal region is a positive real number.
3. The area of a square whose sides are one unit in length is 1.

Assumptions (postulates)
1. If two polygons are congruent, then the areas of the polygonal regions are equal.
2. If the intersection of two polygonal regions does not include any interior points of the regions, then the area of the union of these regions is the sum of their areas.
3. The area of a rectangle is the product of the measures of two adjacent sides.

Theorems
1. The area of a parallelogram is the product of the measure of any base and the measure of the corresponding altitude.
2. The area of a triangle is the product of half the measure of any side and the measure of the altitude to that side.

Postulate
The area of a circular region of radius r is $K = \pi r^2$.

Other theorems and problems are developed from these.

VENN DIAGRAMS

A good way to illustrate logical reasoning is to use Venn diagrams. These are visual presentations of relationships that are easy and interesting for junior high students. We must remember, however, that such diagrams do not constitute a formal proof.

Venn diagrams are based on the Greek logic, which stated proofs in the form of syllogisms. These syllogisms consist of three statements: a major premise, a minor premise, and a conclusion. Since these statements use quantifiers such as "all," "none," or "some," we can represent the statements by sets and the sets by geometric diagrams. Then the union and intersection of sets will describe the relationships involved. Here are some examples:

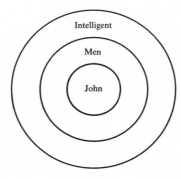

Fig. 6–6

1. All men are intelligent. (Men are a subset of the set of intelligent people.)
2. John is a man. (John is a subset of the set of men.)
3. Therefore, John is intelligent. (John is a subset of the set of intelligent people.)

The diagram for the syllogistic reasoning above is often given the name Euler's Circles. This representation is used only for the special case of set inclusion.

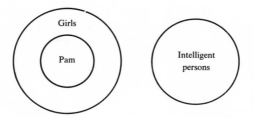

Fig. 6–7

1. No girls are intelligent.
2. Pam is a girl.
3. Pam is not intelligent.

When we have the quantifier "some," we have difficulty selecting the correct Venn diagram because there are several possibilities.

Fig. 6–8

1. Some quadrilaterals are parallelograms.
2. *ABCD* is a quadrilateral.
3. *ABCD* is a parallelogram.

These alternate possibilities suggest that venn diagrams are not adequate to prove all relationships. Fortunately, mathematics has more refined ways of establishing the proofs.

SYMBOLIC LOGIC, TRUTH TABLES, AND ELECTRIC CIRCUITS

In mathematics we often use open sentences called equations to solve problems. In the equation $x + 5 = 13$, x is a placeholder for some number of the domain, $+$ is a symbol for an operation, 5 and 13 are numerals for specific numbers, and $=$ is a symbol of comparison. Similarly, in logical reasoning we use sentences such as $(p \land q) \rightarrow r$. Here p, q, and r are variables which represent statements, $\land$ is the symbol for the conjunction "and," and $\rightarrow$ is a symbol relating $(p \land q)$ to r. Just as the equation $x + 5 = 13$ is an easy way to solve a problem, so $(p \land q) \rightarrow r$ is a convenient way to represent a logical relationship.

In symbolic logic then we use letters as placeholders for simple declarative sentences such as:

$$p = \text{"It is raining."}$$
$$q = \text{"It is warm."}$$
$$r = \text{"We will go swimming."}$$

Next we combine these sentences to form compound statements such as:

Statement	Statement in symbols
It is warm *and* we will go swimming.	$q \land r$
It is raining *or* we will go swimming.	$p \lor r$
If it is raining *then* we will go swimming.	$p \rightarrow r$
If it is raining *and* it is warm, *then* we will go swimming.	$(p \land q) \rightarrow r$
It is *not* raining.	$\sim p$

In these symbolic sentences we use:

1. $\wedge$ to represent "and," called "conjunction"
2. $\vee$ to represent "or," called "disjunction"
3. $\rightarrow$ to represent "if–then," called "implication"
4. $\sim$ to represent "not," called "negation"

Many other symbols are used in logic but these are enough to illustrate symbolic logic.

A chain of reasoning uses a series of statements like this:

1. If it is raining, then it is not warm.
2. If it is not warm, then we will not go swimming.
3. Therefore, if it is raining, then we will not go swimming.

We can write this sequence of statements in symbols like this:

1. $p \rightarrow \sim q$
2. $\sim q \rightarrow \sim r$
3. Therefore, $p \rightarrow \sim r$

The basic pattern for a logical argument follows patterns like this: If $a \rightarrow b$ and $b \rightarrow c$, then $a \rightarrow c$. This particular pattern is called the transitive property of an implication. This pattern is the one used in the preceding argument.

Let's illustrate how this pattern is used for a proof in algebra.

Theorem: If $3x + 5 = 29$, then $x = 8$.

Statement	Reason	Symbolism
1. $3x + 5 = 29$	1. Given	p
2. If $3x + 5 = 29$, then $3x = 24$	2. Subtraction property for equality	$p \rightarrow q$
3. If $3x = 24$, then $x = 8$	3. Division property for equality	$q \rightarrow r$
4. If $3x + 5 = 29$, then $x = 8$	4. Transitive property of implication	$p \rightarrow r$

We can also prove the converse: If $x = 8$, then $3x + 5 = 29$. This is the way we check our equation solution.

Whenever $p \rightarrow q$ and $q \rightarrow p$, we have a biconditional statement (represented by $p \leftrightarrow q$). This is the format for "if and only if" conditions. Thus the theorem above can be restated to be "$3x + 5 = 29$ if and only if $x = 8$." These statements also have the transitive property—namely: "If $p \leftrightarrow q$ and $q \leftrightarrow r$, then $p \leftrightarrow r$." This relationship is needed especially in algebra, where we often start with an open sentence and end up with an equivalent sentence whose truth set is obvious.

We can also use this example to show the relationship of the contrapositive statement to the implication: "If $(p \rightarrow q)$, then $(\sim q \rightarrow \sim p)$" or "If $x \neq 8$, then $3x + 5 \neq 29$." Whenever an implication is true, the contrapositive statement is true and vice versa. This relationship between the contra-positive and the implication is the basis for indirect proof.

In order for the conclusion to a chain of statements to be true, the statements used must be true. Consequently, the statements used are usually definitions, postulates, or previously proved theorems. Hence, it is of importance to consider the truth of simple statements and compound statements. This is often done by the use of truth tables. Here is a comparison of the truth of p and $\sim p$:

p	$\sim$p
T	F
F	T

If it is true that it is raining, then it is false that it is not raining.

Next consider the truth table for the compound statement $p \wedge q$.

p	q	p $\wedge$ q
T	T	T
T	F	F
F	T	F
F	F	F

The table illustrates that the conjunction $(p \wedge q)$ is true only if both p and q are simultaneously true.

A different result occurs for the "or" $(p \vee q)$:

p	q	p $\vee$ q
T	T	T
T	F	T
F	T	T
F	F	F

This compound statement is false only when both statements are simultaneously false.

The truth table for the implication $p \rightarrow q$ is a little tricky. Recall that a statement can be only true or false.

p	q	p $\rightarrow$ q
T	T	T
T	F	F
F	T	T
F	F	T

The implication "If it rains, then it is warm" is false only if it rains and it is *not* warm. Thus the statement "If $1 + 1 = 3$, everything is possible" is a true statement.

These truth tables can be extended to many more complex combinations of statements. One of the dramatic applications of truth tables is the translation into electric circuits. If a lighted lamp represents a true statement then the following simple circuits apply:

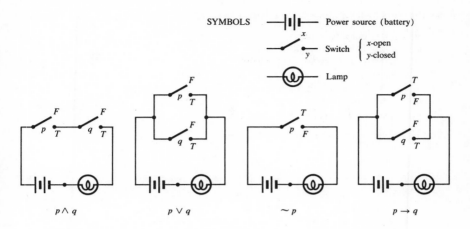

Fig. 6–9

Hence the study of logic in terms of truth tables leads to the use of the computer in analyzing a proof.

PUZZLES AND PARADOXES

Another way to enliven the study of logic is to use it to solve puzzles and paradoxes.

To do this we will accept as valid these arguments:

$$\text{Given} \left\{ \begin{array}{ll} p \to q \\ p \quad \text{(is true)} \\ \hline \text{Then} \quad q \quad \text{(is true)} \end{array} \right. \qquad \begin{array}{l} p \to q \\ \sim q \\ \hline \sim p \end{array} \qquad \begin{array}{l} p \to q \\ q \to r \\ \hline p \to r \end{array}$$

But we will not accept as valid these arguments:

$$\text{Given} \left\{ \begin{array}{ll} p \to q \\ q \quad \text{(is true)} \\ \hline \text{Then} \quad p \quad \text{(is true)} \end{array} \right. \qquad \begin{array}{l} p \to q \\ \sim p \\ \hline \sim q \end{array}$$

Here is a fascinating puzzler from Lewis Carroll.

Theorem:
If John wears kid gloves, he is not an opium eater.
The following conditions are given:
1. If John goes to a party, he does not fail to brush his hair.
2. To look fascinating, it is necessary to be tidy.
3. If John is an opium eater, then he has no self-command.
4. If John brushes his hair, he looks fascinating.
5. John wears kid gloves only if he goes to a party.
6. Having no self-command is sufficient to make one look untidy.

Use the following placeholders for statements.

$p =$ John goes to a party.
$q =$ John brushes his hair.
$r =$ John looks fascinating.
$s =$ John is tidy.
$t =$ John is an opium eater.
$u =$ John has self-command.
$v =$ John wears kid gloves.

Then the given statements are the following:

1. $p \rightarrow q$
2. $r \rightarrow s$
3. $t \rightarrow \sim u$ or $u \rightarrow \sim t$
4. $q \rightarrow r$
5. $v \rightarrow p$
6. $\sim u \rightarrow \sim s$ or $s \rightarrow u$

And we are to prove: $v \rightarrow \sim t$
By rearranging the given sequence of statements we find this chain of arguments.

$$v \rightarrow p$$
$$p \rightarrow q$$
$$q \rightarrow r$$
$$r \rightarrow s$$
$$s \rightarrow u$$
$$u \rightarrow \sim t$$
$$\therefore v \rightarrow \sim t$$

Logical puzzles like this can readily be constructed by students. To do this the students first write a chain of statements for a logical proof. Then the conclusion is stated as a theorem and the steps in the proof are mixed up. Here is an example:

a. If John is well, he hasn't eaten a green apple.
b. If John is not well, he calls a doctor.
c. If John's life is safe, he will not call a doctor.
d. Hence, if John eats a green apple, his life is not safe.

Let p represent John eats a green apple
q represent John is well
r represent John calls a doctor
s represent John is safe

Then the implications are

a. $q \rightarrow \sim p$
b. $\sim q \rightarrow r$ given
c. $s \rightarrow \sim r$
d. $p \rightarrow \sim s$—to be proved

$q \rightarrow \sim p$ implies $p \rightarrow \sim q$ (contrapositive)
$p \rightarrow \sim q$ and $\sim q \rightarrow r$ imply $p \rightarrow r$
$s \rightarrow \sim r$ implies $r \rightarrow \sim s$ (contrapositive)
$p \rightarrow r$ and $r \rightarrow \sim s$ implies $p \rightarrow \sim s$. Q.E.D.

Teachers should provide a stimulating setting for learning logic and structure. Students must understand the need for this structure. Perhaps the best way to illustrate this need is for the teacher to provide many counter-examples and contradicting illustrations, forcing students to fall back on fundamental principles. "Proofs" such as "all triangles are isosceles" and "all numbers are equal" or even "all billiard balls are the same color" force students to examine closely what appear to be examples of correct logical reasoning. This should be a continuing class activity. Examine, for example, proofs of those three statements.

   (1) All triangles are isosceles.

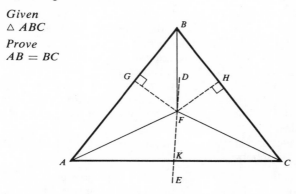

Given
△ *ABC*

Prove
AB = *BC*

Fig. 6–10

1. Construct $\overleftrightarrow{DE}$, the ⊥ bisector of $\overline{AC}$.
2. Construct the bisector of ∠ *ABC* meeting $\overline{DE}$ in *F*.
3. Construct $\overline{FG}$ ⊥ $\overline{AB}$ and $\overline{FH}$ ⊥ $\overline{BC}$.
4. Draw $\overline{AF}$ and $\overline{CF}$.
5. Since △ *BFG* ≅ △ *BFH*, *BG* = *BH*.
6. Since △ *FKA* ≅ △ *FKC*, *AF* = *FC* and △ *GAF* ≅ △ *HCF*.
7. Since △ *GAF* ≅ △ *HCF*, *GA* = *HC*.
8. Adding these, *BG* + *GA* = *BH* + *HC*, or *BA* = *BC*.

A more complete consideration of this false proof is found in Y. Dubnov, *Mistakes in Geometric Proofs* (Boston, Mass.: D. C. Heath and Co., 1963, pp. 9–11, 24–25). In that treatment five other cases are considered, making the proof seem even more acceptable. The error in this proof lies in the drawing—often a source of erroneous thinking. If in the original triangle *BC* > *BA* (as drawn), *F* will fall outside △*ABC*, *G* will fall on the extension of $\overline{BA}$ through *A*, and *H* will fall on $\overline{BC}$ between *B* and *C*. In that case no congruency argument may be constructed.

   (2) All billiard balls are the same color.
By induction, certainly true for $n = 1$ (any one ball is the same color as itself). If true for all $n \leqq K$, then true for $n = K + 1$, because of the overlap as shown in the following illustration:

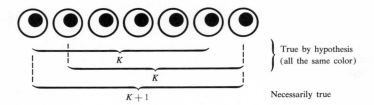

Fig. 6–11

Real insight is required here. The induction principle is met *except* for passing from $n = 1$ to $n = 2$, where the overlap illustrated does not exist.

Students are interested in such "proofs." They like to see how closely mathematics borders on illogical thinking and how careful development and use of structural principles is all that protects us.

Every teacher should collect from his own experience less formal illustrations to support this rule. These illustrations are most easily found in newspaper and television advertising, but other sources are available. Here are two examples:

1. The "Peanuts" cartoon in which Charlie Brown is asked by Lucy how he is doing in school.

> "I'm doing quite well in everything but arithmetic."
> "I should think you would do well in arithmetic. It is a very precise subject."
> "That's just it. I'm at my best in subjects that are mostly a matter of opinion."

2. Mark Twain in *Life on the Mississippi:*

> Please Observe:
> In the space of 176 years the Lower Mississippi has shortened itself 242 miles. That is an average of a trifle over one mile and a third per year. Therefore, any calm person, who is not blind or idiotic, can see that in the Old Oölitic Silurian Period, just a million years ago next November, the Lower Mississippi River was upward of 1,300,000 miles long, and stuck out over the Gulf of Mexico like a fishing-rod. And by the same token any person can see that 742 years from now the Lower Mississippi will be only a mile and three-quarters long, and Cairo and New Orleans will have joined their streets together, and be plodding comfortably along under a single mayor and a mutual board of aldermen. There is something fascinating about science. One gets such wholesale returns of conjecture out of such a trifling investment of fact.

Paradoxes have been of interest to mathematicians for centuries. The classic is the statement "If the barber shaves everyone in town who does not shave himself, who shaves the barber?"

There is a new twist to this.

> Take a sheet of paper; on one side write:
> "The statement on the other side is false."
> Turn the paper over and write:

"The statement on the other side is true."
What is your conclusion?

These are both examples of self-contradictory logical systems and are representative of a type of problem that caused real difficulty in the study of the foundations of mathematics, particularly in set theory.

SPECIAL CONTRIBUTIONS OF STRUCTURE AND LOGIC

Today's world is one of inconsistency. Students are faced with inconsistency everywhere: their parents alternate from permissiveness to extreme strictness; their teachers, seeking to treat each child as an individual, do not discipline students equally; adults talk of the need for moral, law-abiding conduct but at the same time dodge income-tax payments and exceed the speed limit; politicians often make utterances simply because their constituents want to hear them.

The youngsters of today, brought up in this world of inconsistency, seek stability everywhere. Master teachers know that students react favorably to even the most demanding standards when they know that the standards are the same for all. These same students can, and under the guidance of good mathematics teachers often do, find this same stability in mathematics. Dickey and Taylor, in their article "Mental Hygiene and Arithmetic" in *Instruction in Arithmetic* (25th Yearbook of National Council of Teachers of Mathematics), point out the therapeutic values of mathematics in greater detail.

The cohesiveness of mathematics is made apparent through careful study of its structure; and the integrity of mathematics is made apparent through careful study of the binding logical principles. These two important threads should be thoroughly developed in the classroom, not only to give students deeper insights into the subject but also to give them a model for their personal behavior and beliefs.

Learning the mathematical method and mathematics as a system of thought should be considered far more important than learning specific mathematical techniques; for all learning has within it similar but less apparent structures of sequence, emphasis, style, logic, and problem-solving procedures. It is in this sense that mathematics is universal in its applications—to all learning, to society, to the individual.

LEARNING EXERCISES

1. Collect five examples of misused logic from advertising, political speeches, or editorials.
2. Construct a criminal situation in which indirect proof may be used to determine the guilty person.
3. For the following geometric theorem write the proof in the forms listed below. If a tangent and a secant are drawn to a circle from the same exter-

nal point, the square of the tangent is equal to the product of the secant and its external segment. Supply reasons only for part (a):
  (a) in synthetic form
  (b) in analytic form
  (c) diagramatically
  (d) in paragraph form

4. Use symbolic logic to solve other puzzles in references listed in the appendix.

5. Construct a logic problem along the lines of the Lewis Carroll example on page 85.

6. Construct a finite mathematical system. Invent a set of elements and an operation. Determine whether or not your structure is a group.

7. Investigate paradoxes in mathematics as described in Eugene P. Northrop's *Riddles in Mathematics; A Book of Paradoxes* (Princeton, N.J.: D. Van Nostrand Co., Inc., 1944). What are the common errors in the reasoning used in these paradoxes?

8. Investigate Boolian algebra and discuss its use in the logic circuits of electronic computers.

9. Write several proofs of the Pythagorean theorem to illustrate intuitive, deductive, algebraic, and geometric proofs.

10. Select a common theorem from geometry. Write the proof in a format other than the usual T form.

11. Select a topic in mathematics. Establish the structure of this topic.

7

developing computa- tional skills

Mathematics is something like a game: it has rules, goals, and players, and it requires certain skills. Just as games are fun, so the "game" of mathematics can be played for intellectual satisfaction or for the attainment of skills. But games are enjoyable only for skillful players, and often acquiring skill isn't much fun at all.

To learn mathematics and to use it requires a mastery of computation. To master a skill such as computation requires practice, repetition, and drill. However, this practice does not need to be given by countless time-consuming and boring exercises. When practice becomes a meaningless activity, it causes unfavorable attitudes and habits to develop. Even mathematicians dislike rote computations. Consequently, our first responsibility in teaching computational skills is to make the practice as palatable as possible.

We need to inspire our students to practice computation with purpose and energy. To do so, we must (1) make use of a variety of techniques and materials; (2) make sure that the learner knows the purpose of practice—he should recognize that competence in computation will make other activities such as learning new concepts, playing games, calculating odds, or carrying out operations necessary to business easier and more pleasant; (3) help the learner understand the need for repetition and know how to practice independently; (4) make sure he is aware that through this practice he will make progress.

IMPORTANCE OF COMPUTATIONAL SKILL

Although computational skill has always been considered essential for the superior student as well as for the slow learner, employers and teachers often complain that young people in elementary school, in high school, in college, and on the job generally lack this skill. Why? Psychologists and educators give these reasons:

Inadequate understanding of number and operations with numbers.
Lack of interest in attaining computational efficiency.
Lack of ability to cope with the abstract ideas and symbols of computation.
Ineffective teaching of computational processes.

Does it really matter these days whether people have computational skill? Some people might say that it does not, since calculating machines such as the cash register and the electronic computer have taken over computing tasks. However, computational skills are still essential for the following purposes:

1. To facilitate the learning of new mathematical concepts. If his computation is efficient, the learner can devote his mental energy to reflective thinking when facing a new problem or when exploring a new idea.
2. To perform many tasks in the home, on the job, and in recreational activities. Elementary arithmetic examples pervade activities such as shopping, cooking, managing a business, or playing a game.
3. To promote productive thinking in problem solving, research, and other creative activities.
4. To provide sources for insight into the structure of our number systems. Carrying out a computation may be a means of understanding place value, the properties of certain numbers, or the operation involved in an algorithm.

This fourth point is especially important. Many of the great mathematicians of the seventeenth, eighteenth, and nineteenth centuries based their insights into number on the simple arithmetic calculations they performed. Without their broad experience with calculation processes, a good part of their conceptual work would probably not have been achieved. Foremost in this regard was the German mathematician Karl Gauss, who developed many illuminating theorems in number theory from ideas suggested by his work with paper-and-pencil calculations. When Karl Gauss was a boy of eight, his class was given the task of finding the sum of all numbers from 1 to 100 inclusive. Gauss soon found the answer, 5,050, while his classmates struggled to add all these numbers. Gauss undoubtedly noted that

$$S = 1 + 2 + 3 + \cdots + 98 + 99 + 100$$
$$S = 100 + 99 + 98 + \cdots 3 + 2 + 1$$
$$\text{Hence, } 2S = 101 + 101 + 101 + \cdots 101 + 101 + 101$$
$$\text{Then } 2S = 100 \times 101 \text{ or } S = 5,050.$$

Perhaps this discovery, which reduced routine computation into a creative experience, inspired Gauss to become a mathematician. Gauss is now considered one of the greatest mathematicians of all time. Some of his greatest discoveries were in the field of number theory.

It is in much the same way that drill exercises, when they are carefully structured, often can be used to develop a mathematical point. For example, consider the following exercises:

$$371 + 2,934 + 7,066$$
$$899 + 456 + 544$$
$$3\tfrac{1}{7} + 5\tfrac{3}{5} + 2\tfrac{2}{5}$$

Most students will attack these exercises in a straightforward manner. However, if they are urged to find a shortcut or to find the solutions quickly, they soon notice that they can solve the problems most easily by applying the associative property and combining the latter addends first.

The importance of mathematical skills is verified by the statements of recent studies of the current mathematics curriculum:

> Strong skills are surely needed but they must be based on understanding and not merely on rote memorization. Once meaning has been achieved, then drill should be provided to establish skills—skills that can be performed, as Whitehead says, "without thinking." In this way, the mind is liberated to grapple with new ideas. (*Program for College Preparatory Mathematics*. College Entrance Examination Board, 1959.)

> . . . children must know how to do simple and rapid mental computations: they must be accustomed to finding very quickly an order of magnitude for a total or a product. (*New Thinking in School Mathematics*. Organization for European Economic Co-operation, 1961.)

> Mastery of the four fundamental operations with whole numbers and fractions, written in decimal notation and in the common notation used for fractions . . . includes skill in the operations at adult level (i.e., adequate for ordinary life situations) and an understanding of the rationale of the computational processes. (*Program for College Preparatory Mathematics*. College Entrance Examination Board, 1959.)

At the same time that new mathematics programs are advocating a high level of computational efficiency, they are emphasizing the need for a new approach to skill learning:

> Lest there be any misunderstanding concerning our viewpoint, let it be stated that reasonable proficiency in arithmetic calculation and algebraic manipulation is essential to the study of mathematics. However, the means of imparting such skill need not rest on methodical drill. We believe that entirely adequate technical practice can be woven into the acquisition of new concepts. But our belief goes farther. It is not merely that adequate practice can be given along with more mathematics; we

believe that this is the only truly effective way to impart technical skills. Pages of drill sums and repetitious "real-life" problems have less than no merit; they impede the learning process. . . .

We propose to gain three years through a new organization of the subject matter and the virtually total abandonment of drill for drill's sake, replacing the unmotivated drill of classical arithmetic by problems which illustrate new mathematical concepts. (*Goals for School Mathematics*. Cambridge Conference on School Mathematics, 1963.)

Actually, this emphasis on learning through meaningful problem situations has been advocated for a long time.

Continued emphasis throughout the course must be placed on the development of ability to grasp and utilize ideas, processes and principles in the solution of concrete problems rather than on the acquisition of mere facility and skill in manipulation. The excessive emphasis now commonly placed on manipulation is one of the main obstacles to intelligent progress. (*The Reorganization of Mathematics in Secondary Schools*. The National Committee on Mathematical Requirements, 1922.)

However, the present emphasis in psychology of learning suggests a new approach to computational skills. This emphasis—on structure, on discovery, on participation, on meaning, and on reinforcement—has important implications for skill learning. Similarly, new materials such as programmed texts, teaching machines, games, computing devices, and audio-visual aids could be used for skill learning.

PURPOSE OF PRACTICE

Although we cannot improve our skills by practice alone (in fact, repetition can fix wrong ideas just as well as right ideas), practice does provide for refinement of technique and fixation of concepts and procedures in the following ways:

1. Practice is essential for *retention*. We remember only a small part of what we read, hear, see, or do only once.

2. Practice is a means of building *accuracy*. The correct fact should become the only response that is remembered.

3. Practice is the basis for improving *efficiency*. After learning why an operation works, we eliminate crutches and discover shortcuts through exercises that are designed to promote good procedures.

4. Practice is one way to establish *confidence*. Success in computing correctly and efficiently improves motivation, participation, and attitude.

But such positive results do not arise from random practice. They demand careful planning and execution. Often, a teacher can change the very nature of an assignment from drill to concept learning by the instructions given. Consider, for example, the difference between the following sets of instructions:

Do the odd exercises on page 37.

Do the odd exercises on page 37 until you are able to state the pattern involved in each solution. As soon as you can do this, record the rule you would use to solve the exercises you have done. Then do only exercises that differ from that rule.

In the second case the student has a reason to consider each problem carefully. Once he has found a pattern, he need not write other solutions. He must, however, examine all problems in order to test his method and must work out those that do not fit the pattern.

BASIC PRINCIPLES IN PRACTICE

If practice and drill are to be effective, they must be an integral part of mathematics instruction. This practice should be at the right time, in the right amount, and with the right exercises. The following suggestions will add meaning and interest to practice activities.

1. Practice (unlike our daily practice of walking, reading, speaking, or driving a car) must be done with the *intent to improve*. Before he can *want* to improve, the learner must believe it worth his while to attain skill in computation. He needs to be aware of the advantages of being skillful in computation and the handicaps that will result from failure to attain it.

2. Practice should be performed *thoughtfully* and with insight, so that it never becomes mere mechanical repetition. The learner should be able to justify the process, know the properties involved, or relate the process to the definition of the operation. Thus, it is probably better for a teacher to assign a few exercises requiring thoughtful solutions than many exercises calling for automatic responses. This role of reflective thinking in learning a skill is the reason for the current emphasis on practice of computation within the framework of problem solving and applications.

3. Practice should follow *discovery* and *understanding*. It is this understanding as reinforced and extended by thoughtful practice which is the key to learning mathematics, not skill in computation—even though this skill is helpful.

4. Practice should involve *correct responses* rather than incorrect responses. Errors should be eliminated and correct responses reinforced by immediate knowledge of the right answer. Thus, whenever he assigns exercises for independent practice, the teacher should furnish answers for students to use in checking their work.

5. Practice should be *individualized* according to the needs or ability of the learner. Diagnostic tests, observations, or interviews should be used to identify the need for remedial instruction and the reason for the difficulty. The practice of assigning the same exercises to an entire class or assigning more exercises to the student who finishes early is not reasonable. The skillful teacher recognizes that the bright individual needs a few difficult exercises, while the slow learner needs more easy exercises.

6. Practice should be *brief* and at *spaced* intervals. Spaced practice seems to produce better retention, and brief practice is necessary to avoid fatigue. Practice should be used when and where needed and not wasted on

insignificant skills or on well-learned skills. It is not reasonable, for example, for students to drill on division in non-decimal scales.

7. Practice should be given in *meaningful exercises,* so that transfer and application are promoted. If specifics are emphasized, they should soon be integrated into the whole of which they are a part. Thus, practice situations should closely resemble the situation in which the skill is used.

8. Practice should emphasize *general principles* rather than tricks or shortcuts. For example, the associative and distributive principles provide a general procedure for a variety of situations such as adding polynomials, factoring polynomials, and finding equivalent equations. These general principles eliminate the need for memorizing mechanical processes or tricks.

9. The learner should be given instruction in *how to practice.* The learner should know how to use answers for independent learning. He should know what he is expected to write and what he should do mentally. Crutches should be permitted but recommendations made for their elimination by more efficient procedures. (Note, however, that it is better for a weak student to function with a crutch than not to function at all.)

10. Practice should be given in a *variety of activities,* such as games, contests, puzzles, timed exercises, tachistoscope projections, mental computation, group activities, oral or written exercises. Even a short "warm-up" with rapid-fire exercises for mental computation is an effective reminder of facts and processes.

11. Practice becomes more effective if the learner is *informed of his progress.* He should know what competence is expected; how he compares with class, school, or national norms; and what progress he has made. A graph of errors and time can be a dramatic way of showing improvement. Then improvement should become a game as it is in golf or bowling.

12. Practice must *never be a punishment.* Learning mathematics should be a privilege and a pleasant experience. Never assign a set of exercises as punishment for any offense.

By whatever means computation is practiced, the goal is improvement in skills. No teacher should forget this. Many textbook writers recognize this fact and provide sections of review exercises. Whether these are available in the text or not, provision should be made for this review and maintenance in the classroom.

REMEDIAL INSTRUCTION

Even though the principles outlined above are followed, individual differences are such that remedial instruction is frequently necessary. These differences may be due to the learner's low ability, inadequate educational experiences, emotional problems, or lack of interest. The learner may be a poor reader or a slow worker, or he may have physical defects. In any case, the first step in remediation is to locate the specific area of difficulty. In order to identify the specific need for remedial instruction, the teacher should collect information as follows:

1. Use diagnostic tests to identify the process or number set causing difficulty. Any achievement test can be diagnostic if an item analysis is made and the errors analysed.

2. Use evaluative tests to measure the level to which the skill functions when needed. Does the student need an inordinate amount of time to perform? Can he do only easy problems and direct applications of a principle? Varying the time or the difficulty of items, as well as recording types of errors, gives added information on the level of skill development.

3. Observe the way the individual learner solves exercises. Does he make errors in copying problems? Does he use mechancial processes such as "cancellation" or "transposition" without understanding the processes?

4. Interview the learner to identify his thought patterns. Use questions like:

    a. Can you tell me the answer? Is this answer correct?

    b. How did you get the answer?

    c. What did you think about first when you saw the problem?

    d. What did you think before you told me the answer?

    e. Do you like this kind of problem? What kind do you prefer?

After the specific needs are identified, remedial instruction is given. To make this instruction successful, the teacher must accept the learners as they are, show some affection for them, and teach them with patience. He will need to use a new approach with different content to get around emotional blocks and hostile attitudes. He will need to use a variety of materials at appropriate levels—possibly even fourth-grade material for a high school student. He will need to impress on his students that the goal is improvement, not competition with others; that they are working in order to make progress—not just to get a passing grade.

LEARNING COMPUTATIONAL SKILL THROUGH GAMES

Games may be an effective means of making the practice of computational skills palatable. They are also means of attaining other objectives. Games can be adjusted to the interest and abilities of small groups of students and consequently can be used to advantage with the slow learner, the average student, or the gifted student. The creative student can even devise a new mathematical game. In addition, a game can be an ideal device to involve the parent in out-of-class learning activities. A mathematical game can be sent home with the student to gain an informal setting where student and parent to work together at learning mathematics.

The success of a classroom game, like any instructional material or technique, is highly dependent on how it is used. If a game is to play the roles described above, the following factors should be considered:

1. *The game to be used should be selected according to the needs of the class.* The basic criterion is that the game make a unique contribution to learning—a contribution that cannot be attained as well or better by any

other material or technique. The material involved should be closely related to that of the regular classwork. Specifically, the game selected should involve important mathematical skills and concepts; and major emphasis should be on the learning of these concepts or skills rather than on the pleasure of playing the game.

During the game situation *all* students must be participating. Even though only one person is working on a certain problem, every team member also must be responsible for its solution. Games must also avoid extreme embarrassment for the person who cannot solve a problem. Whenever possible, students should compete with other students of equal ability.

2. *The game should be used at the proper time*—that is, usually during the regular class period when the ideas or skills are being taught. There are other times, however, when games promote learning in an otherwise difficult environment. Many teachers prefer to use games on the day before a vacation, or during days of heavy absence due to athletic games, storms, concerts, or excursions. Usually, games should be relatively short so that pupils do not lose interest.

3. *The game must be carefully planned and organized* so that the informality and excitement of the setting does not defeat its purpose. Before the game begins, the participants should be briefed on the purpose of the game, the rules, and the way to participate. Often the students can establish ground rules, so that everyone (including the teacher) may enjoy the activities. "Coaching" or "kibitzing" should not be allowed. The loss of points for breaking rules is usually sufficient to maintain appropriate behavior.

4. *The participants in the game must accept the responsibility of learning something* from the game. Follow-up activities such as discussions, readings, or tests will emphasize this responsibility. The teacher will need to evaluate the results by asking himself how successful the game was in promoting desired learning.

Games appropriate for learning mathematics are limited only by the ingenuity of students and teacher. They can convert almost any practice lesson into a learning game by choosing teams, participating as individuals or teams, and keeping score. Most of the common parlor games or athletic games can be adapted for use in a mathematics class at any grade level.

For example, Bridget is a game similar to bridge. There are four suits (four colors). Each card has an algebraic expression such as x^3 or $(x^2 - 2x)$. Value cards designate the numeral to substitute for the variable. The player whose card gives the highest value of four cards played takes the "trick." Another example is given by mathematical baseball. Here the "pitcher" proposes problems to the "batter." When the batter solves the problem, he makes a "hit." The number of "bases" of the hit depends on the difficulty of the problem. Even if the "hitter" does not solve the problems, he gets on base if an opposing player cannot solve the problem. Quiz games, card games, word-association games, mathematical bingo, spell downs, and identification contests have been successfully used by many teachers.

A card-game variation of bingo is popular with many teachers. The playing cards consist of an array of numbers, algebraic expressions, terms, or geometric figures, depending upon the topic or course involved. The call cards consist of problems, definitions, equations, or algebraic expressions. Player cards are distributed to the members of the class. A student caller selects a call card at random. (Sometimes call cards are large enough to display the problem. At other times the problem of the call card is written on the chalkboard.) Players compute the answer and cover the appropriate space on their playing card.

Identification games may be played like Twenty Questions. A term, number, or principle is selected to be identified in less than twenty questions. Students or teacher may select the term to be guessed. In a similar way, any set of exercises can be used for a relay contest, quiz game or card game.

Printed cards containing numbers (for instance, Rook, Flinch cards, or flash cards) are often useful. Dice or spin dials can also be used to supply numbers. As an interesting variation for dice, the students can make and use regular polyhedra such as octahedrons, dodecahedrons, or icosahedrons. Numbers, algebraic expressions, or problems can be written on the faces of these polyhedra depending on the game involved.

These games can be useful as a means of learning new ideas as well as mastering key ideas and skills. They are effective in lending variety and competition to classroom activities. The teacher is no longer the judge or leader to be outsmarted. Instead, the students vie with each other, work together as a team, and accept responsibility for doing their best. This is why the Minnemast Project and the Cambridge Conference recommend games for learning mathematical concepts.

Many mathematics games can now be purchased ready for use in the classroom, from kindergarten through high school. Commercial games for the mathematics class are listed in the Appendix. However, many games that can be prepared by students or teachers are described in *Games for Learning Mathematics*.[1] Making games based on current classwork may be an excellent learning experience. The materials you need are simple— paper, pencil, 3×5 cards or cardboard. With the help of students and the use of some imagination you are all set to start an adventure. Don't be surprised if your students ask for mathematics games to play at noon hours or at home.

LEARNING FUNDAMENTAL MATHEMATICAL STATEMENTS

Closely related to the development of computational skills is the mastery of basic definitions, properties, axioms, and theorems. Here, the student has to memorize the statements (sometimes in a particular order), understand them, and know how to use them to support the statements of a problem or a proof.

---

[1] Donovan Johnson, *Games for Learning Mathematics* (Portland, Maine: Walsh Publishing Company, 1960).

To help students learn these fundamental statements, the teacher has to ask himself a number of basic questions: What definitions, rules, constants, and properties are of such importance that they should be overlearned? How can I best help students memorize necessary definitions such as those for π, sine, adjacent angles, linear equations, and rational numbers? How can I help them recall from their "dictionary" of memorized statements the ones appropriate to a particular problem situation? For example, what theorems should I consider when I set out to prove that a given quadrilateral is a rhombus? How can I help students use informal shortcuts but at the same time be cognizant of the mathematical principle involved? Compare, for example, transposition with the addition property for equations.

SELECTION OF STATEMENTS

As a first step in teaching for mastery of fundamental ideas, the teacher must *select the statements, formulas, or procedures* that are of sufficient importance to warrant the time and effort needed for mastery. Wherever possible, the learner should participate in this choice, but he will seldom have had the experience necessary to make choices. The reason for each choice should be made clear to the learner so that he is motivated to master the idea. Consequently, the teacher may want to demonstrate immediate applications or show how future developments depend on the statement. He may, for instance, point out the value of definitions to students who must write proofs: in return for memorizing the definition of a word, the student is allowed to replace a longer phrase with the shorter word or words. It is certainly shorter to write or say "π" than it is to write or say "the ratio of the circumference to the diameter of any circle." Memorizing the formula $A = \pi r^2$ or $\sqrt{2} \doteq 1.414$ will save time and effort in innumerable situations. In the same way committing to memory a proven theorem substitutes for repeating the steps of that proof again and again. In short, if we use an idea often, we need a definition for economy; if we seldom use the idea, it is more economical to repeat the idea than to memorize the proof. One appropriate technique to encourage students to learn a particular theorem or definition is to examine a development where it is used and see how the same development would have to be written or explained without the theorem or definition.

MASTERING FUNDAMENTAL IDEAS

As a first step in mastering a fundamental idea, the learner must understand the idea: that is, he must be able to use it in statements, illustrate it with examples, and use it to solve problems or complete proofs. To build this mastery, teachers need to show in as many settings as possible how the statement is applied. The addition axiom is used in arithmetic, in algebra, and in geometry to operate with the lengths of lines, the measure of angles, the area of polygons, and the volume of polyhedra. These varied settings not only underscore the need for the axioms; they give students exposure to varied practice in the use of the axiom. This varied application will extend understanding and memorization better than mere repetition.

The examples below illustrate the importance of understanding each phrase of a definition:

Why are the following not adjacent angles?

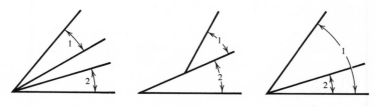

Fig. 7–1

What is wrong with the following general definition of a circle: A circle is the set of points at a fixed distance from a fixed point. (Does a sphere fit this definition?)

MEMORIZING FUNDAMENTAL IDEAS

When helping students to memorize fundamental ideas, the teacher can use a variety of approaches:

1. Since memorizing requires repetitive experiences, he can utilize the same principles detailed under the section on practicing a skill (p. 95). All of these are appropriate here.

2. He can provide both simple and complex settings for application of the basic ideas to be memorized.

3. When several statements are related, he can help students see and use these interrelationships to cut down on the amount to be memorized. A geometer of international reputation, Nathan Altschiller Court, has suggested the theorem "When two parallel lines are cut by a transversal, the angles that look equal are equal and the angles that don't look equal are supplementary." This informal statement, used with appropriate discretion, summarizes a number of independent theorems. It does not replace them, but it reduces their individual difficulty and it provides the student with an over-all understanding of the ideas lost in long lists of statements.

4. He can seek out appropriate procedures to provide quick review and applications. The chalkboard, posters, or flash cards can be used for ready reference by the teacher. References for the student can be provided by underlining the text or recording key ideas in a notebook. Games, contests, mental drills, or quizzes are other settings for quick review.

5. He can encourage students to list available and appropriate ideas, formulas, and definitions when attacking a problem. Such a summary is especially important for an attack on a nontrivial problem for which an answer is not immediately forthcoming.

6. He can provide mnemonic devices when they help students to learn

otherwise burdensome lists of definitions. These learning techniques must be used carefully because they make no pretense at being mathematical in nature; but where definitions are arbitrary and have little relation to the word being defined (or if the word itself is unfamiliar), this approach is helpful.

SHORTCUTS AND INFORMAL STATEMENTS

The use of informal statements for mathematical terms and shortcuts is widespread in mathematics. Although informal statements have considerable value (they save time, they save space, they communicate general ideas much as do variables and symbols of operation), there is a basic danger in using them. Students may fail to understand what underlies the informal statement or procedure and may use it without this necessary background of understanding. Informal statements and shortcuts, therefore, should be used with some caution; but they cannot and should not be rejected, since much of mathematics is virtually dependent on such shortcuts in procedure and in organization of information. (For example, what would we do if we could not use shortcuts in carrying out such a basic procedure as multiplication?)

When informal statements or shortcuts are introduced, a single teaching procedure should be constantly utilized. *Students should be asked repeatedly to provide the reasoning underlying shortcuts or informal statements. Unless they can provide such explanations, they should never be allowed to use the shortcut or informal statements.* Since working problems the long way requires more effort, the motivation to learn the basis for informal statements or shortcuts is built in.

Drill activities have often been overemphasized in the mathematics classroom. Practice and drill are carried to extremes when computational skill is considered sufficient to gain the goals of mathematics. Routine learning of skills results in poor retention, little understanding, and almost no application in daily problems. It is evident that the key to learning skills is through *meaningful* experiences, discovery, and applications.

Teaching the meaning of numbers, the understanding of a process, and the mathematical structure involved precedes practice. Practice, then, is the part of the learning process which builds accuracy, efficiency, and retention. If we provide the proper amount of practice at the appropriate time, it is likely that many of our students will have the mathematical competence that business, science, industry, and colleges are now demanding.

LEARNING EXERCISES

1. Use new symbols and a base other than ten for a new numeration system. Make up tables for addition facts and multiplication facts. Study the problems of learning skills by recording errors and time records of students learning to compute with this system.

2. Set up a finite number system, such as a modular five system. Work a series of computation exercises. Then search for relationships and patterns. Work another comparable series of computation exercises. Compare the errors and time to get a measure of improvement.

3. Set up a finite mathematical system such as a rotation group. Work a series of exercises with the operations involved. Search for relationships and patterns. Work another comparable set of exercises and compare results.

4. Observe students working exercises. Record errors. Confer with students to identify causes of errors.

5. Present a series of mental computation exercises over a sequence of days. Have each student record the number of correct responses. After several sessions in which the rate has been increased, repeat the first exercise. Compare the time and errors with the record of the first exercise.

6. Interview students to identify how they think as they perform computations.

7. Set up an experiment in which computing the square roots of real numbers is taught differently to each of two randomly selected groups. Have one group learn the method of averaging. Have the second group use the traditional algorithm. After comparable instructional time and the same amount of practice, compare the results.

8. Invent a new game for practice.

9. Evaluate a commercial game. Try it out with students to observe its effectiveness.

8

learning to solve mathematical problems

Learning to solve problems (that is, finding an appropriate response to a situation which is unique and novel to the problem solver) is the most significant learning in *every* mathematics class for several reasons:

1. It is a process whereby we *learn new concepts*. A problem may be a setting for the discovery of a new idea. These problems may be a question for class discussion, the topic of an entire unit, or an assigned exercise. An excellent way of promoting much independent individual discovery is to assign in exercise form the concept to be discussed in the next lesson. Thus, an appropriate assignment for discovering the method of finding the truth sets for inequalities might be a series of inequalities to be solved.

The skillful teacher makes such assignments carefully. Most students have become accustomed to homework that includes only content previously discussed in the classroom. Parents also expect this type of assignment and occasionally are upset by homework problems on material not already taught. "Are you asking me to teach it?" is their response. The key to using problems to learn new ideas is clear identification of the *type* of problem the new material presents and, when necessary, guides for the student.

Here is an elementary example of

the use of problems for learning a new idea or preparing for the next lesson. The day's lesson has been concerned with finding unions and intersections of sets. The assignment consisted of finding unions and intersections by tabulation. The learning problem assigned was: Does the distributive property apply to unions over intersections?

Does $A \cup (B \cap C) = (A \cup B) \cap (A \cup C)$? (Suggestion: Select sets A, B, and C, which have some common members. Compare results by tallying the sets involved.)

Here is an example from an eleventh-year algebra assignment:

We have studied graphing quadratics in some detail. Now let's look at a few simple functions of higher degree in order to determine whether some patterns are evident. We will first consider only equations of the form $y = x^n$ for positive integral values of n in the range $0 \leq x \leq 1$.

On your graph paper mark a large square with the left and lower sides the y and x axes. Mark scales in tenths on each axis.

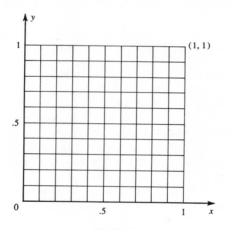

Fig. 8–1

a. On this square, carefully plot two graphs with which you are familiar, $y = x$ and $y = x^2$.

b. On a separate sheet of paper make a table of values to be used for additional graphs. Use the following form:

x	x^2	x^3	x^4
0	0		
.3	.09		
.5	.25		
.8	.64		
1	1		

Fig. 8–2

c. Fill in the table for x^3 and x^4. (Do you have to start with x for each computation?)

d. Plot the points for $y = x^3$ and sketch the graph as a smooth curve through these points. (You may wish to use additional x values to ensure accuracy.)

e. Do the same for $y = x^4$.

f. What appears to be happening as n increases for $y = x^n$? What would you expect to be the limiting position for $y = x^n$ as n increases, $0 \le x \le 1$?

g. FOR THINKERS. Without making a table or plotting points, extend the ideas developed here to the domain $-1 \le x \le 0$ for the same graphs. Use your knowledge of symmetry and exponents. Be careful: two different patterns emerge.

h. FOR DEEP THINKERS. What would be the pattern for $y = x^{1/n}$ for positive integral n? (It is not necessary to extract roots to answer this.)

2. Problems may be a meaningful way to *practice computational skills*. The rote learning of skills through purely manipulative exercises has been found inadequate. Bright students especially resent repetitive activities which demand little thought. Hence, the Cambridge Conference Report recommends the "virtually total abandonment of drill for drill's sake, replacing the unmotivated drill of classical arithmetic by problems which illustrate new mathematical concepts."

Suppose, for example, that we wish to review operations with fractions and fractional equations in the eleventh grade. Students have already been extensively exposed to fraction units in grades six, seven, eight, nine, and, to a lesser extent, ten. We may wish to motivate review of fractions now by introducing some problems related to sequences or continued fractions or Farey series. For example, what is the sum of the series $1 + 1/2 + 1/4 + 1/8 + 1/16 + \ldots$? Students who don't have computational skills have to review these topics carefully, but in this way they gain an intensive rather than superficial understanding. At the same time, any work students do in these subjects has to involve practice with fractions. Note, however, that the practice contributes to the more valuable problem-solving objectives and does not stand alone, unmotivated and unwanted.

3. By solving problems we learn to *transfer concepts and skills* to new situations. We know that the transfer of knowledge from the classroom or textbook situation to new applications is too limited. The amount of this transfer—a fundamental necessity for learning—is highly dependent on the emphasis on transfer. Problems of varied types, which illustrate varied applications, are a means of giving practice in transfer. Furthermore, a general skill such as problem solving is more permanent and more transferable than the knowledge of specific facts or concepts.

The thoughtful teacher continually extends the textbook problems to new situations. The mixture problems of algebra can be extended to the proportion problems of chemistry. The problems about digits have unusual applications to number tricks. The problems involving quadratics have current applications to space travel. The study of relations between the vertices and edges of regular polyhedra can be extended to problems of symmetry and duality.

A student looking for transfer might well see the common basis in the following two problems without having it pointed out to him.

    a. In how many ways can you spell the word *mathematics,* starting from the top and working down through the following array?

Fig. 8–3

    b. A car drives into a city at *A* and leaves at *B*. How many *"direct"* routes are there through the streets?

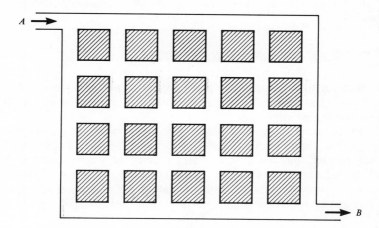

Fig. 8–4

4. Problem solving is a means of *stimulating intellectual curiosity.* A problem, like a puzzle, brings into play inventive, creative responses. Most people have enough intellectual curiosity to enjoy solving puzzles and problems. The curiosity and interest aroused by the brain busters of the SMSG texts demonstrate the pleasure students get from solving challenging problems. Some teachers use a "problem of the week" to whet the intellectual appetites of their students. If every problem assigned to the mathematics students could be an intellectual challenge of this type, it is likely that the students would grow greatly in problem-solving skill.

Problem-solving skill probably develops in direct proportion to amount of practice in solving problems. For that reason, the more the better. Selection should, however, be done carefully to avoid too much frustration and wasted effort. A number of sources for problems are listed in the bibliography in the Appendix.

5. *New knowledge is discovered* through problem solving. The research of the scientist and the mathematician is largely one of solving problems. Even the steps of the scientific method closely resemble the steps in solving a mathematical problem.

Scientific Research	*Mathematical Problems*
a. Define the problem.	a. What do we want to find out?
b. Suggest a tentative hypothesis.	b. Estimate the answer or solution.
c. Plan a course of action.	c. Select the method, formula, relationship.
d. Collect facts according to the plan.	d. Find all facts given and compute others. Experiment with the data and conditions.
e. Organize and analyze the facts.	e. Complete the analysis or computation. Search for a pattern.
f. Draw conclusions, state generalization.	f. State answer or generalization.
g. Apply the generalization to a new situation.	g. Apply the generalization to a situation.

THE PROBLEM-SOLVING PROCESS

In learning to solve problems and in teaching problem solving, both the teacher and the learner must recognize the factors involved in the problem-solving process:

1. Problem solving is a *complex mental process* that involves visualizing, imagining, manipulating, analyzing, abstracting, and associating ideas. It is no wonder that learning problem solving is a long, patience-trying process that demands motivation, reasoning power, and time. Consider, for example, the complex process in this situation, "If one plane divides space into two parts, into how many parts do five nonparallel planes divide space?"

2. Problem solving requires *novel, original, unique, and varied responses.* The best problem solver is likely to be a nonconforming, creative person who is highly flexible in his responses to the problem situation. The following problem, for example, is possible only if the problem solver switches to thinking in three dimensions: How can six matches be used to form four equilateral triangles if the side of each triangle has a length equal to that of the match?

3. Problem solving involves a *background of knowledge*—for instance, of concepts, facts, and structures—so that the learner can recall selected ideas and thus discern relationships and structure. Only when the learner

can select the structure of the relationship or operations can he express the situation in symbols and thus find answers to questions. For example, in order to prove that the product of two negative factors is positive, the student needs to know the format for proof, the meaning of additive inverse, and the distributive property.

4. Problem solving often requires skill in reading and computing, and ability to state associations. Through reading, the learner usually identifies the problem. To understand all the conditions of the problem situation, he must be able to read in an understanding manner.

Consider the following problem: "Suppose I have two American coins in my pocket whose total value is 60 cents. If one of them is not a dime, what coins do I have?" One must read carefully to discern that one of the coins is a half dollar and the "other one" is a dime. A learner also needs to compute accurately if he is to find correct answers to quantitative questions. He needs a storehouse of words and symbols so that he can express associations in symbolic form.

5. Problem solving involves *motivation and curiosity*. Only when the problem is accepted as worth time and effort is it a problem for the learner. One way to get a student involved is to have him estimate the answer. Once he has done this, he has committed himself. It has been suggested that problem solving is one third mathematical knowledge, one third desire or curiosity, and one third common sense. Without question a major factor in learning problem solving is intellectual curiosity. The satisfaction of this curiosity is usually sufficient to supply the incentive needed. At the same time it should be noted that failure to solve assigned problems should not be a threat to the status or acceptance of the student in the mathematics class.

Many famous problemists have recognized that the form of the problem statement itself often increases the level of curiosity. Thus, Sam Loyd poses a problem:

> In describing his experiences at a bargain sale, Smith says that half his money was gone in thirty minutes, so that he was left with as many pennies as he had dollars before, and but half as many dollars as before he had pennies. Now, how much did he spend?

This problem illustrates one other feature of problem posing. For most students it is *not* necessary to take problems from their immediate environment. Often, students are less interested in grocery bills than in cannibals and missionaries, less interested in volumes of oil tanks than in walks through Koenigsburg.

A related technique used by clever teachers is to state problems in humorous terms. Sometimes interest is attained if class members are named as the persons involved in the problem.

6. Problem solving *requires a procedure, an analysis, and a sequence of steps*. In view of the complexity, the individuality, the originality involved, there is no generally accepted procedure or fixed sequence of steps for solving problems. The key point of emphasis is flexibility, originality and variation. However, since it is the method of solution which is impor-

tant, the problem solver should analyze his methods by indicating the procedure he used to solve a given problem.

ANALYSIS OF WORD PROBLEMS IN ALGEBRA

To many teachers problem solving means only solving the verbal problems that form an important part of arithmetic and algebra. Many attacks have been made on this particular genre of problem. Some teachers use geometric approaches—in particular, scale diagrams and graphs; others use tables—too often a specific type of table for each type of problem: mixture, distance, coin, age, or income. Even the geometric approaches are somewhat limited by the difficulty of translating many ideas—like price—into reasonable geometric terms.

It is much better to attempt to give the student a general method of attack on such problems; otherwise, he can solve only those problems that fit neatly into the specific patterns provided. It is possible to determine appropriate equations for solving the problem by a direct approach, utilizing steps like the following:

> 1. Represent what you wish to find, or something closely related to what you wish to find, by x.
> 2. Represent other unknown values in the problem in terms of x.
> 3. Seek relationships between the values represented by variables. These statements are often in the form of simple arithmetic relations like $d = rt$, $i = prt$, $S = C + P$.
> 4. Use these relationships to write an equation that can be solved for x.

Here is an example worked by this procedure, the steps in the solution corresponding to the steps in the given procedure.

> Two sums of money totaling $10,000 are invested at 5 percent and 6 percent respectively. If the total income for a year is $540, how much is invested at each rate?
> 1. Amount invested at 5 percent is x (choice arbitrary!).
> 2. Amount invested at 6 percent is $(10,000 - x)$.
> 3. Income for a year is investment multiplied by rate of return, $i = pr$, or $.05x$ and $.06(10,000 - x)$. Total income is the sum of the individual incomes.
> 4. $.05x + .06(10,000 - x) = 540$.

Many students have difficulty with this procedure. Another helpful procedure (although more often taught to college calculus students than to high school students) involves the following steps:

> 1. Represent all the quantities unknown in the problem with letters: x, y, z, etc.
> 2. Taking each phrase of the sentence of the problem statement, trans-

late the problem into equations relating these letters. (Note that if there are *n* letters, you will need *n* independent equations. Occasionally, fewer equations will suffice.)

Example
Jack is ten years older than his sister. In three years he will be twice as old. What are their ages now?

1. J = Jack's age now.
   S = Sister's age now.
   j = Jack's age in three years.
   s = Sister's age in three years.

2. $j = J + 3$
   $s = S + 3$
   $J = S + 10$
   $j = 2s$

Note that the use of extra letters avoids some of the complications of representation. When only the letters J and S are used, the resulting equation,

$$J + 3 = 2(S + 3),$$

confuses the student. When the additional letters are used, the resolution of this additional complication is merely postponed until the equation-solving stage. But most students can perform the simple substitutions and computations readily when expressed as equations.

Another approach that deserves special attention is that utilized in the University of Illinois Committee on School Mathematics (UICSM) program. This program attacks word problems by extending a procedure known to many teachers—e.g., "Write an equation relating feet, f, and inches, i." When using this procedure, teachers usually suggest that the student pick an arbitrary number of inches (or feet), carry out the conversion as he would in arithmetic, and then merely substitute the letters in the appropriate place in the computations.

Since 36 inches is 3 feet,

$$\frac{36}{12} = 3 \qquad \frac{i}{12} = f.$$

Extended to problem solving, this method provides an interesting basis for equation writing. The student guesses a solution and checks it, recording his check carefully in equation form. (When he is first learning how to solve word problems, he may be asked to try several trial solutions.) Once he has the equation representing his check, he merely substitutes x for the guessed solution at each point it occurs.

Example: A train leaves San Francisco for Philadelphia at 50 miles per hour two hours before another train leaves Philadelphia for San Francisco at 60 miles per hour. If the two cities are 3,400 miles apart and the trains maintain these speeds, how soon will they meet?

Guessed solution: 40 hours.

$$40 \cdot 50 + 38 \cdot 60 \overset{?}{=} 3{,}400$$

Substituting x for 40 and noting that $38 = 40 - 2$,

$$x \cdot 50 + (x - 2)\ 60 = 3{,}400.$$

The last example suggests two other features of the solution of word problems—features that teachers should stress. The first of these is best summed up by the famous problemist George Polya: "We must teach guessing!" Too many teachers, when they emphasize set procedures, encourage students not to guess. Such teachers fail to recognize that the trial-and-error approach sometimes yields adequate answers. It is true that such methods may fail a student or may at least slow him down, but they should not be totally discarded. The second feature is what may be termed *reduction of parameters*. Reducing the complication of a problem often makes it transparent. In the "train" example, for instance, once both trains start, they approach each other at 110 miles per hour. The second train starts after the first has gone 100 miles. The solution, then, is the result of dividing 3,300(3,400–100) by 110.

In this section on word problems, we have not stressed two features that many teachers are adamant about: form and labeling. For these two aspects of problem solution, we believe, individual preferences and needs should be followed. When students make careless errors because they fail to follow a set form or to label units correctly, they should be asked to modify their procedures. On the other hand, if such formal procedures appear to stifle the creative part of the problem-solving activity, they should be curtailed. To illustrate this it may be noted that one of the best papers written by a student for the CEEB Advanced Placement examination was virtually illegible; another very fine paper was the work of a student who was neat almost to the point of compulsion. Here, as always, the individual makes the difference: Some students are able to display their organization while others are not.

A special word of caution is appropriate for the so-called word problems of algebra. Too often, specified procedures are worked out for each type of problem. These pattern solutions tend to restrict rather than expand a student's competence in problem solving. When a method is prescribed, the word problems are merely exercises in which the student practices a given procedure. It is better to let the student find several ways to solve a given problem and to let him make up original problems based on a given equation than to repeat several stereotype solutions.

However, one basic skill needs practice; namely, the matter of translating the word sentences to open, symbolic sentences. Translation needs to be done in both directions. First, we should start with the algebraic statement and construct related word problems. Teachers who use this technique report that students produce varied and often quite sophisticated results—not only in constructing interesting word problems but also in solving word problems of the standard form.

This two-way approach to problem solving is also fruitful in that it gives students insight into the relationship between the real and the abstract worlds.

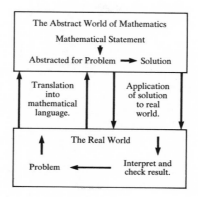

Fig. 8–5

As Fig. 8–5 illustrates, problems from the real world are translated into the abstractions of mathematics. Then mathematical tools are used to produce an answer—the truth set. However, this answer has little meaning unless it in turn is applied to situations in the real world. The abstract world of mathematics provides generalizations to be applied in the real world. Thus, a complete problem solution should include the process, the generalization, and the application.

MIND SETS

When teachers follow fixed solution patterns, there is real *danger that students will form mind sets,* which will be obstacles to their further development. Mind set (*einstellung*), or mind fix, is a form of undesirable transfer. Consider the following example:

Fig. 8–6

Note that there are two *the*'s; one is usually missed on first inspection.

Another example: At the time students are studying the Pythagorean theorem, ask them to find the measure represented by x in the following diagram.

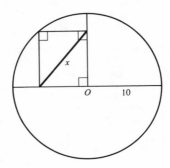

Fig. 8–7

Thinking of the single method, they fail to notice that the other diagonal of the rectangle is a radius. It is not necessary to use the Pythagorean theorem to find the value of x.

To avoid set of this type, activities designed to force students to keep their minds alert should be continually utilized. For example, students who have solved several equations of the form

$$\frac{x}{a} = b$$

should be asked to solve an equation of the form

$$\frac{a}{x} = b.$$

SUGGESTED APPROACH TO PROBLEMS

Often problem solvers get stuck because they have fixed on a single procedure or approach. Many authors have suggested methods to approach problems. From these the following list of suggestions have been gathered:

1. *Identify the question or problem.*
   Do you understand the wording of the problem? (Is there a trick?)
   Is the problem of a known type?
   What is given?

2. *Search for related ideas.*
   What type of problem is it?
   What are the conditions (parameters)?
   What is an analogous problem?

3. *Delimit the problem.*
   Can you simplify the problem by performing some of the computations?
   Are there superfluous details given?
   Can the problem be reduced to an equation or a geometric representation?

4. *Search for a strategy.*
   Can the data be organized into a pattern?
   Does trial and error point to a solution?
   What is it about the problem that is different from problems previously solved?
   Can the conditions be modified to make a simpler problem?

5. *Use reference tools.*
   Can a similar problem be found in a textbook?
   Do tables provide assistance?
   What formulas or theorems apply to problems of this type?

Once a problem has been solved, many students and teachers leave it to advance to "another challenge." In this they fail in a very important way. Problems that have been solved have real value to the solver. They are the source of additional problems as they generate ideas. Here are some questions that may be applied at this point:

1. Can this result be applied to analogous situations?

2. Under what conditions is the problem solvable? Unsolvable? Meaningless? Trivial?

3. Is there a generalization of the result?

4. Is there a more sophisticated solution?

5. What type of reasoning was involved?

6. When and why did I have difficulty? How could this difficulty be resolved in the future?

STEPS IN SOLVING PROBLEMS

Although there is no generally accepted sequence of steps for solving mathematical problems, psychologists suggest that some common stages or steps operate in most problems.

1. *The problem solver must first know exactly what the problem is.* The situation, the question, or the problem is usually presented in a written statement. To become oriented to the problem, the solver should read and reread the statement. The following questions or activities add meaning to the problem:

> What information is given?
> What are you trying to find out?
> State the problem in your own words.
> Write a similar problem about people and places familiar to you.

The following problem illustrates how important it is to relate the ideas about straight lines and directions to geometric relations between lines and angles.

> It's as far from *Witt* to *Pitt* as from *Kitt* to *Mitt*.
> It's as far from *Sitt* to *Bitt* as from *Ditt* to *Mitt*.
> *Mitt* is on a straight line north from *Sitt* to *Pitt*.
> *Mitt* is on a straight road east from *Witt* to *Bitt*.
> *Kitt* is 8 miles north of *Witt* and 8 miles west of *Pitt*.
> *Ditt* is 6 miles south of *Bitt* and 6 miles east of *Sitt*.
> How far is it from *Witt* to *Sitt*?
> How far is it from *Pitt* to *Bitt*?

When a drawing is made, it shows that the answers are obtained by means of the Pythagorean theorem.

2. *The problem solver relates the problem to a familiar idea* or a previously solved problem. He must search his memory to recall ideas, facts, assumptions, theorems, formulas, or experiences that are related to the problem. He must ask himself whether or not he has solved an analogous problem. He must reduce the situation to simpler conditions or solve a simpler related problem. He must consider what happens if given conditions vary, and he must estimate the answer.

Here is a problem that requires the solver to search his memory for conditions on the earth's surface.

> An explorer walks 1 mile south, then walks 1 mile east, then turns and walks 1 mile due north. He finds himself back where he started. At what locations (more than one) on the earth's surface is this possible.

Only when he recalls how latitude and longitude are related to directions and locations does he discover the locations at the North Pole and near the South Pole.

3. *The solver must search for a strategy by identifying the structure of the problem.* He must identify the known facts, the conditions, and the variables. By organizing the facts given, he should identify a pattern. Then he selects a search model—a sketch; an equation or inequality; a graph or a flow chart—to represent the structure of the problem—represents the elements of the problem in symbols, and determines what method of proof applies.

What digits may be substituted for the letters?

What strategy should be used for these exercises?

a. addition	b. subtraction	c. multiplication	d. division
SEND	SPEND	SEAM	bfb
MORE	MORE	N	ab)cdeeb
MONEY	MONEY	MEANS	ceb
			gge
			gch
			ceb
			ceb

These problems require an exploration of many possible combinations to arrive at the equality given. The essential structure here is the place value of the digits.

In the following problem, a sketch would quickly give the clue.

> A chessboard has 64 squares. We have 32 dominoes, each of such size that it covers exactly two chessboard squares. The 32 dominoes may then be used to cover all 64 squares. Suppose that we cut off two checkerboard squares, one at each of two diagonally opposite corners of the board. Discard one domino. Is it possible to place the 31 dominoes on the board so that the remaining 62 chessboard squares are covered? Show how it can be done or prove it impossible.

4. *The solver should use the search model (determined in step 3) to find the answer to the question.* He must perform the computations involved, complete the deductive proof and find the solution set for the equations or inequalities. He must check the answer to see whether the results satisfy the conditions given and state a complete answer to the question of the problem. In this way the search model (sketch, equation, concrete representation) bridges the gap between what is given and what is required.

Make an analysis of this problem.

> Each of two boys had 30 balloons for sale. One boy sold his at the rate of 2 for a nickel and the second boy at the rate of 3 for a nickel. At the end of one day their receipts were 75 cents and 50 cents, or $1.25 in all. The next day the boys decided to combine their efforts. They pooled their 60 balloons and sold them at the rate of 5 for a dime (2 for a nickel plus 3 for a nickel). Upon counting the receipts at the end of the day, they found that they had only $1.20. Why did they lose 5 cents by their merger?

What information about rates is the key to this problem?

5. *The problem solver should interpret the results in the form of a generalization.* He should apply the solution to situations in which the conditions are changed, determine when a solution is impossible, meaningless, or trivial, and write a generalization in terms of a formula, theorem, or principle.

What is the generalization for this problem?

> Philip and his wife, Mary, both work at night. Philip is off duty every ninth evening; his wife is off duty every sixth evening. Philip is off duty on this Sunday evening; Mary is off duty the following Monday evening. When (if ever) will they be off duty the same evening?

What relationship between 3, 7, and 9 is involved in this problem? Under what conditions will they have the same night off?

6. *The problem solver should analyze the method of solution.* He should write the sequence of steps in a logical order, indicate the process whereby information was generated, and identify the type of reasoning involved.

The complete analysis of this problem may be a good example of finding a key idea that simplifies the problem. Try finding several methods of solving it.

> A commuter always arrives at his subway station at 6 P.M. each day. His wife meets him at the station to drive him the remaining distance home. One day he arrives at 5 P.M. and begins walking home. His wife meets him on her way to the 6 P.M. train. He gets into the car and they drive home, arriving at home ten minutes earlier than usual. Assuming that the wife drives at a constant rate on the same route, for what length of time did the husband walk before he was picked up?

PROGRAMMED INSTRUCTION AND PROBLEM SOLVING

Those familiar with programmed instruction may be surprised to see this technique associated with problem solving. There are, however, two very important connections that may be made between the two. The first may be seen best-developed in books by Polya, in the Hungarian Problem Books, and in some experimental geometry programs at the University of Minnesota by Murray Klamkin and Wells Hively. All of these use the method of successive hints: a problem is stated, and the student is urged to seek a solution without help. Failing this he is provided with a first hint, which may help him to organize and direct his thinking into productive channels. Subsequently, more leading hints are also provided. Finally, the complete solution is given. At any point the student may progress to the solution and skip the subsequent hints to check his result. On the other hand, if he was unable to solve the problem at any stage, he was at least forced to examine the problem in greater detail as he progressed through the program. The student who did not solve the problem may be directed to a similar problem in order to help him reinforce his procedure.

Consider, for example, the problem cited earlier: spelling the word *mathematics* in the array of letters (p. 107). The following hints might be given:

> Hint One: Are you familiar with Pascal's triangle?
> Hint Two: In how many ways can you get to each of the A's in the second row?

Note that neither hint takes the student to the answer, but each gives him more direction.

A second application of the idea of programmed instruction comes after a specific problem is solved. Finding the solution to a particular problem, the student should be urged to generalize his result and to develop an algorithm for solving problems of this particular genre. To many who use computers regularly, this programming is the real solution to the problem, anything less having no real application. Such an algorithm may take the form of a carefully structured program, a flow diagram, or a work sheet. In each case, however, the design should be aimed at a layman unfamiliar with the processes involved except for arithmetic computation.

SOLVING PROBLEMS WITH FLOW CHARTS

Flow charts, which provide a condensed visualization of a sequence of operations, facilitate analysis much as an equation facilitates the finding of truth sets. These charts are like classification diagrams, organization charts, historical charts, or industrial process charts. Here is how a flow chart may follow the directions for drawing a common pattern:

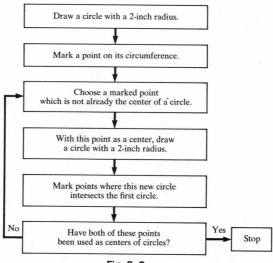

Fig. 8–8

Flow charts are the basis for programming a problem for computer solution. Here is a simple flow chart for finding an average:

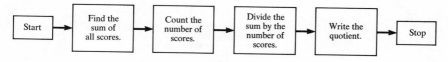

Fig. 8–9

A somewhat more complex chart is one for finding the square root of a number by Newton's method.

What is the $\sqrt{x}$? The flow chart below gives one algorithm for finding this root.

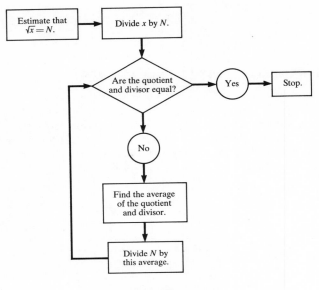

Fig. 8–10

In a similar way it is possible to draw a flow chart for any problem-solving procedure.

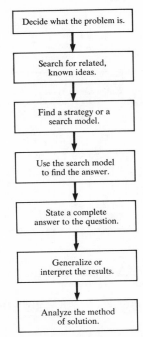

Fig. 8–11.   Flow Chart for Problem Solving.

COMPUTER-MEDIATED PROBLEM SOLVING

As an example of how a problem is attacked by a student with access to a computer, here is a problem assigned to a high school student. He solved the problem via a classroom teletype contact with a time-shared computer. Compare this work with the typical format for solving this problem and compare the insights gained.

Problem

Joe Doakes is looking for a job that pays well. Opportunities Unlimited offers him a starting salary of $1,000 a day with a $100-a-day increase in wages. Double-or-Nothing, Inc., offers him a penny for the first day but doubles his wage each day. Which is the better offer? That is: (1) Would the Double-or-Nothing daily wage exceed the Opportunities Unlimited within a year? (2) If so, after how many days? (3) If so, how long before the total wages were greater?

First the student prepared a flow chart:

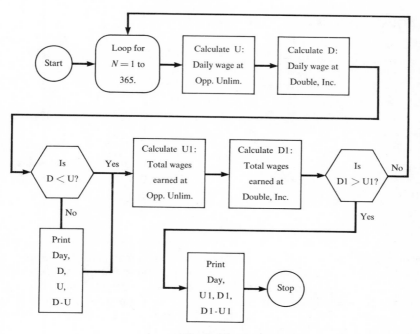

Fig. 8–12

Next he translated the flow chart into an algorithmic language (Basic) and ran the program on the machine.

```
WAGES              13:56          Fri 06-17-66
10 LET  U1 = 0
```

```
20  LET   D1 = 0
30  FØR   N = 1 to 365
40  LET   U = 100000 + 10000 *(N − 1)
50  LET   D = 2 ↑ (N − 1)
60  IF   D < U THEN 100
70  PRINT   "DAY", "D", "U", "D − U"
80  PRINT
90  PRINT   N,D,U, D − U
100  LET   U1 = U1 + U
110  LET   D1 = D1 + D
120  IF   D1 > U1   THEN 140
130  NEXT   N
140  PRINT   "DAY", "D1", "U1", "D1 − U1"
150  PRINT
160  PRINT   N, D1, U1, D1 − U1
170  END
```

RUN

WAGES	13:57	FRI 06–17–66	
Day	D	U	D − U
20	524288	290000	234288
Day	D	U	D − U
21	1048576	300000	748576
Day	D	U	D − U
22	2097152	310000	1787152
Day	D	U	D − U
23	4194304	320000	3874304
Day	D1	U1	D1 − U1
24	8388607	483000	3558607
TIME	1 SECS.		

Fig. 8–13

To many readers who have had no opportunity to utilize computers, the foregoing solution by a seventh grader may appear very advanced or unusual. To those who have used this tool the simple nature of the calculations is apparent. An examination of the work being done by paper-and-pencil calculation for the first few days shows this to be the case. What the computer provides—and all that the computer provides—is rapid calculation and exact following of directions. (That is why, in Fig. 8–13, unwanted data for days 21 and 22 and part of 23 are printed.)

On the other hand, the student must be able to analyze the problem carefully; translate the problem into arithmetic calculations; provide a form for sequencing these calculations; give a reasonable interpretation of the data; and spot errors in his analysis, interpretation, or attack on the problem.

Note that this is not the most sophisticated possible program, nor is the print-out as simple as it might have been. Each of these questions offers a basis for further student thought. Progression sum formulas have not been used for either the arithmetic or geometric series; instead the sums are calculated directly (subsequences 100,110).

In this type of problem solving, the student's thinking is focused on the data from beginning to end. This study often helps him to generate extensions of the problem. To some extent he has already done so here, printing how much more he would earn as well as the days required. It would also have been possible to print weekly status reports or even the effects of a progressive income tax on the wage comparisons.

This type of activity also forces the student to interpret both question and solution carefully. In this case, for example, he had to use cents as his basic wage unit even though dollars would have sufficed for the first alternative.

KEY IDEAS IN TEACHING PROBLEM SOLVING

1. *Provide a wholesome emotional climate for learning problem solving.*
    a. Allow ample time for thinking, analyzing, and experimenting.
    b. Be receptive to questions.
    c. Reduce hostility and fear.
    d. Be patient with the student who can't solve problems.

2. *Establish and maintain students' motivation.*
    a. Emphasize the importance of learning to solve problems.
    b. Provide problems in which some success is assured for each learner.
    c. Prepare the learner for necessary difficulties and frustrations.
    d. Arouse intellectual curiosity by using puzzle problems and "brain busters."
    e. Make reasonable assignments and provide ample time.
    f. Concentrate on a few problems and treat them leisurely and thoroughly.

3. *Provide ways of increasing students' understanding of a problem situation.*
    a. Show students how to read and reread problems.
    b. Help students restate problems so that conditions become clearer and the question more reasonable.
    c. Give the learner an equation or geometric relationship and ask him to write a problem which is based upon this idea.
    d. Ask questions to ensure that the learner understands the statements, the vocabulary, and the type of problem involved.

    e. Have the learner identify key terms or ideas or break the problem down into simpler sub-problems.

    f. If the solver does not know where to begin, encourage him simply to write the facts of the situation.

    g. Have the learner write a related problem.

    h. Give a general question and let the learner specify the variables or conditions involved.

4. *Emphasize flexibility and variety in solving problems.*

    a. Do not prescribe a rigid step-by-step procedure or format.

    b. Suggest that students change perspectives when in difficulty. When students make no progress, encourage them to change the search model.

    c. Provide some problems with insufficient data and others with extraneous data.

    d. Encourage using several methods of solving the same problem.

    e. Relate problem solving to solving mystery or detective stories and to criminal investigation.

5. *Give instruction in establishing a search model.*

    a. Use flow charts to illustrate a solution.

    b. Use diagrams, models, or sketches to identify structure of the problem.

    c. Establish the variables of the problem. Then use symbols and write equations or inequalities for the relationship involved.

6. *Show the learner how to ask himself questions.* Suggest questions like these:

    a. What facts are given?

    b. What are you trying to find out?

    c. What ideas have you studied that are related to this situation?

    d. What problems have you solved that are analogous to this one?

7. *Emphasize the method of solution rather than the solution.*

    a. Instead of assigning numerous problems, ask the student to find several methods of solution for each problem given.

    b. Give credit for each part of a correct method rather than only for the right answer.

    c. Use test items which demand demonstration of the method of solution rather than merely the right answer.

    d. Give opportunities of showing methods of solution that do not require the performance of laborious computations.

    e. Provide for an analysis of the analogies used.

8. *Encourage experimentation, trial and error, estimation, intuition, guessing, and hunches to suggest a method of solution.*

9. *Provide problems at frequent intervals, so that students get adequate practice in solving problems.*

10. *Promote analysis, organization, and communication skill by having students state or write their solutions in logical and orderly form.* Outline the logic or structure of the problem. Suggest possible analyses, flow charts, transformations.

11. *Use problem situations to discover new mathematical concepts, principles, or relationships.*

12. *Use problem situations as a basis for practice and as a substitute for drill exercises.*

Learning how to solve problems can be one of the most satisfying though difficult experiences which we can give our students. It is also probably the most significant learning which we can direct. The key to problem solving seems to be flexibility and reflective thinking. The result of successful learning should be the ability to explore all fields of knowledge independently. To attain this we should emphasize the structure of the problem rather than the computational phase. Then we should emphasize the method of solution rather than the answer.

LEARNING EXERCISES

1. What is the difference between solving a problem and learning a concept?
2. State a problem situation which could be a means of practicing computational skill.
3. State a problem situation which could be a means of learning a new concept.
4. State a problem and analyze the background of knowledge and skill which the solver is expected to have.
5. Write a report on how flow charts are used to program problems for computer solution.
6. Select problems from the references in the Appendix to illustrate different types of problems and different techniques of solution.

9

developing positive attitudes and creativity through enrichment

It is widely recognized that students need to learn something besides facts and skills. They need to develop desirable attitudes and creativity—goals of the affective domain, which are much more difficult to attain than those of the cognitive domain (concepts, facts, and skills).

An effective way of attaining the affective goals of instruction is an enrichment program that is part of the regular day-to-day instruction. This planned enrichment gives breadth and depth to mathematics learning. This program should capitalize on the varying capacity of each student to visualize, to use intuition, to pursue intellectual curiosities, and to be creative. It should encourage each student to develop his mathematical ability, to consider mathematics as being worth studying, and to extend independently the mathematics known to him. Although this program has special implications for gifted students, it should be appropriate for all levels of mathematical ability. In the following discussion the word enrichment is used in its broad sense, not in the narrow sense of "extra materials" to which it has too often been assigned by the teacher.

Consider the role of enrichment in our own daily lives. We frequently hear the expression "he has lived a rich life" or "her life is drab and routine." What are the experiences which contribute to an enriched life? We would likely agree to include the following:

1. *Success* in our work and day-to-day activities. Since we spend a major portion of our time on the job, the joy and satisfaction of success is one of the greatest factors for an enriched life. This success gives us a feeling of security that is so essential for participation in a variety of activities.

2. A *sense of values* which gives meaning to our lives. A life without a purpose or a goal is an empty existence.

3. A variety of *social activities* at home and elsewhere, such as those we enjoy through travel, conversation, and group organizations.

4. Participation in *cultural activities,* such as music, art, drama, or literature.

5. *Intellectual activities,* such as reading, listening to lectures, and participating in discussions which satisfy our curiosity about life around us.

6. *Recreational activities,* such as hobbies and sports.

7. *Creative activities,* such as craftwork, writing, gardening, and sewing.

Whether or not one can live an enriched life which involves these activities depends upon the ability and resources of the individual and the resources of the community in which he lives. Enrichment of some type is usually desired by all age groups and at all socio-economic levels.

In exactly the same way, the learning of mathematics should involve satisfying experiences which enrich the learning process. Activities are needed to satisfy the learner's need for enriched learning. It is the learner's experiences, not the teaching activities, that satisfy this need. Thus, the enrichment of mathematics instruction should provide the learner with the following experiences, which parallel the enrichment factors of daily living:

1. *Success in learning* the ideas, skills, and structure of mathematics. Success in the understanding and mastery of mathematical concepts is developed through the learner's participation in discovery, discussion, illustration, problem solving, practice, and application. Thus, instruction which builds confidence, independence, and security in this way enriches the learning of mathematics. This means that adequate time must be devoted to the mastery of ideas. Our task as teachers, then, is to "uncover" material rather than "cover" a specific sequence.

2. *A sense of the value* in learning mathematics gives meaning to learning activities. Learning without a goal or purpose is empty activity. Discussions of the role of mathematics in our society, the power of mathematical analysis, the applications of mathematics, and the mathematics needed in different vocations enhance the importance of learning mathematics.

3. *A variety of learning activities* can be planned by the use of teaching aids, historical sidelights, dramatic topics, or excursions. In these learning activities there should be much interaction between students as they discover, discuss, and apply mathematical ideas.

4. *The cultural aspects* of mathematics are made evident, so that the learner can look upon it as a human invention important in itself. Mathe-

matics has aesthetic aspects—for instance, in the properties of symmetry and reflections—comparable to music or art. And, in turn, music and art have mathematical aspects of their own.

5. The relation of *intellectual curiosity* to mathematics is unique and exciting. Mathematics is one of the greatest intellectual inventions of the human mind. Its logic, its abstractness, its paradoxes, its study of patterns, its unsolved problems can satisfy intellectual appetites at many levels.

6. *Recreational activities* involving mathematics are plentiful. These include tricks, puzzles, games, and stunts. Mathematics is a hobby for many people who are not mathematicians. Unusual properties of geometric figures and number operations provide such entertaining interludes.

7. *Creating new mathematics* can be made an intriguing activity. Constructing a model, planning and producing a mathematics assembly program, building a mathematics exhibit—all of these are creative activities. Originality may be nourished by new inventions, an elegant new proof, or a new mathematics structure.

The student's participation in enrichment activities depends upon the ingenuity and background of the teacher, upon the ability and interest of the individual, upon the time available, and upon the resources of the school. When a student's curiosity, concern, and creativeness are aroused, learning becomes automatic.

THE ROLE OF ATTITUDES IN LEARNING MATHEMATICS

Attitudes are fundamental to the dynamics of behavior. They largely determine what students learn. The mathematics student with positive attitudes studies mathematics because he enjoys it, he gets satisfaction from knowing mathematical ideas, and he finds mathematical competency its own reward.

The development of positive attitudes toward mathematics is a fundamental concern of the mathematics teacher for a number of reasons:

1. *No student can be forced to learn mathematics which he doesn't want to learn.* He may superficially satisfy you that he is learning by adhering minimally to your classroom demands and standards, but he will carry away virtually nothing unless he is interested in doing so. In this regard all teachers should consider how deeply involved students—even low achievers—become in their hobbies, whether they be stamp collecting, model building, scouting, or sports. Students would make rapid progress in mathematics if they could equal their knowledge of mathematical principles with their knowledge of baseball rules. Such knowledge, which often includes a vast store of memorized detail, is motivated by strong intrinsic attitudes.

2. *Even if students learn the mathematics of a given text, the primary concern of continuing learning is lost when students do not develop positive attitudes.* The mathematics of tomorrow cannot be taught today; so an abiding interest in mathematics should be instilled to encourage learning in the future.

3. *Vocational choices are largely dependent on attitudes*. Mathematics teachers close doors for students when they allow them to develop poor attitudes toward such an all-pervasive subject as mathematics.

4. *Application of mathematical ideas in large measure depends on a positive attitude*. We tend to remember favorable, pleasant experiences and block out the unpleasant. If this leads to blocking out mathematical concepts, they will not be available when needed.

5. *Many people take pride in professing ignorance of mathematics*. Few adults admit that they are poor history students, but the parents of many pupils announce the fact that they "never did understand math." It is in this negative environment that the teacher must work.

6. Finally, there is a selfish aspect of attitude improvement: *Positive attitudes reflect favorably on the teacher*. They form an excellent basis for a teacher's rating by students, parents, and colleagues. The mathematics teacher who inspires his students and whose students are enthusiastic about his class is the teacher who is in line for salary increases, institute recommendations, and—best of all—the prestige of success.

STUDENT BASIS FOR POSITIVE ATTITUDES

It is very important for the classroom teacher to assess his students in order to determine established attitudes toward mathematics and to assure himself of a sound basis on which to build a program of attitude improvement and motivation. While many individual students will bring to the classroom very specific acceptable and unacceptable interests, there are many attitudes that are common to the major segment of the student population. To become involved in emotional dynamics, the classroom teacher must be aware of these and be sensitive to quantitative differences among students. These basic desires include:

1. Wanting to avoid embarrassment or punishment.
2. Wanting to win approval of teachers and parents.
3. Wanting to gain confidence in his own ability.
4. Wanting to succeed in progress toward goals acceptable to him.
5. Wanting to attain approval of his peers individually and as a group.
6. Wanting to be secure.

Many teachers fail to recognize the difficulty they face in developing real sensitivity to these strong drives within their students. It is not easy to be sensitive to the subtleties of student desires and motives. How often has the remark been passed in the faculty room that a student showed quite unexpected concern for something or someone? The fact that such feeling was quite unexpected means that the teacher did not really know his student and that he had therefore underestimated him.

It should be noted that all the desires listed are basically oriented toward the development of positive attitudes. In the beginning they are working for the teacher. Too soon, however, they can all be misdirected. For example, the desire to avoid embarrassment often turns a bright girl into an underachiever when she is criticized by her friends for being the teacher's pet.

This leads to a special point that should be stressed about attitudes. The mathematics teacher cannot choose to avoid the problem of developing positive attitudes toward mathematics. *Whether the teacher likes it or not, each student responds emotionally to his teachers.* Students react strongly, acquiring or rejecting on the basis of this response the attitudes, values, and appreciations of the teachers.

No matter what topic is being taught, much concomitant learning and changes in attitude are taking place. For example, when being taught how to solve a mathematical problem, a student may be learning:

1. To dodge responsibility or to be cooperative.
2. To maintain his integrity or to cheat.
3. To trust the teacher or to lose respect for him.

Attitudes may not be taught systematically or directly. Teaching is not a mechanical operation. It is not even a science, although science too has its artistic side. Teaching attitudes is more like painting a picture, playing a musical selection, planting a garden, or writing a letter to a friend. The teacher must put all his heart into his instruction. It is human warmth that adds the emotional vector needed in the development of positive attitudes toward mathematics.

DESIRED POSITIVE ATTITUDES TOWARD MATHEMATICS

Most mathematics teachers would accept the following attitudes as being those which characterize an ideal product of their instruction, whether they are teaching new or conventional mathematics:

1. *Appreciation* of the power, elegance, and structure of mathematics.
2. *Curiosity* about mathematical ideas.
3. *Confidence* in mathematics.
4. *Loyalty* to mathematics, the mathematics teacher, and classmates.
5. *Enjoyment and satisfaction* in learning mathematical ideas.
6. *Respect* for excellence in mathematical achievement by himself and others.
7. *Optimism and cheerfulness* about one's progress in mathematics.

In addition to these specific attitudes, teachers must take responsibility for many general attitudes or values like honesty, kindness, respect, and self-reliance.

NEGATIVE STUDENT ATTITUDES TOWARD MATHEMATICS

Whenever mathematics students are questioned concerning attitudes toward mathematics, the five most recurring reasons they give for negative attitudes are:

1. *Lack of understanding of mathematical principles.* This lack of understanding kills curiosity and appreciation no matter what content is being taught.

2. *Lack of application of mathematics to a life situation, leading to a loss of confidence in the importance of mathematics.* This lack of emphasis on the practical aspects of mathematics is even more pronounced in modern programs.

3. *Too many boring problems assigned daily.* The constant emphasis on manipulation and daily homework kills the zest of students for learning mathematics.

4. *Uninspired, impatient, uninteresting teachers.* Poor teaching kills confidence, loyalty, and enjoyment of learning, no matter how good the content may be.

5. *Lack of success, leading to development of feelings of frustration and insecurity.* Failure leads to dislike, dislike to fear, and fear to hatred of a subject.

Being sensitive to these sources of negative reactions should help us avoid further reinforcement of negative attitudes.

WAYS TO BUILD POSITIVE ATTITUDES TOWARD MATHEMATICS

The teacher's appreciation of mathematics as an important, dynamic, remarkable subject must be real and deep, his attitude toward students must be sympathetic and understanding, his interest in learning must be great, his enthusiasm for teaching sincere. If the teacher's attitudes are less favorable or his motivation the same as that of the student, no transmission of enthusiasm can take place.

Once the teacher has set his own standards high, he must still establish himself as a person who has the respect and esteem of his students. Maintaining the students' esteem in the face of their constant judgmental response is a sobering problem for the teacher. Students are quick to sense the smallest insincerity just as they note the slightest insecurity. It is extremely important that the classroom atmosphere be friendly, accepting, and supportive, even when it is demanding and challenging. A spirit of security, enjoyment, and loyalty should be the basic goal of classroom organization. The teacher should make his students feel that his attitude will still be friendly regardless of the success or failure of the students' efforts. If we want students to think for themselves, we must allow them to try out their own ideas and answers.

Some of the really important ways in which teachers influence their students' attitudes have to do with pleasant communication habits: the teacher's voice inflection, the way he looks at students, his responses, or even his failure to respond. The classroom itself should be attractive. It should contain books, pamphlets, pictures, and displays reflecting an intellectual atmosphere and providing a proper setting for an enriched program.

Here are some specific examples of things to do to build positive attitudes toward mathematics:

1. To develop *appreciation* of the elegance, power, and structure of mathematics we need to:

   a. Emphasize the nature of mathematics and how it is a model of a deductive system. Often, we forget to teach what mathematics *is*.

    b. Illustrate the harmony, symmetry, and beauty of mathematical patterns.

    c. Include current applications of mathematics.

2. To nourish *curiosity* in mathematical ideas we need to:

    a. Give experiences in discovering new ideas.

    b. Make each lesson have significance for the learner.

    c. Include enrichment topics such as computer programming or game theory.

    d. Assign open-ended questions and problems.

3. To build *confidence* in and loyalty to mathematics we need to:

    a. Be the kind of person students accept and are willing to imitate.

    b. Work with students with patience and kindness so that *each day each student* has some success.

    c. Make learning mathematics a *privilege* rather than a punishment.

    d. Be fair in *marking* and in *discipline*.

4. To make learning mathematical ideas a *pleasure* we need to:

    a. Present the material so that it is understood. Be sure that students attain a reasonable level of competence before going on to new topics.

    b. Use a variety of materials and methods that provide student participation in discovery, discussion, or laboratory lessons.

    c. Make reasonable assignments.

5. To nourish *respect* for excellence in achievement we need to:

    a. Stress the things a student does well. Do not humiliate him because of failure.

    b. Show how mathematical achievement relates to the student's goals.

    c. Establish reasonable competition for marks and keep the student informed of his status.

6. To establish an *optimistic* attitude we need to:

    a. Present problems in a way that does not threaten the student's ego.

    b. Assign tasks that are within the range of the student's ability.

    c. Have a repertoire of illustrations, problems, sidelights, and applications that add variety and sparkle to daily lessons.

    d. Be an optimistic, enthusiastic, sincere person.

USING MATHEMATICAL RECREATIONS TO BUILD POSITIVE ATTITUDES

Many teachers have found the use of mathematical recreations in the classroom the key to attitude development. Of course, learning mathematics is not all play, and no student should bypass the hard work of the subject. But much good mathematics can be learned from enjoyable recreations. In fact, enrichment activities of this type have been the source of much high-quality mathematics. Such outstanding mathematicians as Gauss, Leibnitz, and Euler found in such pastimes sources of new ideas and even new fields of mathematics. Two examples of such mathematical topics growing out of recreation are probability theory and game theory.

Recreations may sometimes be brought into the program as optional activities; for instance, many teachers pose a weekly problem for extra credit. On the other hand, it is quite appropriate to incorporate recreational activities that introduce, underscore, or extend the regularly required program.

The possibilities for worthwhile recreational activities in the mathematics class are very great. Most lessons can be dressed up with a puzzle, trick, paradox, or anecdote. The references and books listed in the Appendix will supply you with a wealth of ideas.

Here are some examples of recreations that stimulate students to participate, be observant, learn rules, work independently or cooperatively, and, most of all, find satisfaction in mathematics:

1. A game like "Battleship," in which teams "shoot" at various-sized ships marked on coordinate grids, provides good practice in locating points on a graph. Another game that provides this same practice is a form of the Japanese game Go-Moku. To play, the class is divided in half, and each side attempts to locate a row, column, or diagonal of four counters, at the same time preventing the opponents from doing so.

2. Alphametics encourage junior and even senior high students to examine the structure of mathematical operations. In these each different letter represents a distinct digit. Here are some examples:

$$\begin{array}{r} \text{HAVE} \\ + \text{ SOME} \\ \hline \text{HONEY} \end{array} \qquad \begin{array}{r} \text{SANTA} \\ - \text{ CLAUS} \\ \hline \text{XMAS} \end{array} \qquad \begin{array}{r} \text{FORTY} \\ \text{TEN} \\ + \text{ TEN} \\ \hline \text{SIXTY} \end{array} \qquad \begin{array}{c} 2(\text{HOHOHO}) = 9(\text{OHOHOH}) \\ \\ \dfrac{\text{EVE}}{\text{DID}} = .\text{TALK TALK TALK} \ldots \end{array}$$

3. Paradoxes force students to examine more closely the operations they carry out without thinking. For example:

> You are as old as I am!

> If x represents your age and y mine, then let our average age, $(x + y)/2$, be M. Then $x + y = 2M$. Multiplying by $x - y$ gives $x^2 - y^2 = 2Mx - 2My$, or $x^2 - 2Mx = y^2 - 2My$. Add M^2 to each member and factor:

$$x^2 - 2Mx + M^2 = y^2 - 2My + M^2$$
$$(x - M)^2 = (y - M)^2$$

> But this means $x - M = y - M$ or $x = y$. In other words, you are exactly the same age I am.

4. Number tricks often help students to understand the operations of simple algebra and encourage them to explore the field further:

Think of a number between 0 and 10. Multiply it by 5. Add 6 to your answer. Multiply this answer by 2. Add any other number between 0 and 10. Subtract 5 from this result. The answer can be represented as $10x + y + 7$, which quickly identifies the chosen numbers.

Select a number between 100 and 1,000 that has a first digit and a last digit that differ by at least as much as two. Reverse the digits of this numeral. You now have another number represented by a three-digit numeral. Subtract the smaller number from the larger of these two numbers. The difference should be another number between 100 and 1,000. Reverse the digits of this difference. Add the difference and the number represented by its reversed digits. The sum is 1,089.

5. Recreations can show the versatility of logical analysis. The following situation is an example of a problem using indirect reasoning:

A professor wishing to choose an assistant decided to test the mentality of the three top candidates. The professor told the candidates that he would blindfold each one and then mark either a red or blue cross on the forehead of each. He would then remove the blindfold. Each candidate was to raise his hand if he saw a red cross and drop his hand when he figured out the color of his own cross. The professor first blindfolded each candidate and proceeded to mark a red cross on each forehead and then removed the blindfolds. After looking at each other, the prospective assistants all raised their hands. After a short interval of time, one candidate lowered his hand and said, "My cross is red," and gave his reasons. Can you duplicate his reasoning?

6. Recreations may be appropriate "homework." A puzzle, game, or stunt is an excellent way for student and parents to work together at learning mathematics. Since parental attitudes are a key to student attitudes, this joint enjoyment of "doing" mathematics together can be extremely productive. Such assignments also give an answer to the oft-repeated parent question: "How can we help?"

THE BEHAVIOR OF STUDENTS WHO HAVE ATTAINED FAVORABLE ATTITUDES

The student with the proper attitudes will enter wholeheartedly into the learning activities because he is sensitive to mathematics wherever he finds it and derives pleasure from his contacts with it. His conversation, written work, and activities in and out of the classroom will be indicative of his attitudes. For example, in the student's written work his attitudes will be expressed by the pride he takes in completing work, doing extra work, searching for the most elegant exposition or solution, and by the effort he makes to discover new relationships, new forms, new procedures. He may find unique problems or applications to bring to class, or participate in a mathematics club, or read mathematics books. He may keep a mathematics notebook or use ingenuity to create original models—and he will do these things cheerfully and be annoyed by distractions that hinder his progress or that violate good mathematics.

CREATIVITY IN MATHEMATICS

When we consider the history of mathematical ideas, we realize that many mathematical concepts have been created by young people. Therefore, continued development of mathematics depends to a great extent on the early identification, stimulation, and education of our mathematically creative youth.

In many ways mathematics offers unique opportunities for creative and original thinking. Writing and solving original problems, establishing theorems with original proofs, discovering and stating relationships in one's own words are beginning experiences in creative thinking. A further opportunity for originality is found in the communication of mathematical ideas, be it in a demonstration, a proof, an exhibit, a poem, or a research project.

The development of a new numeration system, the building of an original model, or the discovery of new ideas or new applications of mathematics illustrate creative work at an even higher level.

DISCOVERING CREATIVE STUDENTS

Research on the problem of creativity indicates that the creative student is the nonconformist, the independent, the offbeat, and sometimes even the unruly student. In locating the specially creative youngster the teacher must not rely heavily on standard measures of achievement, for the creative student does not always rate unusually high on an intelligence test. On those tests the ideal performance is conformity to the examiner's criteria and norms. Creativity requires more than high intelligence, special talent, or technical skills—even though creative thinking is related to achieved intellectual skills.

Here are some of the characteristic ways in which creative students perform:

They are unpredictable, flexible, versatile in responses to situations, ideas, problems, adaptive in association, redefinitions, reorganization, and elaborations of ideas.

They are curious about ideas, objects, devices; they are sensitive to problems, relationships, errors, independent and confident in judgment and approach.

They are able to sustain uncertainty and withhold decisions in a complex situation, and able to abstract generalizations from complex situations or apply generalization to new situations.

Although much recent research, notably by Paul Torrance, has sought objective measures of creativity, the capable teacher attuned to the attributes of creative students can probably locate this talent as well as any testing device. Through individual conferences and out-of-class contacts, through evaluation of student classroom activities, homework, and projects, the teacher will frequently find the student who has special creative attributes.

Often, creative students develop negative attitudes toward the highly structured activities of science and mathematics. They prefer the unusual activities, the unexpected circumstances. Classrooms that offer little opportunity for student participation repress creativity, whereas classrooms that provide for student participation and that encourage original ideas and approaches foster creativity. Within this encouraging environment, the teacher can identify the creative student as the one who takes real advantage of the opportunity provided him.

CREATIVE ACTIVITIES OF MATHEMATICIANS

The mathematician, in his search for new knowledge, uses intuition, imagination, recall, and estimation. Often his insight, originality, and flexibility lead to breakthroughs to new ideas. The history of mathematics offers a wealth of anecdotes which illustrate the creative activities of young mathematicians. One of the best examples is Evariste Galois (1811–1832), a great French mathematician. Even though he died at the age of twenty-one, he created the basis of modern group theory—one of the most fundamental concepts of mathematics today. He was inspired by reading the literature of mathematics and encouraged by a teacher who recognized his genius. The creative efforts of Galois and other mathematicians may be illustrated by these historical events:

> The determination of the value of π by Archimedes.
> The measurement of the earth's circumference by Eratosthenes.
> The binomial expansion and Pascal's triangle.
> The analysis of the networks of topology by Euler.
> The sum of an arithmetic series by Gauss.
> Fermat and his last unsolved theorem.
> The invention of calculus by Newton.
> Goldbach and his conjecture about primes.
> Cartesian coordinates as proposed by Descartes.
> The musical scale as established by Pythagoras.
> The invention of binary numbers by Leibnitz.
> The theory of relativity proposed by Einstein.
> Cantor and the mathematics of sets.
> The non-euclidean geometry of Riemann and Lobachevski.
> The theory of games as built by Von Neumann.

SUGGESTED ACTIVITIES FOR DEVELOPING CREATIVITY

There are some who say that creative activities must be delayed until the students know all the mathematics already developed. However, numerous times during the course of study a student may depart from the traditional sequence to explore new fields. For example, permutations and combinations are essentially independent of advanced mathematical concepts; and, at an elementary level, properties of numbers can furnish an excursion independent of algebraic concepts. Linear programming, elementary topology, groups, and game theory are other possibilities for original thinking. In geometry, there are extensions to the geometry of a sphere or a cylinder, non-euclidean geometries, four- or five-dimensional geometry, and projective geometry. At a more advanced level, the creative student might study finite geometry, quaternions, matrices, probability, or transformations. The applications of mathematics in science, economics, genetics, and psychology are also avenues for further original explorations.

For a secondary school student to discover or develop a new mathematics today would be most unusual, though not absolutely impossible. But for a secondary school student independently to rediscover or redevelop good mathematics is an extremely valuable experience, as valuable to him as the original act was to the mathematician who first performed it. The mathematician R. L. Moore of the University of Texas recognized the need for redevelopment and rediscovery and made it the basis of his teaching. He provides his students with a set of axioms and definitions and asks them to develop a certain subject independently, without the aid of texts.

Here are a few ideas that may suggest possibilities for creative activities:

1. Determine why an accepted algorithm or procedure works.

2. Invent new number symbols and a new numeration system.

3. Invent new operations or new ways to perform divisions, multiplications, or the finding of roots.

4. Write an original mathematical poem, essay, or story.

5. Write and present an assembly program, television program, or classroom dramatization on a mathematical theme.

6. Discover a new proof for a theorem, such as the Pythagorean theorem.

7. Construct an original model, such as a device for finding the roots of a cubic equation.

8. Invent a new scheme of measurement with appropriate units and measuring devices.

9. Find a way of graphing the complex roots of a quadratic or cubic equation.

10. Write and prove original theorems involving sets, non-euclidean geometry, or game theory.

11. Extend the theorems of plane and solid geometry to four-dimensional space.

12. Extend Euler's formula connecting edges, vertices, and faces to four-dimensional tessaracts.

CLASSROOM ACTIVITIES THAT PROMOTE CREATIVITY

The teacher can encourage investigation and exploration by making available materials, topics, problems, and reading matter. Any discovery by the student in the realm of ideas should be recognized and care taken to avoid discouraging such activities. Often, time and solitude are needed to bring creativeness to the surface, but this freedom for independent work and expression must be combined with sustained effort by the learner, organized presentations of information, and adequate resources for reference work. The psychological climate must be such that the student feels that his qualities are valued by other members of the group as well as his teacher and feels enough confidence in his relations with others so that he can afford to be different and to express his own opinions.

Often, teachers reward memory, skills, and information far more than imaginative responses, "irrelevant" questions, and differences of opinion. By requiring specified assignments, courses, and procedures, we tend to explore new ideas in a formal group situation with a textbook containing all the facts and rules. Rather, the teacher should explore new ideas without the aid of the textbook. Finally, test constructors have not built test items which search for creative, unique responses.

If students are given only facts, rules, and drill, then the teacher has no reason to expect creative thinking. If we as teachers think there is only one solution to a problem, then students have little incentive to demonstrate originality. Do not stifle enthusiasm, originality, or creativeness by requiring conformity in analysis, method, or language.

Here is a list of activities that the teacher may check against his current classroom practice to highlight areas which may need improvement. It should be noted, however, that great variation in the number of times a specific activity is used is to be expected in any program. After matching the items in the list against his own classroom practices, the teacher may wish to modify his program to provide greater emphases in these areas.

1. The students are actively participating in discovering concepts through reflective thinking, problem solving, experimentation, analysis, or generalization.

2. The students are encouraged to ask questions, correct errors, propose new solutions or proofs, and introduce concepts that are different from those of the text or class discussion.

3. The students are required to give reasons for answers, statements, methods, rules, so that they will know the "why" as well as the "how" of what they do.

4. The teacher is prepared with reading material, applications, illustrations, procedures, and problems that enhance and extend the meaning of a concept.

5. The students are encouraged to explore topics independently.

6. The students are given open-ended research projects, reports, creative writing, and supplementary assignments.

7. The tests used include open-book tests, reading tests, performance tests, or reasoning tests that measure productive thinking.

8. The teacher shows enthusiasm for and enjoyment of his work and his pupils, and appreciation for new ideas.

Most mathematics students aren't going to do creative original work in mathematics, but they should have the opportunity to discover something which is new to them even though it is not new to the mathematical world. They may even discover something you, the mathematics teacher, do not know.

LEARNING EXERCISES

1. Collect information about original mathematics projects which have received awards at science fairs.

2. Make a case study of a student classified as creative by you or another mathematics teacher.
3. Analyze a test of creativity. Write a similar test of creativity in mathematics. Administer the test to a group of students and make an item analysis to determine the reliability and validity of the test.
4. Request that a group of students invent a new operation to be performed on rational numbers. Test the properties of this operation to determine the mathematical system.
5. Invent and build a model to demonstrate a mathematical idea.
6. Select a modern mathematics textbook. Make an analysis of it to find what it does to build favorable attitudes.
7. Review a test which is designed to measure attitudes.
8. Make a collection of puzzles, paradoxes, tricks, games, or anecdotes to enrich a specific mathematical unit.
9. What are the aspects of mathematics which cause reactions to it to be strongly positive or negative rather than neutral?
10. Make a survey of the attitudes of students in a given class by having the students answer anonymously this question: "How do I feel about mathematics or about learning mathematics?"
11. Observe a class taught by a master teacher. What techniques, materials, or assignments did he use to build positive attitudes?
12. What personal characteristics does a teacher need to cultivate if he is to establish rapport with his students?

10

teaching the methods of learning mathematics

Since most students lack skill in listening, reading, and studying, we must teach these skills; they are essential for the independent learning of mathematics.

LEARNING THROUGH LISTENING

One of the most effective ways of learning mathematics is for the student to listen and participate in class discussions. Here are some suggestions that may help your students:

1. Listen to the statements made and try to correct or improve them.

2. Participate in the discussion, and ask questions when ideas are not clear.

3. Try to anticipate what comes next in a discussion or explanation. Study the pattern, sequence, and facts to discover relationships involved.

4. Take notes of significant ideas or key examples, but don't concentrate on writing so that you miss the idea being presented.

5. Reflect on what has been discussed both in and out of class. Relate what is discussed to previously learned ideas. Discuss the concepts with other students.

LEARNING THROUGH READING

With renewed emphasis on reading material in contemporary mathematics textbooks, supplementary books, and programmed texts, the mathematics teacher must know not only the sources of difficulty his students encounter in reading mathematical material but also ways of overcoming these difficulties.

Mathematical statements are unique in several respects. First, mathematical writing is compressed and concise, and unfamiliar words may not be skipped in reading mathematical narrative. Second, the vocabulary of mathematics is highly specialized and technical. Even in primary school, terms such as "associative" or "operation" are used to express basic ideas. Consider as a case in point the definition of "adjacent angles" in plane geometry: "Adjacent angles are two angles with a (1) *common vertex* and a (2) *common side* (3) *between them.*" Each of the three italicized phrases is necessary for the definition. Examples can be given of angles that fulfill any two of the three phrases that are not adjacent angles. There is, in other words, no "fat" in a mathematical statement. There is no room for carelessness in mathematics.

Third, the ideas involved in mathematics are abstract. The reader may be familiar with an elementary example of this confusion: failure to recognize the difference between the abstract idea of number and the symbol representing it; that is, a numeral. When asked why he said that half of 8 is 3, a student answers, "It's the right half." Presumably the left half is $\mathcal{E}$.

Students of mathematics must be able to relate the abstract ideas to concrete examples, but they must always recognize the differences and the losses that come with the gains when such examples are used. A dot (a pencil or chalk smudge) is a useful representation of a point, but it immediately introduces contaminating aspects of dimension to the pure idea.

A related difficulty is that the ideas frequently lack immediate application outside the mathematics classroom. Although students may learn how to divide one fraction by another fraction, the possibilities for real situations which require this computation are very limited. Often, the applications of mathematical ideas are beyond the scope of the course or the level of understanding of the learner. Complex numbers have wide applicability in electrical theory, but the physics background demanded for such applications is not yet available to the high school student.

Fourth, familiar words (*root, base, irrational, real, log, point, opposite, similar,* and *function*) frequently have a special meaning in mathematics; and some mathematical words have several different meanings. For example, the word *root* may refer to the truth set of a linear equation or to the value of a radical. And some words that are often taken as synonyms (for instance, *root* and *radical*) turn out to have different meanings. A square root of 16 is -4, but -4 is *not* a value of $\sqrt{16}$ (radical 16).

A final source of reading difficulty is the frequent use of symbols. Often these symbols represent complex ideas, such as

$$\int_a^b \frac{dx}{x}$$

At other times a given symbol has several meanings. Thus, "$-$" may mean "subtract," or "negative," or "opposite." At other times, symbols are so similar that meanings are confused. For example, within a given problem x^1, x', and x_1 would all have different meanings. At other times symbols are omitted. This X represents $+1X^1$. Sometimes several arrangements of symbols will mean essentially the same thing—for instance, $\frac{a}{b}$ or $a : b$, or a/b, or ab^{-1}, or even (a,b).

FACTORS IN TEACHING THE READING OF MATHEMATICAL MATERIAL

In deciding what instructions to give a student regarding a given reading assignment, the teacher must consider several factors. First of all, he should consider the *purpose* of the reading assigned. If the purpose is to learn a new, complex idea, then the reading must be careful, slow, and deliberate; each word and symbol must be noted and, frequently, paper and pencil should be used to respond to questions, examples, or computations. In addition, the material should be reread to be sure the ideas are thoroughly clear to the reader. If the material assigned is read merely for the main ideas, then such an intense reading would not be required.

Second, the *difficulty* of the ideas must be taken into consideration. If the reader is not expected to digest all the ideas in the first reading, then there should be instructions for looking up words, working out problems, making drawings, and applying the ideas to specific situations. After that, a second reading would make further clarification more likely to occur.

Third, the teacher should stress that the reading should be done with *intent to learn,* for it is the teacher's role to stimulate interest in the readings and to ensure the maintenance of this interest.

A fourth factor relates to the student's background—his storehouse of ideas and vocabulary and his reading habits. It is essential that the student be *prepared* for the ideas, words, and symbols involved in a new assignment by reviewing background material and defining new words.

To enhance the student's success in reading mathematical material, the teacher should take the following steps:

1. Establish the purpose of the reading, so that the student approaches the reading with interest.
2. Be sure the student is ready for the material involved.
3. Teach the necessary vocabulary and symbols.
4. Give instruction in the type of reading which is appropriate.
5. Let the student read the selection silently and independently.
6. Discuss the purpose of the material read.
7. Have the student reread the material if necessary.

However, all of these steps will be of no avail if they are not followed by a test of achievement of reading skill. The teacher should design and administer a reading test that measures comprehension, rate, and retention.

To ensure learning through independent reading, the student should be urged to follow these steps:

1. Be sure the purpose is clear in your mind.
2. Read the entire passage to get an overview of the ideas involved.
3. Look up all unfamiliar words and symbols.
4. Reread the passage very carefully to see how the details fit together.
5. Work through each step of examples given.
6. Explore the relationship of this material to previously studied ideas. Anticipate where these ideas will probably be used in the future.
7. Whenever footnotes, suggestions, or hints occur, be sure to check them.
8. Whenever drawings, tables, or charts are used, compare them with verbal statements.
9. Write a summary statement in your notebook.

LEARNING VOCABULARY

The student's vocabulary must be built by direct, planned instruction. New words and symbols should be noted on the chalkboard or screen and then pronounced, defined, and discussed. Whenever possible, words should be related to previous experiences or previous vocabulary. Thus, *binomial* may be related to *bicycle, bimonthly,* or *bigamy.* Whenever appropriate, words should be illustrated by visual or graphic illustration. For example, the teacher might make the term *sample space* more meaningful to the student by illustrating the events or "sample points" of the tosses of dice. A new word should be applied to a variety of situations to broaden the concepts it represents. Thus, *irrational* is illustrated by numbers such as $\sqrt{3}$, π, and e, and also incommensurable line segments in geometry.

Word mastery grows in the following way: First, words are heard with comprehension; then the words are read; then they are used in speaking; and, finally, they are used in writing. If students are required to write precise statements before they have mastered the ideas, their learning of the ideas may be hampered. New vocabulary will have to be reviewed frequently in order to maintain vocabulary mastery, and vocabulary tests will reinforce the retention of technical terms.

INDEPENDENT ASSIGNMENTS

If independent assignments are to be effective, the teacher must first recognize the role they play in the learning of mathematics. Assignments are significant if they stimulate independent thought, clarify and extend new ideas, and build skill through meaningful practice. These assignments should increase mastery and retention of ideas, and provide a means for individualizing learning through enrichment or remedial instruction. By so doing they will build habits of organized, clear communication of ideas.

The teacher should always keep in mind that assignments are learning exercises, not measures of achievement. This means that students must be made aware that the assignment has been given to assist them in learning, rather than for grading them.

As mathematics teachers we tend to have too much confidence in the necessity of homework. Although research on the benefit of out-of-class assignments has been limited, evidence suggests that these assignments contribute little to achievement in mathematics—at least at the junior high level. However, before we abandon assignments, we must recognize that they are ineffective largely because they are improperly planned. To be effective, learning assignments should have the following characteristics:

1. The assignments should always be given in writing so that there is no question about what is to be done.

2. The assignment should be given for a specific purpose, and the student should know what this purpose is.

3. Whenever necessary, specific instructions should be given on how to prepare the assignment, how to find the necessary information, what materials are needed, and what difficulties are anticipated.

4. If possible, the assignments should be differentiated to provide for varying ability to handle abstractions. Capable students need to work a few challenging exercises, while slow students need easier exercises.

5. The assignment should be reasonable in terms of the time and facilities which the student has available. Whenever possible, make assignments for several days in advance. Be flexible in setting dates for the completion of assignments.

6. Include material such as answers to problems assigned so that students are able to check their progress.

7. Give the assignment at a time when it will contribute the most to the learning at hand.

8. In no case should the assignment be given after the period has ended.

9. Whenever possible, use assignments to relate the daily lesson to local situations and up-to-date events.

10. Use assignments as a way of discovering new ideas rather than for mere practice.

11. Perhaps most important, show your students that you are making assignments part of the required learning activities of your course. Correct some papers and return them. Include in your tests ideas developed in homework and not in class.

INSTRUCTIONS ON HOW TO STUDY

The teacher should use some class time for specific instruction on how to study mathematics. He should help students plan a study schedule and acquire the resources needed for home study through individual conferences and check their progress by tests and diaries of study activities.

Here are some easy suggestions for the students:

1. Know exactly what your assignments demand of you. Record your assignment in writing.

2. Budget your time so that you do not feel rushed or distracted.

3. Have all the necessary materials at hand, and arrange a study place that is quiet, well lighted, and adequately spacious.

4. Begin work promptly, concentrate on your lesson, and avoid interruptions.

5. Understand what you are reading or computing, and reflect as you read. When you get lost, go back to the point of difficulties.

6. Organize the new material by outlining the major ideas.

7. Review frequently. Stop to recall what you have been studying. Look for new applications of past lessons. Summarize key ideas and memorize commonly used facts.

8. Check the accuracy of your work. Estimate answers to see if your result is reasonable, and use these answers to help locate difficulties (like misplacement of a decimal point) but not to suggest methods.

9. Complete your written work in an organized, neat manner. Use ample writing space to avoid confusion.

10. Work independently. We learn best and remember longest those ideas we have discovered by ourselves.

11. Be optimistic about your progress. Enjoy overcoming obstacles. Expect problems to be frustrating.

12. Accept the responsibility for learning. No school book, course, or teacher ever gave anyone an education; they only provide the opportunity for one. Your teacher cannot do your learning; only you can do that.

13. Try to learn the material in such a way that you could teach it to your friends.

TEACHER ATTITUDE AND LEARNING SKILLS

Concentration on the learning of skills and concepts in the day-to-day classroom setting should not prevent a teacher from continually seeking to make students capable of translating their classroom learning into knowledge and attitudes viable in the modern world.

Teachers must recognize that the specific problems, theorems, computation techniques, and even concepts learned in the classroom will be largely forgotten by students, but that classroom learning techniques—good or bad—will be largely retained. Students who indiscriminately take notes and never make any real use of them will probably continue to do so; students, on the other hand, who develop thoughtful approaches to learning will probably continue to do so. These latter students have two great advantages: (1) they are learning more efficiently now, and (2) they are building a basis for learning new material in the future.

Here are some questions for teachers to consider in regard to their own thinking and classroom instruction:

1. Am I considering *learning efficiency* in my instruction? Early in the year do I spend the time necessary to establish good study and learning skills or do I race ahead only to have poor learning habits catch up with me later in the school year? Dog owners know the advantages of extra time

spent early on house breaking, time rewarded by hours and tempers saved later.

2. Do I encourage students to extrapolate ideas, to apply the concepts learned to broader concerns? Do I encourage them to apply mathematical principles to the sciences and to the arts? Do I seek to direct students to explore these relationships independently?

3. Do I work cooperatively with other teachers to coordinate efforts to attack this problem of learning how to learn? Occasionally, teachers can work together on a unit. If, for example, students are reading *Gulliver's Travels* for their English class, their science and mathematics teachers can discuss the problems of size and proportion.[1]

4. Do I work individually with both strong and weak students to help them develop better learning skills and habits? Do I attempt to encourage depth of interest in my students by all the means at my command?

5. Do I seek the cooperation of the parents in encouraging student independence and self-reliance? Unwitting parents often undermine school functions with statements like "I hated school too" or "Math was my poorest subject and look at me now." Brought into contact with schools and made aware of your broad objectives, especially as related to their children, parents can be very supportive and can contribute a great deal to your program.

6. Is it possible for me to bring in a mathematician to tell about his work or arrange a field trip to a research center to see mathematics being applied?

7. Do I continue to learn and to treat the acquisition of knowledge as a lifelong opportunity, and transmit this enthusiasm to my students? Or have I based my teaching of mathematics on what I learned and the way I learned it years ago?

It has been said that the successful teacher is one who makes himself increasingly unnecessary to his students. The class which continues to learn when the teacher is called from the room or when a visitor interrupts class activities is often demonstrating the results of superior instruction. To attain this level of independent study, students require instruction in the process of learning and encouragement to stimulate their activities.

LEARNING EXERCISES

1. Before teaching a new unit, examine the text and select the mathematical terms which the author assumes the reader will know. Use these terms for a vocabulary test to determine the readiness of your students for learning this new topic.

2. Write several test items that apply mathematical concepts to other subject areas or that interrelate two fields.

3. Develop an optional summer reading program for students. Annotate at least one reading suggestion with an introduction for students.

[1] For a delightful presentation of these ideas see Peter Weyl, *Men, Ants and Elephants: Size in the Animal World* (New York: The Viking Press, 1959).

4. Teach a lesson and test immediately to find out how well the class listened and understood.

5. Select several passages on topics that your students have not studied previously and use them for reading test items. Examine a reading test to learn how to ask questions that will reflect reading skill.

6. Read *Men, Ants and Elephants: Size in the Animal World* and the first and second sections of *Gulliver's Travels*. Describe in some detail how this material could be used in both science and mathematics courses.

part three

special problems in the classroom

11

special instructional techniques

One of the basic requirements for success in teaching mathematics is the development of a repertoire of special techniques to meet particular instructional problems. While many individual teachers have the intellectual resources to develop truly creative approaches to lessons on their own, they often fail to take advantage of methods developed by others.

One of the best ways for a teacher to find alternate and creative teaching techniques is by direct reference to the extensive literature of mathematics and mathematics education, and to the better texts and teachers' manuals used in classrooms. Naturally, a compendium of "tricks of the trade" would be virtually endless, but the teacher must select from the various techniques those that will work for him, that fit his goals and style of presentation, and that are interesting to him and his pupils.

Many teachers do read extensively and make a real effort to learn from fellow staff members in local discussions and from a broader segment of teachers at state and national conferences. Too often, however, the excellent assistance derived from such interchange is lost if the teacher has made no record of the new ideas. For the teacher quickly forgets his newly found technique and therefore has no way of retaining it. In many cases the same thing happens even to self-developed techniques. A failure to record such activities for future reference means a loss to students and a duplication of effort on the part of the teacher.

To avoid the dilemma of not having various techniques at hand the beginning teacher should develop files of *instructional techniques,* and continue using them for the rest of his teaching career. Such a file would be organized by courses and within courses by topics. The file may at first require only desk-drawer space, but a continued development would almost certainly create the need for a filing cabinet with a drawer devoted to each subject area and an additional drawer for general techniques.

TYPES OF MATERIAL FOR THE INSTRUCTIONAL FILE

Here are some suggestions regarding the kinds of ideas that could be included in the Instructional Techniques File:

1. A unique way of developing the mathematical content of a topic. A typical example is the use of a finite number system as an introduction to a mathematical system.

2. Historical background related to the development of a topic. For example, the story of Eratosthenes and his method of measuring indirectly the circumference of the earth.

3. A striking problem to be used to introduce a topic, to motivate the discussion, or to stimulate discovery. For example, locating the path of a basketball can be the basis for an introduction to quadratic equations. The formula $S = S_o + V_o t - 16t^2$ for given values of height of ball at release (S_o) and initial velocity (V_o) may determine such things as the two times at which the ball will be at the height $(S = 10)$ of the basket.

4. Alternate strategies for teaching a topic, as described in Chapter 4.

5. A fresh and stimulating way to review a topic, such as that provided by an identification game.

6. A game, trick, fallacy, or puzzle related to a topic. The game of Nim can be an excellent setting for examining number patterns and arriving at a generalization.

7. A specific pitfall to avoid in teaching a topic with some suggestions of how to avoid this pitfall. For example, a common error in dealing with algebraic fractions is to "cancel" as follows:

$$\frac{3x + \cancel{a}}{2y + \cancel{a}} = \frac{3x}{2y}$$

8. Some good questions that lead into a topic, point out special aspects of a topic, or otherwise direct the thinking of students toward significant results. A typical example might be to ask under what conditions does $\frac{3}{4} + \frac{2}{3} = \frac{5}{7}$.

9. A useful diagram or a special technique for drawing a diagram. For example, correct drawings of three-dimensional objects are easily done with a stencil.

10. A logical fallacy that forces students to look deeper into a subject for answers. The proof that arrives at the conclusion that every triangle is an isosceles triangle may be used to challenge the students to find the loophole in the proof.

11. A laboratory exercise that promotes learning—for example, the exploration of algorithms by the use of calculators.

12. A project idea or a resource for an enrichment exercise, such as an exploration of topology.

13. An application to a local-interest angle, such as the mathematical relationship between students' achievement in the classroom and car ownership.

14. An interesting extension of a topic to higher dimensions or a more general case—for example, the distance formula and n-dimensional space.

15. A geometric analysis for an algebraic or arithmetic problem or an algebraic analog for a geometric problem. One example is the algebraic proof of the Pythagorean theorem. Another is the geometric illustration of the arithmetic, harmonic, and geometric means.

16. The rationale for a computational procedure or an arithmetic shortcut such as the algorithm for the square root. This algorithm has an algebraic explanation in terms of $(x + y)^2$ as well as a geometric illustration.

17. A new technique to represent a mathematical idea. In this regard, paper folding or curve stitching could illustrate conic sections.

EXAMPLES OF SPECIAL PROBLEMS

Here are some examples of material for the Instructional Techniques File, organized under subject and topic.

ARITHMETIC

1. *Graphing.* The use of figures or pictures to represent the quantities in a bar graph is widespread and may be misleading—sometimes, as in advertising, purposely. In the example shown in Fig. 11–1, the vertical scale represents the number of barrels of oil, showing that the production in the three recorded years is 100, 200, and 300 respectively. The figures, however, are representations of volume instead of length. If the first represents 100 gallons, the second would represent eight times as much, 800 gallons; and the third, 27 times as much—2,700 gallons. The unsuspecting reader sees a representation of a cubic rather than a linear growth. A variety of similar examples can be found in *How to Lie with Statistics.*[1]

2a. *Ratio and proportion.* In order to keep track of the terms in a proportion and to locate them correctly, it is useful to write an auxiliary ratio specifying units.

[1] Darrell Huff, *How to Lie with Statistics* (New York: W. W. Norton & Co., 1954).

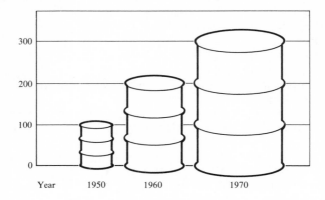

300

200

100

0

Year   1950   1960   1970

Fig. 11–1.   Number of Barrels.

Example:
If I drive 300 miles in 7 hours, how far could I expect to go in 9 hours driving at the same rate?
Solution:

$$\frac{\text{miles}}{\text{hours}} \qquad \frac{300}{7} = \frac{x}{9}$$

Note that this avoids the pure mathematician's criticism of equations that include units.

2b. *Ratio and proportions, measurement.* It is usually best to teach conversion of units by means of ratios. Set up the auxiliary dimensional analysis relationship and from it write the conversion ratios.

Example:
Change 176 feet per second to miles per hour.
Auxiliary relation

$$\frac{\text{feet}}{\text{second}} \; \frac{\text{seconds}}{\text{minute}} \; \frac{\text{minutes}}{\text{hour}} \; \frac{\text{miles}}{\text{feet}} = \frac{\text{miles}}{\text{hour}}$$

Mathematical statement

$$\frac{176}{1} \cdot \frac{60}{1} \cdot \frac{60}{1} \cdot \frac{1}{5280} = x$$

3. *Area.* How is the number of holes in a pegboard related to the area of a polygonal region of the pegboard?

Assume that there are holes at the vertices of each unit of area. Also assume that the polygons involved will all have vertices at points with holes. Thus, there will be holes at vertices, holes on the perimeter, and holes inside the polygon. What is the relationship of the area of a polygon and the holes on the perimeter or inside the polygon? Figure 11–2 shows some examples.

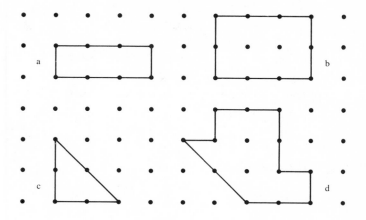

Fig. 11–2

The data for these examples are as follows:

	No. holes on perimeter (x)	No. holes in interior (y)	Area (A)
a.	8	0	3
b.	10	2	6
c.	6	0	2
d.	12	2	7

By collecting additional data, students can discover that the formula is

$$A = \frac{x - 2}{2} + y$$

Then conditions should be varied. Consider polygons with common vertices. Consider regions which are not convex polygons. Finally, state the generalization that takes care of all conditions.

4. *Geometry.* Geometric relationships give students another application of commutative and associative laws. For example, they might note (1) several ways the area formula for a triangle may be justified from the corresponding formula for a parallelogram and (2) the algebraic relations:

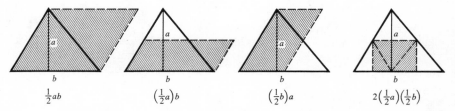

Fig. 11–3

ALGEBRA

1. *Patterns.* The patterns of certain number relations are discovered rather quickly.

a. Sum of consecutive counting numbers beginning with 1:

$$S = 1 + 2 + 3 + 4 + 5 + 6 + 7 + 8 + 9 + 10$$
$$S = \frac{10 \times (11)}{2} = 55 \quad \text{or} \quad S = \frac{n(n + 1)}{2}$$

b. Sum of consecutive odd numbers:

$$S = 1 + 3 + 5 + 7 = 16$$
$$S = 4 \times 4 \quad \text{or} \quad S = n^2$$

c. Sum of consecutive even numbers:

$$S = 2 + 4 + 6 + 8 + 10 = 30$$
$$S = 5 \times 6 \quad \text{or} \quad S = n(n + 1)$$

d. Difference of the squares of two consecutive numbers:

$$4^2 - 3^2 = 7 \qquad 5^2 - 4^2 = 9$$
$$9^2 - 8^2 = 17 \qquad 12^2 - 11^2 = 23$$

If $x^2 - y^2 = n$, then $n = x + y$

e. Sum of rational numbers of the form $1/n(n + 1)$:

$$n = 1 \qquad S = \tfrac{1}{2}$$
$$n = 2 \qquad S = \tfrac{1}{2} + \tfrac{1}{6} = \tfrac{2}{3}$$
$$n = 3 \qquad S = \tfrac{1}{2} + \tfrac{1}{6} + \tfrac{1}{12} = \tfrac{3}{4}$$

Thus $S = \dfrac{n}{n + 1}$

2. *Maneuvers on a lattice.* An imaginative new operation has been proposed by David Page. He suggests that a lattice such as the following be used:

```
51  52  . . .
41  42  43  44  45  46  47  48  49  50
31  32  33  34  35  36  37  38  39  40
21  22  23  24  25  26  27  28  29  30
11  12  13  14  15  16  17  18  19  20
 1   2   3   4   5   6   7   8   9  10
```

Next he introduces operations represented by arrows: $(\rightarrow)$ $(\uparrow)$. Then $7 \rightarrow = 8$ and $12 \uparrow = 22$. Combinations such as $32 \uparrow \rightarrow = 43$ or $32 \nearrow = 43$. What is the result for $25 \uparrow \rightarrow \rightarrow \downarrow$? What is $10 \rightarrow$? Is the operation $\uparrow$ closed with respect to this lattice? What about $\rightarrow$? What about commutativity and associativity? This lattice then becomes a means for exploring a completely new system.

3. *Shortcuts for squaring numbers* when you know the squares of numbers from 1 to 25.

a. For numbers from 26 to 75. Example: Square 46.
    (1) First two digits $N - 25$ $46 - 25 = 21$
    (2) Last two digits $(50 - N)^2$ $4^2 = 16$
    (3)   Answer: 2,116.
    (4) Why? Answer: $N^2 = 100(N - 25) + (50 - N)^2$.

b. For numbers from 76 to 100 (best 91–100). Example: Square 93.
    (1) First two digits $N - (100 - N)$ $93 - (100 - 93) = 86$
    (2) Last two digits $(100 - N)^2$ $7^2 = 49$
    (3)   Answer: 8,649.
    (4) Why? Answer: $N^2 = 100\ [N - (100 - N)] + (100 - N)^2$.

c. For numbers from 101 to 125. Example: Square 106.
    (1) First three digits $2N - 100$ $212 - 100 = 112.$
    (2) Last two digits $(N - 100)^2$ $6^2 = 36.$
    (3)   Answer: 11,236.
    (4) Why?   Answer: $N^2 = 100(2N - 100)^2$.
    (5) Why were examples chosen within ten of 50 and 100? Answer:
To avoid regrouping, but the rule still works for other numbers.

4. *Exponents.* Beware the temptation to prove $a^0 = 1$ and $a^{-n} = 1/a^n$ from the definition of a^n. Instead, define these terms separately.

If we define

$$a^n = \underbrace{a \cdot a \cdot a \cdot a \ \ldots \cdot a}_{n \text{ factors}}$$

then we assume that n is a natural number (a positive integer). We then can establish rules like

$$\frac{a^m}{a^n} = a^{m-n} \quad \text{and} \quad \frac{a^m}{a^n} = \frac{1}{a^{n-m}}$$

only for $m > n$ in the first case, $n > m$ in the second, because we base our argument on counting and applying the definition. For example:

$$\frac{a^m}{a^n} = \frac{\overbrace{a \cdot a \cdot a \cdot a \ \ldots \cdot a}^{m \text{ factors}}}{\underbrace{a \cdot a \cdot a \ \ldots \cdot a}_{n \text{ factors}}} = \frac{\overbrace{(a \cdot a \ \ldots \cdot a)}^{n \text{ factors}} \cdot \overbrace{a \cdot a \cdot a \ \ldots \cdot a}^{m - n \text{ factors}}}{\underbrace{a \cdot a \cdot a \cdot a}_{n \text{ factors}}} =$$

$$\frac{\overbrace{a \cdot a \cdot a \ \ldots \cdot a}^{(m - n) \text{ factors}}}{}$$

Now we ask what would we like to have a^0 equal in order to fit (and not contradict) our definition.

Since $a^m/a^m = 1$ for any m, to fit our rule for division, we would like

$$1 = \frac{a^m}{a^m} = a^{m-m} = a^0$$

To make this the case we must *define* $a^0 = 1$. This development also suggests *how* mathematicians arrive at many definitions naturally rather than arbitrarily.

The preceding lesson is a good one for discovery techniques and shows how the brakes must be occasionally applied to avoid trouble.

5. *Division of polynomials.*
   Use $1/(1-x)$ as an example.

$$
\begin{array}{r}
1 + x + x^2 + \ldots \\
\hline
1 - x\,)\,1 \\
\underline{1 - x} \\
x \\
\underline{x - x^2} \\
x^2 \\
\underline{x^2 - x^3}
\end{array}
$$

But do not stop there. Raise some questions about the resulting statement.

$$\frac{1}{1-x} = 1 + x + x^2 + x^3 + \ldots$$

Is it a true statement for all values of x? Students recognize the fact that it isn't true for $x = 1$ (dividing by zero) but usually look no further.

What about $x = -1$? $\frac{1}{2} = 1 - 1 + 1 - 1 + 1 - 1 + \ldots$
What about $x = 2$? $-1 = 1 + 2 + 4 + 8 + \ldots$

Now they wonder if there are any true values.

What about $x = \frac{1}{2}$? $2 = 1 + \frac{1}{2} + \frac{1}{4} + \frac{1}{8} + \ldots$

At this point students should be ready to do some exploring on their own and are more willing to question apparently satisfactory computations. Some students may wish to look ahead to an independent study of sequences and series.

Historical note: The resulting equation for $x = -1$

$$\frac{1}{2} = 1 - 1 + 1 - 1 + 1 - 1 + \ldots$$

led some mathematicians (even Euler temporarily) to accept this result. Such unsatisfactory results led to a more careful logical development of infinite sequences and the calculus.

What about the sequence $1 - 1 + 1 - 1 + \ldots$?

If $S = 1 - 1 + 1 - 1 + \ldots$
then $S = (1-1) + (1-1) + (1-1) \ldots$ or $S = 0$
If $S = 1 - 1 + 1 - 1 + \ldots$
then $S = 1 - (1-1) - (1-1) \ldots$ or $S = 1$

Which of these is correct?

6. *The Hindu method for deriving the quadratic formula.* Once you know the statement of the quadratic formula, you can reconstruct its derivation "from the inside out" merely by reconstructing the statement by "bombardment."

$$ax^2 + bx + c = 0$$
$$ax^2 + bx = -c$$

Complete the term containing c by multiplying by $4a$.

$$4a^2x^2 + 4abx = -4ac$$

Add b^2.

$$4a^2x^2 + 4abx + b^2 = b^2 - 4ac$$

Square roots:

$$2ax + b = \pm\sqrt{b^2 - 4ac}$$

$$2ax = -b \pm \sqrt{b^2 - 4ac}$$

$$x = \frac{-b \pm \sqrt{b^2 - 4ac}}{2a}$$

GEOMETRY

1. *Equality of area, perimeter, and volume.* When will the area and perimeter of a triangle be numerically equal? The first example to come to mind is the 6–8–10 right triangle. What other right triangles with sides of integral measures have this property?

If the sides of a right triangle are x, y, and z, then $x^2 + y^2 = z^2$. The perimeter is $x + y + z$, and the area is $\frac{1}{2}xy$. Thus

$$\tfrac{1}{2}xy = x + y + z \quad \text{or} \quad \tfrac{1}{2}xy = x + y + \sqrt{x^2 + y^2}$$

Then

$$y = \frac{4(x - 2)}{x - 4} \quad \text{if} \quad x \neq 4$$

We also know that $x + y > z$ and $x > 0$ and $y > 0$. It is obvious that $y > 0$ if $x > 4$ and that $y < 0$ for $2 < x < 4$.

The graph of $\quad y = \dfrac{4(x - 2)}{x - 4}$

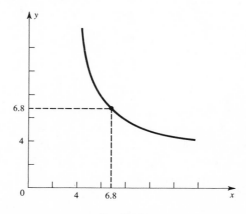

Fig. 11–4

The isosceles right triangle results when $x = y = 4 + 2\sqrt{2}$ or $x \approx 6.8$ and $y \approx 6.8$. Thus the interval $4 < x < 6.8$ represents all possible measures of the short side of the right triangle having area and perimeter equal. The only integers in this interval are 5 and 6.

Hence, the only right triangles with sides having integral measures and the perimeter equal to the area are (6–8–10) and (5–12–13).

Under what conditions are the area and the perimeter of any triangle numerically equal? The result is that the radius of the incircle is 2. When any triangle is extended to three space, the measure of lateral surface and volume are equal when the radius of the insphere is 3. An extension to n-space gives $r = n$. (For details of this extension see *Mathematics Teacher*, April 1965, pp. 303–306.)

2. *A comparison of means.* Suppose we wish to show geometrically the comparison of the arithmetic mean, geometric mean, and harmonic mean of a and b. (The relationship of these means is illustrated by Fig. 11–5.)

$$\text{Arithmetic mean} = \frac{a + b}{2}$$

$$\text{Geometric mean} = \sqrt{ab}$$

$$\text{Harmonic mean} = \frac{2ab}{a + b}$$

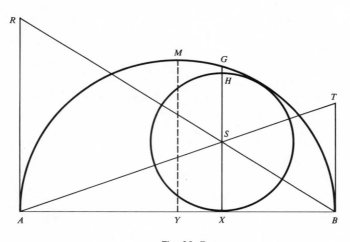

Fig. 11–5

On a horizontal axis locate X and Y so that $AX = a$ and $XB = b$ and Y is the midpoint of $\overline{AB}$. At A and B construct lines $\overline{AR}$ and $\overline{BT}$ perpendicular to $\overline{AB}$ and such that $AR = a$ and $BT = b$. Draw $\overline{AT}$ and $\overline{BR}$ which intersect at S. Then $\overline{XS}$ is parallel to $\overline{AR}$ and $\overline{BT}$. Why? With $\overline{AB}$ as a diameter and Y as the center draw a semicircle. Draw $\overline{YM}$ as a radius perpendicular to $\overline{AB}$. Draw a circle tangent to $\overline{AB}$ with center at S. Extend $\overline{SX}$ which intersects the semicircle (Y) at G. The semicircle (Y) and circle (S) are tangent.

Since $\overline{YM}$ is the radius of the semicircle whose diameter is $a + b$, YM is the arithmetic mean of a and b. The half-chord $\overline{XG}$ in the semicircle (Y) represents the geometric mean. In the circle (S) the radius XS is the harmonic sum, $(1/a + 1/b)$, and the diameter XH is the harmonic mean. Since circle (Y) and circle (S) are tangent, $XH < XG < YM$. (If $a = b$, the same diagram applies except that $X = Y$ and the three points M, G, and H coincide. In this case the three means are equal.)

Suppose AY and XY represent air speed and wind speed, respectively. Then AX is the ground speed with tail wind, BX is the ground speed with head wind, and XH is the average speed for a round trip.

3. *Angle measurement on the circle.* With the resurgence of interest in small boats, application of theorems about inscribed angles to navigation will be of interest to many students.

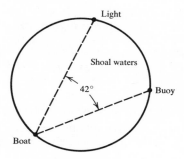

Fig. 11–6

Figure 11–6 shows a chart indicating shoal waters within a circle passing through two navigation lights. Boats in the area avoid the danger by keeping the angle between the two lights greater than 42 degrees.

To establish the rationale for this type of navigation, we need only apply an inscribed-angle theorem and the theorem relating an exterior angle of a triangle to non-adjacent interior angles.

In each case $m(\angle b) = 42°$. In Case I $m(\angle a) = m(\angle b)$; in Case II $m(\angle a) > m(\angle b)$; and in Case III $m(\angle a) < m(\angle b)$.

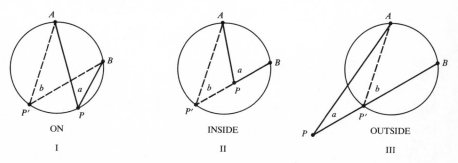

Fig. 11–7

This is a good example of a rather trivial application of a geometric idea that still gives students a feeling of the power of mathematics in a situation they can understand and appreciate.

4. *Indirect proof.* Start with a detective story, a familiar setting for the application of indirect proof.

Four people, alone on an island, have a violent argument. The group separates, each going his own way. When three of them return to the original place later, they discover the fourth seriously wounded. The wounded man is not able to identify his assailant. The hero of the story, knowing that he didn't commit the crime, eliminates himself as a suspect. He eliminates a second suspect who was within his view during the entire time the group was separated. He eliminates the wounded man because the wounds are of a type that could not be self-inflicted. He knows the criminal is the fourth man.

Students can discuss the reasoning contained in this example and may provide better examples themselves. Such a discussion is important because some students have a difficult time accepting this type of proof. Once the discussion has given students a chance to explore informal reasoning, they are encouraged to abstract from their discussion the technique of indirect reasoning: (a) State all possibilities, *one of which must be true.* (b) Eliminate all but one possibility by showing that they contradict given facts. (c) Accept the remaining possibility as proved.

Now return to the story to see how these steps are carried out.

5. *Ruler and compass constructions.* Through a point inside an angle but not on the angle bisector, construct one of the two circles tangent to the sides of the angle.

Given
∠ *ABC* and
point *P*.
Solution

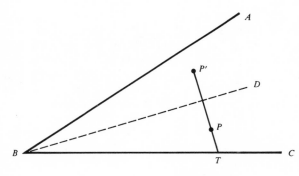

Fig. 11–8

1. Construct $\overrightarrow{BD}$ the bisector of ∠ *ABC*.
2. Locate *P′* symmetric to *P* on the opposite side of *BD*.
3. Extend $\overrightarrow{P'P}$ to *T*.
4. Construct the mean proportional $\overline{TP''}$ to $\overline{TP}$ and $\overline{TP'}$.
5. Mark off $\overline{TP''}$ on $\overline{BC}$.
6. Construct the circle through *P*, *P′* and *P″*.

The basis for this proof is the theorem "The tangent to a circle is the mean proportional between the secant and its external segment."

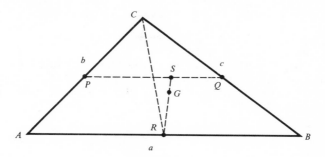

Fig. 11–9

6. *Center of gravity.* Many geometry books state that the center of gravity of a triangle is the point of intersection of the medians. This is a physical interpretation with no counterpart in abstract geometry because it assumes a uniform weight distribution. Even with such an assumption, it contradicts the usual modern interpretation of a triangle as one-dimensional (like a coat hanger). The following argument illustrates the fact that the intersection of the medians is the wrong answer. On Fig. 11–9 let the weight of the sides be distributed evenly, with the unit of weight equivalent for each unit length. The weight of the sides, *a, b,* and *c,* then is also *a, b,* and *c.* This weight may be considered concentrated at the midpoint of these sides, at *R, P,* and *Q* respectively. The center of gravity of lines *b* and *c* together, then, is a point, *S,* on segment $\overline{PQ}$. Unless *b* and *c* are equal, *S* will *not* be the midpoint of this line. The center of gravity, *G,* then will lie on the line $\overline{SR}$ and not at *R,* which is generally the only point of intersection of this line with the median, $\overline{CR}$.

In fact it may be shown that the equilateral triangle is the only case when the center of gravity of the one-dimensional triangle and the point of intersection of the medians are the same. Students may wish to test this fact by locating the center of gravity of a wire triangle model with threads and attempting to balance the hanger from this point. (See Fig. 11–10.) A further exploration may be made to discover whether the zero-dimensional

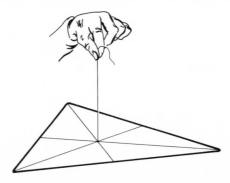

Fig. 11–10

(3-point) triangle and the two-dimensional triangle (region) have their centers of gravity at the point of intersection of the medians.

TRIGONOMETRY

1. *Wrapping functions.* As an introduction to the idea of wrapping functions, graph the length of the string wrapped counterclockwise from the origin as the independent, the distance from the x-axis as the dependent variable on the following diagram.

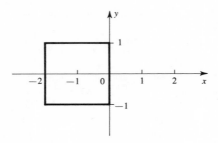

Fig. 11–11

A physical model of this with a graph paper background for graphing and a square block of wood 3/8" to 5/8" thick with twine wrapped around it helps students to see what you are doing. The graph looks like this:

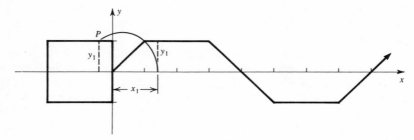

Fig. 11–12

The line y_1 shows how a point is located. The arc shows how the string is unwound from P along the x-axis to give x_1; y_1 is the ordinate to P.

Now develop informally some theorems about the function $S(x)$. For example

$$S(x) = S(x + 8)$$
$$S(x) = -S(x + 4)$$
$$S(6 + x) = S(6 - x) \text{ for } x < 6$$

This provides background for the more complicated wrapping functions on a circle. It may be a source of enrichment activities after a study of the circular functions. Questions for research then might be formulated:

a. $S(x)$ acts somewhat like sine x. What are some similarities? Differences?

b. Define a function, $C(x)$, that corresponds to cosine x on the square. Graph it and state some theorems about it.

c. State some theorems relating $C(x)$ and $S(x)$.

d. Is then a $T(x)$ like tangent x?

e. Try some other figures like the following:

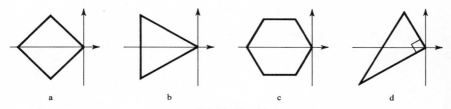

a   b   c   d

Fig. 11–13

  f. Graph the distance of a point on a rectangle from the center of the rectangle as a function of this distance of the point from a given starting point.

$$\text{Graph } y = \overline{OP} \text{ against } x = \overline{BCP}$$

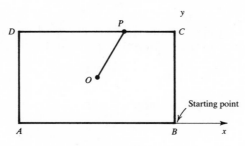

Fig. 11–14

ADVANCED MATHEMATICS

  1. *Analytic Geometry.* A problem that draws together many seemingly unrelated parts of mathematics is always useful. Here is one such problem:

  A fixed circle of radius 3 has its center at the point $(3,0)$ on the x-axis. A second circle has its center at the origin. Its radius is made to approach zero. Consider the line joining two points on this second circle: the intersection with the y-axis and the intersection with the other circle. How far from the origin will this line intersect the x-axis?

  Most students will agree that as the variable circle shrinks, points of intersection of the line with the x-axis go farther and farther out. So far so good. But students also believe that the lines move out an unbounded distance. This is not the case as they can show by developing the following:

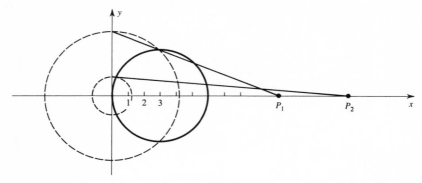

Fig. 11–15

a. Letting the radius of the variable circle be r, the equations of the two circles:

$$x^2 + y^2 = r^2 \quad \text{and} \quad (x - 3)^2 + y^2 = 9$$

b. The coordinates of the two points of intersection described in the problem: $(0, r)$ and

$$\left(\frac{r^2}{6}, \frac{r}{6} \sqrt{36 - r^2} \right)$$

the latter by solving the equations of the two circles simultaneously.

c. The equation of the line through these two points:

$$y = \frac{\sqrt{36 - r^2} - 6}{r} x + r$$

d. The x-value of the intersection of this line with the x-axis $(y = 0)$:

$$x = \frac{r^2}{6 - \sqrt{36 - r^2}}$$

e. The x-value rationalizing the denominator of this expression:

$$x = 6 + \sqrt{36 - r^2}$$

Once this expression is reached, this x-value cannot be made greater than 12, no matter how small r becomes—an entirely unexpected result.

This problem is also one that gives students, informally at least, additional insight into the limit process.

2. *Limits.* Some students become so enamored of limit processes that they want to use them without restraint. An example that should caution them is the following:

We set out to prove that favorite theorem of junior high school students: Since in a right triangle (with hypotenuse c; legs a and b) $c^2 = a^2 + b^2$, we can take square roots to get $c = a + b$. High school seniors in ad-

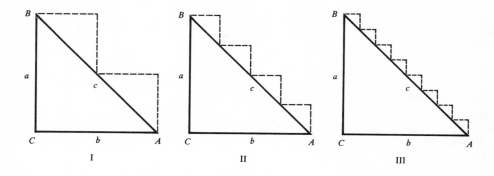

Fig. 11–16

vanced mathematics know the error in this statement, but they are intrigued by the following geometric demonstration (which is somewhat like the development of the circle area formula in plane geometry).

In I, $c(= AB)$ is bisected and the dotted lines parallel to a and b are drawn. The distance along the dotted line is $a + b$. The line c is further subdivided in II and III but still the length of the dotted line is $a + b$. Obviously it will soon be impossible to detect any difference between the dotted line joining A to B and the line AB. In other words we may say

$$\lim_{n \to \infty} \overset{...}{AB} = AB$$

where n represents the number of subdivisions and $\overset{...}{AB}$ the length of the dotted line joining A and B.

This statement is, of course, untrue. Even though the difference cannot be detected by the eye, it is always there and is in fact,

$$a + b - \sqrt{a^2 + b^2}$$

The basic goal of a file of teaching pointers is improvement of one's own instruction. There is, however, a secondary but important goal. Once a technique developed by the teacher himself or even taken from a suggestion by another teacher is refined through use several times, it should be shared with others through publication in a professional journal. Such articles are always in great demand by editors who know that their readers prefer them to all other types of exposition.

LEARNING ACTIVITIES

1. Outline a lesson which uses a unique way of developing a mathematical topic.
2. Select a historical incident that can be related to the development of a specific topic.

3. Select a striking problem which could be used to introduce a specific topic.

4. Make a collection of several alternate proofs of the Pythagorean theorem which could be used in a geometry class.

5. Make a file record of games, tricks, fallacies, or puzzles that can be related to specific lessons.

6. What are the common errors of algebra students? What can be done to prevent these errors?

7. Find an illustration of a geometric analysis of an algebraic problem or an algebraic analog for a geometric problem.

8. Outline an extension of a topic to an advanced level in terms that are meaningful to high school students.

9. Outline an enrichment unit on a topic such as infinity or non-euclidean geometry.

10. Start your own Instructional Techniques File by collecting and filing ideas such as those outlined in this chapter.

12

teaching the applications of mathematics

Mathematics has played an important part in liberal educational programs for at least two thousand years. It has retained its place today because of its continued and ever increasing use in science, industry, and government. Mathematics has always been the handmaiden of science; but today, more than ever before, all fields of knowledge are using mathematics for solving problems, stating generalizations and theories, and creating new knowledge.

At the same time that modern science and technology demand increased attention to the utilitarian aspects of mathematics, our present mathematics courses emphasize logic and structure devoid of specific applications or concrete representation. Consequently, critics of the new programs stress the formality, lack of reality, and lack of application of mathematics.

Actually, new mathematics programs have introduced innovations which should improve the student's ability to apply mathematics. The introduction of sets and set operations should provide a helpful means of classification and description. The emphasis on patterns and discovery should improve the ability to perform experiments in order to determine generalizations. The treatment of rate pairs and proportions provides a better means for using variation to solve problems. The increased content devoted to vectors, probability, and periodic functions improves the understanding of mass, space, time, and motion. The emphasis on problem solving and logical reasoning is a good foundation for the scientific investigation of problems in any field. Related to this is the common use of computer programs for solving problems. Finally, the emphasis on the structure of mathematics should prepare students for seeing the structure of problems and the structure of other fields of knowledge.

THE IMPORTANCE OF TEACHING APPLICATIONS

Teachers of mathematics must develop mathematical ideas and skills in such a manner that they can be used for further study, for everyday problems, for the personal satisfaction of all citizens. Thus, the mathematics we teach should have the concepts, the structures, the language that will give insight into the applications and the concepts of other fields of knowledge as well as daily problems. Teaching for the transfer of mathematical ideas and skills to other fields consists in teaching appropriate content in a way that will ensure transfer. This transfer occurs best when it is emphasized and when specific experiences in transfer are given to students. If we want students to use ratios and proportions in solving problems in chemistry, for example, we should include some chemistry problems in the mathematics assignment.

The applications of mathematics play another role in the classroom. Many students need applications to motivate their study of mathematics. Students frequently ask why they must learn certain facts and skills. When it is shown that these specific facts and skills are used in certain occupations or subjects, the students will more likely exert the effort to learn them. To reply that mathematics is needed only for entrance into college is not satisfactory.

Applications are also a means for illustrating the role of mathematics in our society. How has mathematics influenced civilization? The computer is a revolutionary force in our society. How does it depend on mathematics? What mathematical principles are used in decision making in business or government? One cannot be an informed citizen, one cannot understand the world of space travel, atomic energy, or automation without a background of elementary mathematics.

Finally, applications of mathematics are a means of teaching problem solving. What better sources for problems are there than those in the world about us? How do we measure the distance across a lake? How is a discount at the furniture sale computed? What is the centigrade temperature if the Fahrenheit reading is 68 degrees? How high will a baseball travel if the batter hits it upward at 45 degrees and 100 feet per second? At what speed will a space vehicle have to be launched to escape the earth's gravitational pull? What is the probability that you will have an automobile accident tomorrow? No matter where you turn in modern life, you will find mathematical problems. Often the best assignment is to have the student himself find such applications in his environment.

If we look at the history of mathematics, we find that mathematics grew out of experience in the physical world. Counting, measuring, fractions, geometric relations, equations, probability, and vectors—these and many others had their origin in problems faced by the scientists and mathematicians of the past. It seems reasonable, then, that students can learn mathematical principles in a similar way—in terms of actual problems from the environment in which the student lives.

SOME APPLICATIONS OF MATHEMATICS

The most common applications of mathematics are in the subject matter itself. After students have learned the principle of one-to-one correspondence, it is applied over and over in later topics. After they have learned the distributive property, this idea is used to make many operations such as the factoring of binomials meaningful. After they have learned to graph equations, this principle is applied to the study of functions and relations in advanced courses. The operations used to find truth sets for linear equations are applied in solving higher-degree equations and systems of equations. The method of proving a theorem is applicable to a great variety of situations. Frequently, it is these applications of mathematics which are of the greatest significance to the learner. He is not always interested in the applications of the adult world such as taxation, insurance, or banking.

Another major application of mathematics is its use in establishing new facts. Whenever the scientist performs an experiment, he collects data by observing events and making measurements. He then must fit the data into some conceptual scheme called a law, principle, or hypothesis. In his analysis of his experimental data, the scientist searches for a general law that will fit all the data. Usually he searches for a pattern by graphing, by obtaining differences, by testing regression equations—all tools furnished by mathematics. The scientist experiments and observes results enough times to be convinced that a principle has been established. Since he cannot test all possible events, he runs the risk of drawing an incorrect conclusion. He often uses mathematics to give the probability that his conclusion is true.

From special laws and concepts, the scientist attempts to develop a more general theory. To do this he begins with certain assumptions and then uses deduction, the logical reasoning of mathematics. Deductive reasoning—that is, reasoning from the general to the particular—results in conclusions that are accepted as certain to follow from given assumptions and definitions.

There is another significant aspect of mathematics used in the scientist's research. His experimentation usually involves many measurements; the more precise and accurate they are, the better. However, every measurement is an approximation. It is the mathematical aspect of measurement which gives him the necessary means for dealing with these approximations. Fortunately, the computational tools of mathematics are designed to provide for exact data as well as approximations.

Another major application of mathematics is its use in solving problems. The techniques of solving mathematical problems are immediately applicable to the problems of science. Both mathematics and science teachers agree that the approach to problem solving should be one of flexibility, originality, trying out hunches, probing different possibilities, and discovering generalizations. The method of solving mathematical problems is very similar to the so-called scientific method of inquiry.

If we stop to consider the activities of business, industry, government, science, and education, we recognize very quickly that the following mathematical topics are used daily:

1. *Computation.* Despite the availability of calculators or computers, the most common application of mathematics is calculating with counting numbers, rational numbers, and real numbers. Accurately computing additions, subtractions, multiplications, divisions, squares, and square roots is frequently necessary.

2. *Measurement.* Making measurements, computing with measures, converting from one unit to another. Computing area or volume of common geometric polygons, circles, polyhedrons, spheres, cylinders, cones.

3. *Statistical data.* Reading tables, charts, and graphs; summarizing data, determining patterns of data; computing means or standard deviations; determining cause and effect and predicting results.

4. *Graphing.* Reading or interpreting or drawing graphs; determining trend lines; using nomographs; using graphs for predictions, for solving problems, for showing relationships between variables.

5. *Percent.* Reading, converting, computing with ratios expressed as percents.

6. *Equations.* Finding truth sets for linear equations, formulas, and quadratic equations. Writing the equation for a pattern of data or a graph.

7. *Geometric relations.* Pythagorean theorem, similar triangles, properties of triangles, quadrilaterals or polygons, angles, relationship of lines or planes, properties of circles.

8. *Ratio and proportion.* Writing proportions for direct and inverse variation, solving proportions for any variable, determining constants of variation.

9. *Estimation and approximation.* Using significant digits and scientific notation, rounding off numerals, estimating results.

10. *Computing machines.* Calculating with slide rule, calculator, flow charts, or by programming a computer.

11. *Probability.* Interpreting and computing probability, both theoretical and empirical.

Note that these competencies relate to many of the classical topics of school mathematics as well as the content of the new school mathematics.

TEACHING THE APPLICATIONS OF MATHEMATICS

In order to teach the applications of mathematics, a teacher should have a background in fields other than mathematics, so that the applications have meaning for him. Because of the number and the significance of applications in science, it has been suggested that every mathematics teacher have a minor in science. Whether or not he has this specific background, a teacher with a broad general education will have had contact with many applications of mathematics in many other fields, and be able to present them to his students.

One of the ways to emphasize applications is to have a variety of them available for use as examples and exercises. Whenever a mathematics lesson involves topics such as equations, graphs, or polygons, this storehouse should be used to supply an appropriate example.

We are fortunate that a variety of books containing applications are readily available. A number of these are listed in the Appendix C.

To indicate the wide range of applications for use in algebra classes, here is a collection of science formulas according to type:

A. $y = kx$ (Direct Proportion)
   - $(e = kf)$ Elongation of spring related to force applied.
   - $(s = kt)$ Distance traversed at constant velocity related to time.
   - $(s = kv)$ Distance traversed in a given amount of time related to velocity.

B. $y = k/x$ (Inverse Proportion)
   - $(y = k/p)$ Volume of a gas at constant temperature related to the pressure.
   - $(p/c = 7/4)$ Diet for a patient who should have a protein-to-carbohydrate ratio of 7 to 4.
   - $(IQ = \dfrac{M.A.}{C.A.} \times 100)$ The intelligence quotient (IQ) as related to mental age $(M.A.)$ and chronological age $(C.A.)$.

C. $Z = Kxy$ (Joint Variation)
   - $(C = \pi RD/12)$ The proper lathe speed (C) where (R) is the revolutions per minute and (D) the diameter of the drill.
   - $(P = IE)$ Electrical power used related to the current and the voltage.
   - $(F = PA)$ Force exerted related to the pressure and the area, illustrated by the force of an automobile in collision.

D. $Y = k/x^2$
   - $(I = k/d^2)$ The intensity of illumination of light related to the distance from the light source.
   - $(I = k/d^2)$ The intensity of sound related to the distance from the source.

E. $Y = kx^2$
   - $(s = kt^2)$ The distance traveled by a body which has constant acceleration related to the time.
   - $(c = W V^2/gr)$ The centrifical force of a rotating object (c) related to the weight of the object (W), the speed of the object (V), (g) the

force of gravity and (r) the radius of the turning.

($P = KI^2$)   The electrical power needed to push through a fixed resistance related to the current through it.

($T = .85\, d^2\, L\, P\, /w$)   The pounds ($T$) a locomotive can pull if d = diameter of cylinder; L = length of piston stroke; w = diameter of driving wheel; P = mean stream pressure in lbs., per square inch.

($L = L_c A\, V^2$)   The lift (L) on airplane wing in pounds if L_c = lift coefficient; A = area of wing (sq. ft.); V = velocity of plane (mph).

F. $Z = Kx/y$

($C = O/V$)   The capacity of a condenser related to the charge and the difference in potential.

($R = E/I$)   The resistance of an electrical conductor related to the voltage and the current.

($P = W/T$)   Mechanical power related to the work done and the time taken to do it. Thus, a person can measure his horsepower by running upstairs.

($D = M/V$)   Density related to the mass of an object and its volume.

G. $1/z = 1/x + 1/y$

($1/f = 1/d + 1/d_1$)   The focal length of a lens related to the object-distance and the image-distance.

($1/R = 1/r_1 + 1/r_2$)   The calibrated resistance of two resistances in parallel related to the two resistances.

H. $y = K\sqrt{S}$

($v = \sqrt{2\,a\,s}$)   The velocity of a body moving with constant acceleration related to the distance traveled.

($T = 2\pi\sqrt{L/g}$)   The period of a pendulum related to its length.

($V = \sqrt{800\,W/A}$)   The speed of fall (V) in feet per second at which a parachute supporting a man of weight W will fall; number of square feet in surface of parachute is A.

I. $y = K_1 x^2 + K_2 x + K_3$

($s = at^2/2 + v_0 t + s_0$)   The distance a body moves from a certain position with constant acceleration and given initial velocity related to the time.

($H = D^2 N/2.5$)   The horsepower of gas engine (H) if

$(T = .0157 \, d^2 h)$

D = diameter of a cylinder in (H) and
N = number of cylinders.
The number of tons (T) of silage in a
silo if d = diameter of silo in feet and
h = height in feet.

J. $y = K^x$

$(r = Ke^2)$ The distance on a monovalve shell related to an
angle.

$(y = e^{-0.38t})$ The amount of radium disintegration related to
time in centuries.

K. $(E = I \cos A / s^2)$ The illumination of light source is related to the
intensity, the angle between the light ray and the
surface, and the distance from the light to the
surface.

EXERCISES USING SCIENTIFIC CONCEPTS

To illustrate some possible applied exercises, here are some samples:

1. If 201 grams of mercury and 16 grams of oxygen combine to form 217 grams of mercuric oxide, calculate the percent composition of each element in the mercuric oxide.

2. The volume of a gas is directly proportional to the absolute temperature provided the pressure is constant. If a sample occupies 10 liters at $273°$ absolute, what will be the volume at $400°$ absolute?

3. If 12 grams of carbon react with 32 grams of oxygen to form carbon dioxide, how many grams of carbon will react with 640 grams of oxygen?

4. How many millimeters of 0.4 normal potassium hydroxide solution, KOH, will neutralize 100 millimeters of 0.05 normal phosphoric acid, H_3PO_4?

Formula

$$\frac{\text{millimeters of acid}}{\text{millimeters of base}} = \frac{\text{normality of base}}{\text{normality of acid}}$$

5. A stone is thrown out of a window which is 50 feet above the ground. While traveling 20 feet horizontally, the stone falls 1 foot. If the ball travels in the arch of a parabola, how far away from the building does it land?

6. The equation of the orbit of the earth around the sun may be taken to be $x^2 + y^2 = 9$. There is a comet whose path is almost parabolic. If the comet has the equation $y = \frac{x^2}{4} - 1$ as it crosses the earth's orbit, what are the points of intersection of the two orbits? (Assume both orbits lie in the same plane.)

7. A certain weight of gas has a volume of 1,200 cubic centimeters at a pressure of 500 grams per square centimeter and a temperature of 21 degrees centigrade. What is its volume at a pressure of 1,500 grams per square centimeter and a temperature of 315 degrees centigrade?

Formula

$$\frac{P_1V_1}{T_1} = \frac{P_2V_2}{T_2}$$

where T is absolute temperature, $273°$ more than Fahrenheit.

8. What is the combined resistance of a 9-ohm coil and an 18-ohm coil connected in parallel?
Formula

$$1/R = 1/R_1 + 1/R_2$$

9. A flying saucer has a circular body with elliptical stabilizers. The equation of the circular body is $x^2 + y^2 = 9$. The equation of the wings is $x^2/16 + Y^2/4 = 1$.

   a. At what points do the wings intersect the body?
   b. Draw to scale the two curves.

10. In mechanical drawing, a student is faced with the problem of representing a cylindrical can in perspective. This means that he will have to draw congruent ellipses for the top and bottom, whose major and minor axes are 2 inches and 1 inch respectively. Instead of using the usual approximation with circular arcs, the student decides to use a thread to construct the ellipses accurately. Determine the positions of the foci and the length of the thread to do this.

SPECIAL TEACHING PROBLEMS

One of the most commonly used mathematical tools is the proportion. It is a means of solving problems involving percentage, chemical composition, mechanical advantage, pressure, volume, light, profits, and a host of others. At the same time textbooks tend to give limited emphasis to proportionality as an aspect of variation, direct or inverse. This is one topic which should be well taught in the mathematics class by discussion, experimentation, and applied exercises.

Frequently, students will know the technical language and the mechanical manipulation of proportions without really knowing how variation is involved. Ask students to explain direct proportion so that a fourth grader can understand it. What happens numerically to the second variable if the first is doubled? What does it mean to say that distance varies directly as the time? What does it mean to say that light intensity varies inversely as the square of the distance from the light? If the distance is doubled, what happens to the intensity of the light? If the speed of two pulleys connected by a belt varies inversely to their diameters, how does the speed of a 3-inch pulley compare with that of a 12-inch pulley? What is the geometric basis for this relationship? If the volumes of two spheres are directly proportional to the cubes of the diameters, how does the volume of a 2-inch orange compare to that of a 3-inch orange?

Another simple source of difficulty in transfer is the use of different notation and language in courses other than mathematics. For example, the subscript zero is often used in science to denote initial conditions, as in

$s = v_0 t - 16t^2$. Likewise, exponents are used for dimensions, as 5 in.^{2}. Methods of solving equations and the language used will tend to be that of traditional mathematics. Terms such as "the resolution of forces" or the "constant of variation" or "a percent is a fraction" and "signed numbers" will be foreign to a student in a modern mathematics class. To avoid confusion caused by differences in symbols, methods, and words, the mathematics student should be told of these variations both in the mathematics class and in the science class.

MATH-SCIENCE LABORATORY EXERCISES

Another way to treat the applications of mathematics is to perform specific laboratory exercises in the mathematics classroom. Here are some experiments to perform in order to collect data for generalizing or to illustrate concepts. Independently of their value in showing applications, these experiments may be a valuable lesson in discovery and problem solving. To perform them, some equipment from the science department may be needed.

A. Ratio and Proportion
  1. Determine the ratios of frequencies of musical-instrument strings. Determine the ratios of harmonic notes.
  2. Determine the specific gravity of liquids.
  3. Show the use of direct proportions in the Wheatstone bridge.
  4. Use proportions to find chemical composition.

B. Formulas
  1. Develop the relationship between Fahrenheit and centigrade temperatures.
  2. Determine the relationship between volume, temperature, and pressure.
  3. Show the intensity of light related to the distance from the light (use photometer or lightmeter).
  4. Indicate the relationship between weight in air and weight in water and weight of displaced water.

C. Geometry
  1. Grow crystals to show regular polyhedra. Examine substances like salt under the microscope to see polyhedra and polygons.
  2. Use reflections in two mirrors to show congruent triangles and translations.
  3. Use horizontal pans of a platform balance to illustrate properties of parallelograms.
  4. Show reflection properties on a billiard table.

D. Curves

    1. Show the trajectory of a stream of water (parabola).

    2. Show water film between capillary plates of glass (hyperbola).

    3. Project a cone of light on planes (conic sections).

    4. Roll a circle and trace a point as a spot (cycloid).

    5. Illustrate motion on a banked curve by means of marble spinning in a funnel.

    6. Show conic sections by means of water in a funnel.

    7. Spin a cylindrical container of liquid to give a paraboloid of revolution.

    8. Illustrate minimal surfaces by means of soap film.

    9. Show properties of the focus through reflections by a parabolic surface.

    10. Show pendulum patterns by sand funnel or photography.

    11. Draw lines of force around a magnet plotted with compass. Plot against patterns of iron filings to show orthogonality (perpendicularity).

    12. Use the *hygrodeik* to illustrate reading nomographs.

    13. Draw graphs of loss of heat from a pan of boiling water as a function of time.

E. Trigonometry

    1. Use oscilloscope to illustrate sine curve. Relate sine values to generator voltage and current.

    2. Use a rotating helix to illustrate wave motion.

F. Measurements

    1. Show that the hexagonal bee cell has minimum perimeter and maximum volume.

    2. Measure shadows to determine time and latitude.

    3. Determine the probability of an event such as the result of tossing a thumb tack.

SUPPLEMENTARY UNITS

A third way to emphasize the applications of mathematics is to prepare and teach units as supplements to the regular text. Topics which are suitable for application units include the following:

    1. Probability and insurance.

    2. Projections and mapping.

    3. Vectors and mechanics.

    4. The slide rule and surveying.

    5. Space travel and conic sections.

6. Perspective and painting.
7. Linear programming and economics.
8. Proportions and music.
9. Installment buying and interest formulas.
10. Chemistry and proportions.
11. Carpentry and the Pythagorean theorem.
12. Astronomy and indirect measurement.
13. Machine work and geometry.
14. Navigation on sea, in the air and in outer space and similar triangles.
15. Decision making and probability.

Sometimes these topics can be dealt with as student projects to be shared with the class. In this case the projects should be presented to the class by student demonstrations, reports, or bulletin-board exhibits.

THE KLINE PROPOSALS

A fourth method is to design a mathematics curriculum that grows out of experiences in the physical world. Thus, Morris Kline, a severe critic of the new school mathematics, proposes that algebra be based on the formulas that deal with motion, gravitation, light, temperature, force, elasticity, friction, the pendulum, patterns, and population growth. He suggests formulas such as $P = rl$ or $v = 32t$ as leading to the general equation $y = ax$. Next he suggests that $y = ax + b$ be introduced by formulas such as:

$P = 500 + 30t$, where P is the population of a town which has 500 people and is growing at the rate of 30 people per year.

$V = 32t + 100$, where V is the velocity of a ball t seconds after it is thrown downward with a speed of 100 ft./sec.

$l = \frac{1}{4}w + 4$, where l is the length of a spring which is 4 inches to start with and stretches $\frac{1}{4}$ inch for each pound of weight (w) attached to it.

Kline's geometry would emphasize both direct measurement and indirect measurement.

SPECIAL APPLICATIONS COURSES

A fifth way to treat applications is to offer specific applicational or "practical" courses. Consequently, schools may have special courses such as Shop Mathematics, Consumer Mathematics, Basic Mathematics for Science, Business Arithmetic, or Computer Programming.

Textbooks used in applications courses do give emphasis to the applications. However, few college-bound students take these courses, and they need to know applications too. Moreover, frequently little mathematics is taught in these courses. They tend to concentrate on remedial arithmetic. Even worse than this, the courses may emphasize shortcuts and meaningless manipulations, some of which are not mathematically sound.

Probably one of the best ways of insuring transfer to the application of a given field is to coordinate the topics of a mathematics course with the mathematical needs of another course. Before the science class uses proportions for problems dealing with simple machines, the mathematics class should study proportions. Before the physics class begins its study of vectors, the appropriate mathematics class should master the mathematical aspects of vectors. If the social studies class is to study map projections, the mathematics class should ensure the necessary background in geometry. Perhaps in the future, team teaching, integrated courses, and flexible scheduling will make it possible for mathematics teachers to work closer with staff members of other fields. Until then, every opportunity should be taken to ensure interdepartment cooperation. Examination of the experimental science courses, such as the Physical Science Study Committee (PSSC) physics course, shows that the mathematical content is very substantial. It would seem appropriate for the mathematics department to teach these mathematical concepts to a level of mastery high enough that the science teacher does not need to reteach them. The science teacher will need to review mathematical concepts and skills and assist the student in transfering this knowledge, but he should not need to teach the mathematical topics involved.

LEARNING EXERCISES

1. Give an example of a mathematical model which can be used to derive a scientific law.
2. How did Eratosthenes measure the circumference of the earth?
3. Which planet was located mathematically before it was sighted by man? How was it done?
4. What is the difference between a fact in mathematics and a fact in science?
5. What are the different means whereby a fact is established in a court trial?
6. Write a unit on one applicational phase of mathematics.
7. Investigate ways in which computer programming may be used to integrate mathematics and some other course.
8. Tabulate and compare the applications included in two textbooks on secondary school mathematics.
9. Select a topic in a secondary mathematics course. Find appropriate applications from at least two fields to supplement this topic.
10. Analyze the mathematical competence required in a secondary science course. Construct a test on the competencies and use it to test the readiness of a class for this course.
11. Analyze one of the new school science courses to determine the kind and amount of mathematics included.
12. Develop two open-ended and two multiple-choice test items to test a student's understanding of (a) direct proportion; (b) inverse proportion; (c) variation; (d) the right triangle; (e) similar triangles.

13

individual differences in the mathematics classroom

Human beings are complex, unpredictable, and unequal. No two individuals are exactly alike in appearance, in ability, in personality, or in any other trait. Hence, as soon as we have a class of two or more students, we are faced with the problem of providing for individual differences. And when we have a mathematics class of 30 unlike, active young people, we have a situation that demands variation in content, method, and materials to meet the needs of each individual.

When a retiring teacher was asked how present-day high school students differ from those of a generation ago, he said, "Students today are more extreme than they were when I started to teach. The top students are way out front. The slow student is way behind his counterpart of a generation ago. This seems to be true of behavior as well as of intellectual attainment." Thus, the differences between students in today's classroom are likely to be greater than those of a generation ago.

HOW DO INDIVIDUALS VARY?

Before considering ways for providing for individual differences, let us consider the differences which are of significance in learning mathematics. These include:

1. *Mental ability, ability to reason or think reflectively, ability to solve problems.* Variability in these traits is usually determined by a so-called intellectual aptitude test and is reported in terms of an IQ. In a typical school we expect IQ's to vary from 75 to 150. Ideally, measures of ability should indicate differences in the learning rate as well as in quality of response.

Many teachers and administrators fail to recognize one result of the difference in learning rate:—the differences between the students' achievements should be expected to diverge rather than converge. When teachers attempt to have an entire class conform to a set curriculum or when administrators set up classes designed to make weak students "catch up" with their more talented friends, they are working against this factor.

2. *Mathematical ability, ability to use symbols, ability to do logical reasoning, ability to compute.* Differences in these traits are often measured by a mathematical aptitude test, a test on quantitative thinking, or a prognostic test. Teacher-constructed achievement tests administered early in the school year give results that compare closely with those of such standardized tests.

3. *Knowledge of mathematical concepts, structures, and processes.* This knowledge is related to the previous educational experiences of the learner and largely determines the readiness of the learner for the content of a new course. The mathematical background of a learner is often measured by his past achievement record or by an achievement test. Today this factor is of increasing importance because of curriculum variation from one community to another. Pre-tests of achievement may be used as general measures, and also as indicators of specific areas of difficulty.

4. *Motivations, interests, attitudes, appreciations.* While these are potent factors in the classroom, they cannot be measured well at the present time. Unreliable teacher ratings are frequently used.

5. *Physical, emotional, and social maturity of the learner.* The measures of maturity are also at best subjective evaluations of the teacher or counselor. Student variation in cultural, social, and emotional adjustment traits are great and are highly significant for the placement of learners in special classes. A student's real physical disability should be noted and its effect on his emotional reactions should be watched. Minor defects in sensory perceptions, such as in sight or hearing, should also be ascertained.

6. *Special talents or deficiencies such as creativity, lack of reading skill, or retention span.* The ability to verbalize is closely related to mathematical achievement. Special talents or special needs are usually identified by observation or interviews, although tests of specific traits are becoming available.

7. *Learning habits, self-discipline, attention and retention span, and organization of written work.* Differences in this category bear a significant relationship to the learner's home environment and previous education.

If individuals are unequal in the traits listed above, it isn't reasonable to give them all the same mathematics courses, the same assignments, the same instruction, the same allocation of time in class, or the same achievement requirements. Therefore, individual differences should first be provided for by gathering as much information about the student as possible.

To do this will mean the use of a variety of tests and a study of the learner's cumulative information folder. It will mean the continued collection of information based on the classroom performance, learner products, and careful observation of and thoughtful conferences with the learner.

WAYS OF PROVIDING FOR INDIVIDUAL DIFFERENCES

Although there are a variety of ways of organizing the mathematics program and a variety of materials for use in meeting individual needs, the teacher is still the key to the success of the program. The teacher's success in dealing with individual differences will be determined by how he accepts the learner, how he uses materials, how he varies his assignments. The teacher must recognize differences and provide for them by offering different experiences for different learners—varying content, language, rate of learning, materials of instruction, and the goals of learning according to individual differences.

Here are some practical ways of providing for individual differences:

1. *A multiple-track curriculum with learners assigned to classes according to certain abilities or interests.* Such a program might include
   a. Accelerated classes for gifted students.
   b. Advanced placement classes for gifted students.
   c. Correspondence study courses or independent study courses using self-instructional materials for classes with limited registrations in small schools.
   d. Remedial instruction courses.
   e. Vocationally oriented courses such as consumer mathematics or shop mathematics.
   f. Enrichment courses such as probability and statistics or computer programming.
   g. Courses designed for students of average ability.
   h. Special courses for the low-ability student.

2. *Classroom activities modified according to learner needs.*
   a. Vary daily learning assignments according to ability or achievement levels. Some system is needed that provides many easy exercises for the slow learner and fewer but more challenging exercises for the talented.
   b. Organize the class into small groups according to ability and then give each group special instruction and assignments. To make this possible it may be appropriate to have capable students act as group leaders. The capable student then receives experience in a leadership role and reinforces his learning by having to teach the material. Such grouping is difficult in a class of over 25.
   c. Enrich the instruction with student reports, demonstrations, projects, and creative writing.

  d. Provide supervised study time so that the work of individual students can be observed and help given when needed.

  e. Involve the students in many of the classroom activities such as writing on the chalkboard, collecting papers, correcting assignments. Each learner needs to feel that he has a place in the class and can participate in some activities without frustration.

  f. Establish a level of participation which is related to the students' ability. Capable students are given difficult discussion questions and are not given undue praise for an average performance. Slow learners are given relatively easy questions and their performance is judged according to their ability. The teacher must seek a balance between coddling students so that they are not challenged and develop unrealistic aspirations, and forcing students into a pattern of failure that turns them away from learning activities.

3. *Instructional materials varied according to student ability.*

  a. Provide text materials, programmed texts, workbooks, and independent units to supplement the regular text. These supplementary texts should have appropriate readability and interesting content.

  b. Provide manipulative materials, models, devices, or equipment appropriate to the needs and interests of the students. Slow learners need frequent reference to visual and concrete representations. High-ability students need to develop their own challenging devices such as logic machines.

  c. Use visual aids such as overhead projections, films, charts, and bulletin-board displays.

  d. Provide construction material for laboratory work or independent projects. A library of supplementary books and pamphlets for enrichment reading or remedial instruction should be available also.

4. *Evaluation made appropriate to the course or students involved.*

  a. Establish reasonable levels of achievement according to the group and individuals involved. Be wary of a continuing high percentage of failing grades: look into the causes of such records.

  b. Establish a marking system in special classes which does not jeopardize the scholastic rank of the capable or frustrate the efforts of the slow learner.

  c. Use standardized tests to determine real level of achievement independent of the group or course involved.

  d. Use common examinations for multiple sections so that the base of comparison is broadened.

  In the past, ability grouping was criticized as an undemocratic procedure. It was presumed to foster an intellectual elite and deprive the regular classes of the leadership and inspiration of talented students. Today, however, it is accepted that the bright student feels less superior when competing with his intellectual equals in a special class than when he easily gets top rank in a regular class. It is also assumed that slow learners will make more progress when they are competing with students of relatively the same ability. However, it has also been found that ability grouping by itself is effective only when the teacher varies the instruction according to the ability group being taught.

A MULTI-TRACK PROGRAM

Many schools, especially those with large enrollments, have developed multiple-track programs in mathematics, designed to serve students of high, average, and low mathematical ability. Whereas such a program is more difficult in smaller schools, occasionally interschool cooperation or even special intraclass divisions make similar programs possible. Here is a flow chart for a sample secondary school program:

Grade	Track I	Track II	Track III (Honors)
7	Math 7	Math 7	Math 7, 8
8	Math 8	Math 8*	Algebra I*
9	Pre-Algebra or Lab Algebra	Algebra I*	Geometry*
10	Algebra	Geometry*	Intermediate Math
11	Pre-Geometry or Lab Geometry General Math	Intermediate Math	Senior Math*
12	Informal Geometry and Shop Math or Consumer Math	Senior Math*	Advanced Placement Calculus or Modern Algebra

* Within starred classes students are grouped according to achievement, not grade level. High-ability sections require extra work.

One of the most important considerations of such a schedule is transfer from track to track as well as from section to section within a subject. Many schools make special provision for late entry into an honors sequence by having students take summer school courses. Although the problem of how to move into an honors track is often considered, how to move out of it is equally important. Students should not be allowed to find "an easy berth" or to repeat courses (with different titles only) for extra credit. And, perhaps most important, courses should be carefully designated on transcripts so that honors students are not punished by grading systems that favor the underachiever.

SELECTING STUDENTS FOR SPECIAL CLASSES

It is extremely difficult to select students correctly for special classes or homogeneous groups. No matter how careful the selection process, there are always a few individuals for whom the assignment made is inappropriate. Thus a first principle of selection to adopt is one which makes it possible to change the assignment during the year. This change should allow a student to move into either a lower or a higher group. Of course, the sooner incorrect assignments can be discovered and a new assignment made, the better for everyone involved.

In the assignment of students to special classes all information available should be used. Intelligence-test scores or aptitude-test scores or achievement records alone are not satisfactory. Teacher ratings of social, emotional, and intellectual maturity helps. A rating of the student's interests, attitudes, and motivations would also improve the possibility of an appropriate assignment. Standardized achievement-test scores, especially those that test problem-solving skill or quantitative thinking ability, are helpful. In the final decision, however, a value judgment must be made by the teacher.

One of the pressures on teachers for student selection for special courses is the parents' desires. To meet this problem, the parent should be informed of the basis for an assignment so that he will recognize it as in the best interest of his son or daughter. Many schools allow parents to change such assignments. When such requests appear unreasonable, special records of the reason for the new assignment should be on hand.

In making decisions some schools establish cut-off boundaries, such as an IQ of 110 or a percentile rank of 50. When this is done without regard to the school population or the community culture involved, these boundaries are likely to be inappropriate. A percentile rank of 50 in a suburban school may be equivalent to a percentile rank of 80 in a culturally deprived area.

CLASSROOM PROCEDURES

Individual differences cannot be eliminated or even taken care of by grouping, special courses, or varied material. What makes the difference is how the teacher differentiates his instruction. Here are some suggestions that mathematics teachers report have been helpful:

1. *Class time will be used more productively if every student participates.* Teachers who make eye contact with every student and speak to each student every day are often successful. One way for a teacher to achieve maximum participation is for him to ask students the kinds of questions they can answer. To do this, he may have to prepare a lesson plan that lists questions to be directed at specific students. And a teacher should try to ensure that students are not afraid of making mistakes or asking foolish questions. By referring to a student's homework, the teacher can identify areas the student knows well and other areas on which he is having difficulty.

2. *Be sure that each lesson is related to what the student thinks is important.* We must exercise caution in imposing our objectives on students of a different culture or of different ability. We must recognize that intellectual goals may not seem worth the effort for a student whose values are different from those of the teacher.

3. *There is no substitute for well-prepared lessons presented with enthusiasm.* Neither the gifted nor the culturally deprived will stand for poor teaching.

4. *Encourage students to recognize their ability.* Help them set up specific, realistic goals and then hold them responsible for attaining these goals.

5. *Provide a classroom climate that stimulates excellence and at the same time avoids the frustration of continued failure.* Require students to complete work commensurate with their ability. Never permit it to be "smart" or socially acceptable among peers to be stupid or apathetic in class.

6. *Take time to meet individuals or groups out of the classroom, either at noon or after school.* It is difficult for a reluctant learner to reject the teacher who shows genuine interest in and concern for his difficulties. Learn to know your students so that you will understand each one better and be able to give them the help and inspiration they need to attain their goals.

7. *Allow class time for motivation, appreciation, and attitude-development activities.* Do not confine instruction to the text. Permit individuals to explore topics or skills of special interest.

8. *Give special help in how to study, how to use the text, how to locate information in order to promote individual progress.*

9. *Demand that classes be of reasonable size.* It is virtually impossible to make provisions for individual differences in classes of more than 20–25 students of heterogeneous ability.

10. *Continuously evaluate your own mental attitude to see that you enjoy your work and like your students—sometimes in spite of their idiosyncrasies.*

As we have suggested, individual differences of students is a constant problem in the mathematics classroom. As teachers improve their instruction and improve their programs these differences between students will become even greater. This is to be expected because the rapid learner is stimulated to learn to his potential and the slow learner drops proportionately behind. As we recognize how different our students are it seems reasonable that we should vary the goals, the content, the materials, the instruction, and the learning activities. Learning the same content but at a different rate is not satisfactory. Failing a student or dropping him from the mathematics course does not seem reasonable or productive. Mathematics teachers must accept the responsibility for teaching all levels of ability by using proper resources and methods. Since ability grouping is no longer considered undemocratic, it should be established wherever possible.

LEARNING EXERCISES

1. Collect the test scores in reading and mathematics for a group of junior high school students. Draw bar graphs according to the grade levels to picture the variation and the comparison of achievement in these two areas.

2. Select an underachiever and an overachiever. Collect all information about each one from his cumulative record file. Interview each one in an attempt to find the reason for the achievement record.

3. Observe the work of two students who differ greatly in achievement. Compare their completed assignments. How are these students different in their organization and methods?

4. Make a case study of an individual student. Identify the major factors which have influenced his achievement in mathematics.

5. Outline a multiple-track program for a given grade. Indicate how these courses vary in goals, content, materials, and methods according to the student for which each course is designed. Indicate how students will be assigned to each class.

14

a program
for the low
achiever

Most mathematics teachers consider teaching the low achiever an uninspiring and unimportant task. But when we recognize the need for greater mathematical competence for a greater proportion of society, we recognize the need for further emphasis on mathematics for every student. Furthermore, as teachers in a democracy which values the worth of each person, we know that we have a professional obligation to teach learners of all ability levels.

A teacher who accepts the fact that low achievers are teachable; a teacher who has a missionary spirit and a respect for the worth of pupils with limited ability; a teacher who is concerned and interested in individuals; a teacher who can make a pupil feel he not only belongs but also is important; a teacher who can instill a sense of worthiness, responsibility, and desire to achieve; a teacher who cares enough to give his very best to the low achievers will make the program a success.—*Preliminary Report of the Conference on the Low Achiever in Mathematics.*

The slow learners will always be with us. In fact, their number as well as proportion may very well increase. They are found at every socio-economic level and will have an influence, for good or bad, in our society. If we do something for them in school now, we may be helping them to avoid problems in their adult years. Many of them have latent talents which can and should be developed.

Until recently very little had been done to improve the mathematics for the low achiever. The emphasis and the financial support had been given to educating the potential scientist. Presently, though, attention to the culturally deprived and to vocational training has resulted in financial support for developing new ways of dealing with the low achiever.

IDENTIFYING THE LOW ACHIEVER

Who is the so-called low achiever? Students generally classified as low achievers do not necessarily share the causes for this disability. Special terms are sometimes used in classification to identify the specific cause of low achievement:

The *slow learner,* who has below average academic ability.

The *underachiever,* who has potential for mathematics achievement but has not realized the potential.

The *reluctant learner,* who lacks interest in the usual school mathematics program.

The *disadvantaged learner,* who has been given little background for adjusting to the usual mathematics program.

The *culturally deprived learner,* who has been reared in a culture with meager educational experiences.

The *disaffected learner,* who has developed a negative attitude toward mathematics.

The *rejected learner,* who has been rejected by teachers, peers, or parents.

The *non-college bound,* who has inadequate ability, interest, or resources for college attendance.

We will consider the low achiever to be the student who normally ranks below the 30th percentile in achievement due to the following factors:

1. *Low mental maturity.* Although the student's ability may not be measured accurately by our culturally oriented mental tests, he has little ability to perceive relations, is unable to generalize, and has difficulty transferring knowledge. He usually has an IQ below 90.

2. *Emotionally immature.* The student usually needs and lacks acceptance, affection, security, and success. He comes to school without hope, hostile to the teacher and the school, depressed, and frustrated. His dislike for authority may result in rebellious and delinquent behavior. He is often confused, lacking in self-confidence, yet unaware of the sources of his difficulties. He has probably been deprived of an adequate amount of affection, love, and emotional support. The best way for a teacher to build his self-concept is to see that this type of student has some success.

3. *Socially immature.* The student's social and cultural experiences at home, in the community, and in school are often meager. He may be

prejudiced and intolerant. He lacks leadership experience and does not like to cooperate in group activities. He may never have found a person whom he wishes to imitate as he grows up. He is often overly aggressive and physically restless.

4. *Physical deficiencies*. The student's poor achievement may be due to poor health, insufficient food, or insufficient rest. He may have poor eyesight and poor hearing and lack motor coordination.

5. *Psychological deficiencies*. The student's attention span and memory are short. His reading level is low, his visualization and imagination meager. Insight, creativity, and problem-solving skills are often almost nonexistent. His motivation for learning is weak.

6. *Limited cultural experiences*. The student has had few experiences such as traveling, reading, craft work, or hobby work. The world of literature, art, music, and drama does not seem relevant to his daily life. He may have a record of juvenile offenses. However, mathematics is probably less culturally conditioned than any other subject, and mathematics has fewer derogatory connotations for the culturally deprived than other fields.

7. *Meager educational experience*. The student's previous mathematical experiences, his study habits, and his achievement are likely to be inadequate. He is more oriented to vocational than to academic education. Learning for its own sake has little if any meaning for him. He may be anti-intellectual and pragmatic. Talk, reading, and intellectualizing in general have little appeal to him. He has not learned how to ask questions, how to study, or how to take tests. His ability to verbalize is likely to be very low. Although tests can be used to determine the extent of some of these deficiencies, these tests themselves require a certain level of reading skill and cultural background. Many of the low achievers are lacking in these qualities, and they may be rated far below their potential. Therefore, conferences, observations, and past performance records need to be considered as a basis for classification.

PROBLEMS TO BE RESOLVED IN PROVIDING FOR THE LOW ACHIEVER

There are many problems which complicate provisions for the slow learner:

1. *The teacher problem*. Teachers do not want to teach classes of slow learners. They consider it futile and difficult. (Mathematics teachers have generally been spoiled by the natural selection of the academic mathematics program.) At the same time, our society requires that ordinary citizens have enough mathematical competence to be employable. And we would never condone a doctor who refused medical attention to an indigent patient. There is no question but that the slow-learner course needs top-quality teaching. Usually, however, a beginning teacher, a barely competent teacher, or a teacher without seniority rights or without a major in mathematics is given the assignment. The result is chaos and even less respect for the class by teacher, student, and parents. Furthermore, it may mean the

loss of a beginning teacher who has the potential to become a highly successful teacher if given a more appropriate first assignment. On the other hand, schools that assign excellent teachers to these sections note real progress on the part of the students.

2. *The curriculum problem.* The major modern curriculum-development groups have not selected objectives or designed courses for the low achiever. Hence, there does not seem to be agreement on what the content of courses for the low achiever should be and on which students should take the course. Furthermore, there is little evidence regarding the effectiveness of the course. One recent study showed that a year of reading instruction was just as effective during the ninth grade as a year of instruction in "easy" algebra. As a result of the chaos in a curriculum for the low achiever, the following courses have been proposed:

a. A course that reteaches *computational skills.* Since the slow learner has been unable to learn computation in his previous six to eight years, it is not likely that another year of similar content and method of presentation will be successful. Frustration will continue, hostility will increase, and improvement will be negligible. There is a need for improving the computational skills of the slow learner, but this needs to be done in a novel way.

b. A course that teaches the good mathematics of the college preparatory courses but teaches it at a *slower pace,* with more concrete examples, less stress on precise language, and simpler problems. For example, it is suggested that most of elementary algebra and geometry be taught over a span of three or even four years rather than the usual two. This seems to ignore the needs and interests of the slow learner. But many teachers accept this proposal because they feel more secure teaching this content, and text material of this type is available. However, this is a poor basis for the selection of this type of course.

c. Build the course around the mathematics which the learner will *need* as a citizen, a worker, a consumer. This course is the typical general mathematics of the ninth grade, which covers topics such as installment buying, insurance, taxes, and investments. This has not been successful since the topics are too remote for the ninth-grade student. Furthermore, these topics merely provide exercises in computation without extending the mathematical understanding of students.

d. Organize the course around a *vocational* area such as shop mathematics, business arithmetic, nursing mathematics, or mathematics for home economics. These courses have the advantage of being related to the students' vocational goals and take care of the problem of transfer to applied problems. Again, however, these courses tend to be narrow, with emphasis on computational drill.

None of the courses described above is a satisfactory solution to the dilemma of what mathematics is appropriate for the slow learner. Therefore, an imaginative new approach is needed—preferably a complete sequence of courses for grades 7 through 12. The content should be mathematically sound, significant for the learner, and within the range of the slow learner's capacity to learn.

3. *The student problem.* It is possible for the low achiever to attain

significant goals of mathematics instruction—but only if he *wants* to learn. To build this motivation the teacher will need appropriate content, materials, and methods of instruction, and an appropriate method of evaluating the achievement of slow learners in a special class.

4. *The parent problem.* Many parents will not accept the classification of their child as a slow learner. They respond negatively to placement in the special class for low achievers, especially if it is for more than one year. They are frequently adamant about their child's taking the mathematics courses which are prerequisite for college entrance.

5. *The materials problem.* The slow learner usually needs a variety of experiences with concrete materials. He needs short exposure to topics, with novelty features which will hold his attention for short periods. He needs brief units which are complete in themselves, so that difficulties do not compound. He needs idea-oriented materials which are not now in existence. He needs reading material that is at least one grade level, and usually more, below the grade being taught in readability rating.

GUIDELINES FOR AN EFFECTIVE PROGRAM FOR THE LOW ACHIEVER

Knowing the nature of the slow learner, his needs and potential, and the problems of the current school program, what can be done to build an effective program for the low achiever? The following principles must be considered:

1. The goals of instruction should be appropriate, realistic, and attainable. Unless he has specific goals in mind a teacher's instruction will lack direction or significance. Emphasis should be placed on attitudes, appreciations, habits, and values. Attention should be given to reading and other communications skills. The objectives of good citizenship (honesty, responsibility, cooperation, and respect for others) should also be accepted as a major aspect of the course.

2. The students for low-achievement courses should be selected carefully. Selection should be based on the student's intellectual ability, mathematical ability, mathematical experiences, vocational interests, and emotional maturity. Provision should be made for transfer into another course whenever the achievement warrants a change. At no time should students be assigned to these courses merely because they are discipline problems—students who can achieve but do not try should be excluded. The practice of transferring students from courses in algebra and geometry into a general mathematics class or even allowing a student who has passed algebra and geometry to elect a general mathematics course for a "soft" credit is entirely unwarranted. Since the highest correlation coefficients are found between achievement in algebra and previous achievement as measured by marks in mathematics or a standardized achievement test, previous achievement in mathematics is the best single factor to consider in placement at the ninth-grade level. Algebra-aptitude tests, reading tests, and intelligence tests also correlate well with achievement in algebra: that is,

they provide evidence about the student's ability to achieve in this course.

3. The *class size* should not exceed 20 students. A classroom of this size will permit laboratory work, individualized instruction, and curtail the number of disciplinary problems. The size of the class is a major factor in the success of a slow-learner course. One justification for having a small class is the wider range of ability to be found in low-ability classes (and in high-ability classes) than in average ability sections.

4. The instruction should emphasize student participation in a variety of learning activities such as laboratory work, class discussion, discovery activities, informal practice, games, and the use of teaching aids. Every effort should be made to choose introductory activities that are new and interesting and that are not based on skills that students do not have.

5. The *teacher* assigned to the course for the low achiever must be especially well qualified. Besides being skilled as a teacher, he will need to understand and accept these youngsters and their culture, to value the purpose of the course, and to have a warm personality and a reservoir of information about mathematics and techniques for teaching.

6. The *facilities* for low-achiever classes must include a variety of instructional aids, such as micrometers, slide rules, models, kits, programmed texts, supplementary books, and games, as well as audio-visual equipment such as projectors, tape recorders, and tachistoscopes (machines that provide timed exposures of drill material in reading, or mathematics).

7. The *evaluation* of progress should be realistic—taking into account the purpose of the course and the ability of the pupils. This evaluation should include measures of attitudes, skills, and habits. Wherever possible, marks should record the amount of growth or progress made and the specific levels attained.

8. The *applications* should include those appropriate to the modern world, such as computers and space travel.

9. The *course content* should include new ideas, new treatment of old topics, and new presentation of computation skills. The content should also include much traditional material such as measurement, equations, rational numbers, geometry, graphs, and statistics.

10. The content of a ninth-grade general mathematics class might include some of the following topics:

Number Patterns
Probability
Calculating Devices
Equations, Formulas, and Graphs
Rational Numbers
Measurement
Ratio, Proportion, and Percent
Statistics

Informal Geometry
Mathematics and Science Experimentation
Design and Construction
Mathematical Recreations
Fact or Fancy
Flow Charts, Problems, and Computers

11. The content for other grade levels should also be outlined in detail, and units should be built emphasizing vocational and applicational aspects of mathematics rather than logic and abstractions. Since algebra is the key to most applications, it is appropriate to emphasize this field.

12. While content patterns and units are usually provided for the teacher, the individual instructor should be allowed considerable latitude to modify his program to take advantage of special student interests, to

reteach topics not well understood, and to extend topics that he finds provide significant learning and success. He should feel free to explore enrichment topics, applications, or informal work that appeals to his students. In other words, more attention should be given to the needs of the student than to covering the content.

SPECIFIC PRACTICES FOR TEACHING THE LOW ACHIEVER

To motivate the low achiever, to gain his acceptance, to help him to identify with the teacher, and to guide him to learn topics which do not always seem relevant to him—all of this requires a teacher with ingenuity and energy. The following activities have been found effective by successful teachers of the low achiever:

1. Present the material in short, independent topics. Do not insist on complete mastery before moving on to the next topic. Since these students learn slowly, an insistence on their mastery of topics might mean that too limited progress is made and major goals are not attained. Be sensitive to the students' need for a change in topic and teaching technique. At the same time, be aware of the security provided these students when you repeat a successful activity as well as one that needs reteaching. Thus, a topic such as probability could be organized into several independent units. One unit could be on permutations, another on probability experiments, and a third on applications of probability. However, if there are several approaches to a new concept being taught, only one should be presented in a given lesson to avoid confusion.

2. Use a variety of methods and activities from day to day and even during a given period. To meet the short attention span and low motivation, variety of activity is essential. Each lesson should consist of several different activities such as a game, a laboratory discovery period, a short study period, and a short mental-computation drill. Be sure each activity is short, preferably not longer than 15 minutes.

3. Use a variety of materials to capture the interest and arouse the curiosity of the learner.
   a. *Pamphlets,* such as *The Amazing Story of Measurement.*
   b. *Models,* such as the dynamic geometry devices.
   c. *Computing Devices,* such as the slide rule.
   d. *Kits,* such as the probability kit.
   e. *Films,* such as *Donald in Mathmagic Land.*
   f. *Construction Material,* such as cardboard and balsa strips.
   g. *Games,* such as *Equations.*
   h. *Projectuals,* such as the set on venn diagrams.
   i. *Programmed Topics,* such as Measurement.
   j. *Charts,* such as Optical Illusions.
   k. *Resource Books,* such as *Field Work in Mathematics.*
   l. *Measuring Instruments,* such as micrometers.

4. Use the *discovery approach* by collecting information through laboratory work. Provide background material as needed rather than as an independent unit. Relate ideas to the students' experiences. For example, to

discover area formulas, cut out rectangles and transform them by cuts into triangles.

5. Have the students read about things they see, feel, and do. Use models, paper folding, and measurements which students can manipulate. Stress tangible, not abstract, qualities.

6. Apply mathematical ideas to local situations. Collect data from class members, parents, or community projects. Capitalize on the curiosity of youth to explore, manipulate, and cope with their environment. Use their names, local situations, local newspaper advertisements, catalogs, radio or television programs for problems.

7. Give remedial instruction to individuals or groups based on a diagnosis of needs, but do not expect slow learners to attain the normal grade level. Gear learning to the students' readiness to learn. Correct errors and give feedback on progress made. One way to help review is to provide semiweekly quizzes on fundamentals, essentially the same test given twice. Students know that if they can correct their errors they can always score well on the second test. Or provide a sequence of very short problem sheets that students work and correct independently during a 5- to 10-minute period set aside frequently for such a procedure. Only when they score perfectly on one sheet can they go on to the next.

8. Provide short periods for independent study on activities in which the students can experience some success. Assign short, easy, concrete exercises. Strive for overlearning of basic ideas to ensure retention and transfer. Students grow in security when they have complete mastery of at least a few basic ideas.

9. Provide informal practice sessions, using games or realistic problems rather than formal drill. Use adequately spaced repetition and review. Give feedback on progress to confirm, clarify, and correct previous learning. A series of easy equivalent tests may be used for students to collect data on their performance; their grades should be noted on a graph. This graph should show improvement in the student's accuracy and quickness.

10. Give specific help in communication: reading, speaking, writing, spelling, neatness, organization, and vocabulary. Be sure to use text materials which students can read. Spend class time in teaching students to state ideas correctly, spell correctly, and write legibly.

11. Give special help on how to study, how to use the text, how to locate information, and how to check work. Do not expect much to be accomplished by homework. Permit the use of "crutches" but avoid the use of shortcuts. Frequently provide answers so that students can reinforce correct responses and locate their errors more quickly.

12. Provide the pupil with opportunities to assist the teacher in board work, art work, demonstrations, displays, projects. These activities give the student a feeling of acceptance and security. Never punish by giving extra work.

13. Enrich the instruction with:

a. Historical Incidents   d. Puzzles
b. Dramatic Topics   e. Stunts and Tricks
c. Unusual Problems   f. Personal Experiences
         g. Local Applications

14. Help pupils select specific, attainable goals and encourage them to recognize their greatest potential. Help them attain these goals. Have good practical reasons for everything done or assigned. Emphasize that the school program is set up to help each student. Don't try to cover up the student's limited ability; he already knows it. By your acceptance of it, help him accept his own limitations.

15. Create a classroom climate that stimulates interest, curiosity, and participation. A pupil should feel secure and accepted even if his dress, cleanliness, appearance, or response is not what we would desire. Try to have some activity every day which can be done successfully by each student. Be slow to take offense and use a light touch to deflate a potential blow up. Control expressions of irritation that rebuff or antagonize students.

16. Make specific provisions for developing attitudes, interests, appreciations, habits. If a topic is completely lacking in appeal, drop it for a time and move on to a new topic.

17. Permit pupils to explore topics or skills of special interest. Do not feel obligated to cover all topics of a given text. Allow for class expression and interplay. Tailor your questions to the ability of the student.

18. Provide adequate time for the pupil to complete assignments. Being hurried produces anxiety, which inhibits learning. Write out the assignments, make them brief, and keep your directions simple.

19. Be patient, kind, understanding, and fair. The learner wants the teacher to be genuinely interested in him. He wants to be respected, not patronized. He wants a teacher who will stand by him, someone upon whom he can depend. Don't moralize, preach, or be too sentimental. *Try to make eye contact with or to speak to each student every day.*

20. Use diagnostic tests to determine needs. Provide programmed texts, workbooks, pamphlets, or supplementary texts to meet individual needs for remedial instruction. Have texts for several grade levels for study. Review frequently to counteract short memory spans.

21. Contact the parents and recommend cooperative activities for meeting the needs of their sons or daughters. Do not let lack of cleanliness, odd dress, appearance, or socio-economic status of the parents influence your acceptance of a learner (or his parent).

22. Collect all the information possible about each student. Use the cumulative folder, the comments of other teachers, and the parents' comments to get a complete picture. Make up your own file with a cumulative folder for each student.

23. Find some activity in which the pupil can do superior work such as drawing, constructing, or computing. Give genuine praise for every inch of progress. Assume that students can learn, and push them to their limit.

24. Establish a classroom behavior standard that permits learning to take place. The low achiever usually thrives on specific rules of behavior; and if he respects you and likes you, and if you respect him and like him, he is not likely to be a rebel.

There is not just one right technique for teaching the low achiever, although there are many wrong ways. In teaching the low achiever, the teacher needs to be straightforward and specific, stating clearly what is to be done as many times as necessary. At the same time, the teacher should be informal, warm, and down-to-earth. He should encourage the learner and indicate that he expects him to learn. Since low achievers tend to be insecure and defensive, they do not respond well to "challenges."

Once you have established rapport with low achievers, you can teach them many ideas. Your own excitement, enthusiasm, and interest will be contagious if the learner identifies with you.

A SAMPLE LESSON FOR THE LOW ACHIEVER

To illustrate how some of the principles mentioned above operate in the classroom, here is a 45-minute lesson plan:

1. Introduction (10 minutes). An activity designed for fun is an appropriate class opening, particularly because it encourages promptness. One such activity is the game "What Number?" One student whispers a rule to the teacher like "add 1" or "take half" or "zero for even, 1 for odd." (If the student cannot think of a rule, the teacher provides one.) Without telling what his rule is, the student asks the other class members for a number between 1 and 20. The student then replies by giving the number he arrived at after applying the secret rule. When students think they have deduced the rule from the examples, the leader tests them by giving them numbers to answer. For example, if the rule is "subtract 2," the exchange might be:

> *Leader.* Bill?
> *Bill.* 5.
> *Leader.* 3. Mary?
> *Mary.* 19.
> *Leader.* 17. John?
> *John.* 10.
> *Leader.* 8. Frank?
> *Frank.* I know the rule.
> *Leader.* Okay. Try 15.
> *Frank.* 12.
> *Leader.* Sorry Frank, that's wrong. Bill?
> *Bill.* I know. 13.
> *Leader.* How about 7?
> *Bill.* 5.
> *Leader.* Okay. Anyone else?

2. Review (10 minutes). Review the short three-problem homework work sheet. Two students write each solution on the board. Other students judge the better solution to each problem on the basis of correctness, presentation, and neatness.

3. New content (5 minutes). Teacher presentation. With an overhead projector the teacher develops some simple area and perimeter relationship based on counting squares on a lattice, as shown below.

4. Class practice (10 minutes). Students draw dots on their papers and make their own figures. The challenge is to make an odd figure to

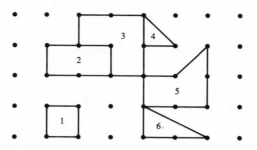

Fig. 14–1

determine the area and, when okayed, to copy the figure on a transparency to challenge the class.

5. Individual practice (5 minutes). Start on a worksheet assignment that has one problem based on classwork and two on review material.

6. Motivation (5 minutes). As a bonus for a good class period, the teacher plays a challenge game of One-Pile-Nim with a student chosen for good participation. The teacher chooses the number of counters in the game, the student tells how many counters may be taken in one turn (no more than 3 or 4 or 5 as his choice) and takes the first turn.

Many readers would challenge the outlined lesson as only nominally mathematical. However, it stresses goals that are even more important: developing interest and participation, good work habits, successful experiences, providing leadership. The mathematics itself is basic but good. Many algebra students have trouble with the problems of "What Number?" in its abstract form: "Write the equation representing the linear relation between the ordered pairs of which (5, 3), (19, 17), and (10, 8) are examples." In the same way, students of coordinate geometry, who would reject some of these area problems as being too simple, would also have difficulty with them in abstract form.

The activities suggested in this chapter are based on the following assumptions:

1. It is *important* that we teach mathematics to the low achiever. Our nation needs citizens who have enough mathematical competence to be employable and who can participate in a democratic society.

2. It is *possible* for the slow learner to attain significant goals of mathematics instruction.

3. It is *necessary* for the slow learner to have a desire to learn before learning will take place.

4. It would be *helpful* if the content, grade placement, and ability level needed for progress were established.

5. It is *required* that the teacher of the slow learner be a competent teacher.

6. It is *appropriate* that the content be selected according to the needs, ability, and vocational goals of the learners.

7. It is *essential* that the negative attitudes of the slow learner be changed. This is the key to the problem. To do this the teacher must be convinced that the learner has real potential and is worth time and effort. The teacher must:

   a. Respect the student for who he is, so that the student can respect and have faith in himself.
   b. Encourage the student to try, and assure him that failure is no crime.
   c. Show confidence in the student's ability to learn.
   d. Show sincere pleasure at a reasonably good attempt even though there has been no demonstrable progress.

8. It is *important* that class size be kept small to allow for the greatest amount of individualized instruction.

LEARNING EXERCISES

1. Make a case study of a low achiever. Identify the sources of his difficulties. Recommend ways to meet his needs.
2. Make a readability test of a slow-learner text.
3. Write an enrichment unit for a low achiever.
4. Make a bibliography of commercial games and toys which could be used to teach mathematical ideas.
5. Analyze a published mathematics-achievement test or intelligence test to determine the reading skill and cultural experience needed to answer the questions.
6. Write a letter to a parent in which you recommend home activities for learning mathematics.
7. Make a list of appropriate goals for a special course for low achievers.
8. Make a list of appropriate materials needed for a low-achiever class. Indicate the source and cost of each item. Justify the selection of each item by listing its contribution.
9. Write an outline of a course for the slow learner.
10. Write a model lesson plan for a topic for a slow-learner class.

15

a program for the talented

Since the number of persons who have special mathematical talent is limited, it is important that we, as teachers, develop and encourage this precious human resource in these students. There are a variety of things which a school can do to improve the mathematics education of gifted youngsters.

IDENTIFYING THE TALENTED MATHEMATICS STUDENT

For the purposes of our discussion we will assume that the talented mathematics student is simply the person with a high potential for learning mathematical concepts and structures. This student is frequently in the top 10 percent in academic achievement of his age group.

The talented student in mathematics shows the following traits:

1. He is able to abstract generalizations from complex situations.

2. He is able to transfer and apply his knowledge to new situations.

3. He demonstrates a high level of intuition, association, insight, creativeness, and original thinking in learning new ideas, solving problems, or finding discrepancies.

4. He has an extensive vocabulary which facilitates his thinking, reading, and communication.

5. He learns new ideas rapidly, easily, and usually with pleasure.

6. He has a storehouse of knowledge, which often extends to advanced mathematics.

7. He has an extraordinary memory—sometimes even total recall of what he has read, heard, or seen.

8. He is curious about new ideas and the world around him.

9. He maintains initiative for independent work toward goals that may even be remote or difficult to achieve.

10. He enjoys a wide range of interests in hobbies or special fields such as mathematics or science.

11. He tends to be physically fit, socially mature, honest, and charitable to others. The usual picture of the gifted student as an awkward introvert is not borne out in studies of the gifted.

12. He may be a nonconformist, independent, confident in his judgments, and impatient with routine activities, drill, and computation.

Although many talented students have these characteristics, their performance level may vary considerably. Some demonstrate outstanding achievement and interest in mathematics; others have had their initiative blunted by a routine and conforming school program. Some have a record of average or even below average achievement because they are unmotivated, have negative attitudes or conflicting interests, or come from culturally deprived homes or communities.

Generally, taking these characteristics into consideration, a teacher can identify the talented student by specific testing procedures and by careful observation of the student. The following specific tests are helpful:

1. *A mental-ability test.* Students with IQ's above 125 are usually talented in mathematics. However, special mathematical talent is not isolated by intelligence tests.

2. *A mathematical-achievement test* with published norms. Students ranking in the top 5 percent would likely have special aptitude for mathematics.

3. *A test of reasoning ability, problem solving or critical thinking.* This type of intellectual activity is highly correlated with mathematical talent.

4. *A reading test.* The talented student is usually a rapid and avid reader.

5. *A communication test.* The talented usually have high verbalization competence.

These test scores combined with achievement records and the judgments of teachers and counselors become a basis for selecting talented students. One large metropolitan school established these standards for their definition of a talented mathematics student:

1. An IQ score of 120 or above.

2. A percentile rank of 90 or better on a standardized mathematics achievement test appropriate to his grade level.

3. An achievement record of *A* in previous mathematics courses.

4. A strong interest in learning mathematics.

5. A record of good work and study habits.

Although these guidelines make the selection of the talented straightforward and objective, errors in selection still will be made. There is always the risk that some plodding overachievers who are not really talented will be selected, while creative, nonconformist, unmotivated underachievers will be omitted.

SPECIAL PROGRAMS FOR THE TALENTED

Every school should establish a special program for its talented students. The type of program will depend on the size, location, and current resources of the school. Scholastic provisions for the mathematically talented students usually take one of the following forms:

1. Acceleration of gifted students into a class normally elected only by students in a higher grade.

2. Individualized instruction using correspondence study, programmed texts, or independent study.

3. A small special-ability group within a regular mathematics class.

4. A special-curriculum track for talented students.

5. Attendance at an optional out-of-school seminar, summer-school class, or camp with an academic program.

6. Registration in a course at another school or college.

7. A special enrichment course such as computer programming, probability and statistics, or game theory.

8. An advanced placement course.

Our description of the gifted has emphasized their possession of characteristics such as intellectual curiosity, ingenuity, independence, high reading interest, imagination, creative talent, leadership, and ability to assimilate and generalize. In order to capitalize on these unique traits, any program for the gifted should provide a variety of enrichment activities. A supply of mathematics books, pamphlets, and periodicals should be available to provide literature to satisfy intellectual curiosity and reading interests. Creative talent and independent work habits may be developed through research projects, written reports, or the construction of mathematical devices. The possibilities of using imagination in dealing with infinity, the fourth dimension, non-euclidean geometry, a new number base, or Boolean algebra are far-reaching. The analysis of original data collected at school or in the community can be a vehicle for social responsibility and leadership, as well as training in applying methods of analysis. To capitalize on the ability of the gifted to assimilate and generalize difficult material, the teacher can direct the student to a much more intensive coverage of a given course. For example, the study of graphing can be extended to topics in analytical geometry such as polar coordinates or three-dimensional coordinate systems, the logic of geometry to statistical inference, the study of variation to limits and elements of calculus. The main point to remember is that the talents of the gifted student must be nurtured; that, rather than narrowing his horizons by a rigid curriculum, the teacher must broaden these horizons by a more flexible program.

The generally accepted method of dealing with the talented student is by homogeneous grouping in special classes. When students are grouped according to ability, the content, materials, method, time, and learning activities can be tailored to the students involved. The talented need open-ended, challenging exercises instead of repetitive reinforcement and review exercises. Talented students need opportunities for enrichment and independent investigations. They need to work at an accelerated pace; and, in a class of his peers, the talented student is stimulated to work more nearly up to his potential. In competing with other students of equal ability, the talented student does not get an inflated notion of his ability. In doing the things he enjoys with others who share his interests, he should be motivated to continue his study of mathematics. However, there are also dangers inherent in ability grouping. The talented group may forget that their special assignment is a privilege and consider themselves an elite group. As a result, they may abrogate their role in leadership and service and may withdraw from student activities. Assigning them to different groups in other subjects and in homerooms is one way of keeping them in touch with the entire student body. Separating the gifted from other students also imposes problems for teachers, who would then need to develop leadership in the average classes to replace that siphoned off by the top sections.

One of the most frequent proposals for dealing with superior students has been to provide them with special courses. These courses permit the extensive study of mathematical topics adapted to the ability of the student and presented at a challenging rate. They provide an organization in which acceleration, enrichment, and independent activities can be coordinated into a balanced program. In small schools this approach has been modified to provide clubs or seminars, which often meet after school. Currently, we devote a tremendous amount of out-of-school time, provide special coaches, and buy all kinds of equipment for the athletically gifted without concerning ourselves with the probable development of conceit on the part of stars or frustration on the part of the third stringer. We should work for equivalent provision for the mentally gifted.

Another frequent proposal is to accelerate the superior student. This method has the advantage of providing challenging material at a pace that does not permit poor work habits and avoids the frustration of lock-step class work. It involves certain risks of social and emotional maladjustment when sooner or later the superior student finds himself studying with older students, who sometimes have greater social maturity. However, several studies have shown that moderate acceleration is desirable—especially when the gifted individual is socially and emotionally mature.

The desire for social leadership has often resulted in the gifted student's becoming so involved in extracurricular activities that he has lacked time to build his foundation in science and mathematics. Opportunities for social responsibility and community leadership must be assured the gifted, but they should be part of a balanced program planned with the help of well-informed counselors and teachers. This planning should involve the selection of goals as well as the building of interests. At higher levels it should also explore means of financial support if such help is needed to attain the goal selected. Counselors can also be helpful in establishing the testing program that will identify the gifted, locate their strengths and weaknesses, and measure their progress by contrasting it with the progress made by students both in their school and in other schools.

Counseling is one of the most important aspects of dealing with the talented, for the talented student needs to know what his potential is and how to capitalize on his ability. He needs to know what professions require mathematical talent and what the requirements are for different occupations. He needs also to know what sources of financial support are available to attain the education he needs. The pamphlets listed in Appendix C (under mathematical careers) are helpful in giving guidance to the talented.

CRITERIA FOR PROGRAMS FOR THE TALENTED

All provisions for the talented will fail unless the student is motivated to use his talent. His intellectual curiosity must be stimulated by good teaching, appropriate materials, and recognition of his high accomplishment. In this regard, awards, A grades, scholarships, and contests are probably secondary to intellectual satisfaction. The stimulation of an enthusiastic, well-informed teacher who knows the needs of his students is indispensable.

An effective program for the talented, then, will have these aspects:

1. The *curriculum* for the talented should be a complete curriculum, extending from grade 7 through 12. This curriculum should provide enrichment as well as acceleration. It may involve correspondence courses, programmed texts, college classes, or independent study. Avenues for late entry into the program should be provided, as well as opportunities for leaving the program.

2. The *goals* of instruction should include those associated with attitudes, habits, values, creativity, leadership, and communication skills as well as the content goals of the mathematics courses.

3. The *students* for this special curriculum should be selected with care. Selection should be based on tests of intellectual and mathematical aptitude, vocational interests, and social maturity as well as teacher judgments.

4. The *teachers* for special classes should be assigned on the basis of qualifications rather than seniority or prestige. The successful teacher of the talented is one who can give the necessary stimulus and guidance for effective and enriched learning. The teacher of the talented must have a strong background in mathematics and, if possible, special training in teaching this type of group. Extra preparation time should be provided for this teacher, especially during his first assignment to this group.

5. The *resources* for the talented must include special facilities and materials. An independent study room, laboratory, or seminar room is helpful. Supplementary texts, enrichment pamphlets and books, computers, laboratory equipment, and construction materials are needed.

6. The *evaluation* of the talented must be realistic. A student's class standing or grade-point average must not be jeopardized by his being assigned to an accelerated program. One way to handle this situation is to give an "S" grade in special courses or to base class standing on test scores. Some schools offer two grades for the talented—within the course, a grade that expresses his standing among his peers; and a school grade, which compares him with the entire class. Another procedure that has been used is to assign standard (within course) grades but add a point to these grades when computing grade-point average and class standing. In the majority of cases, average marks are not acceptable in a special class for the talented.

ENRICHMENT FOR THE TALENTED

Since the talented student has such broad interests and the ability to do independent study, enrichment is one excellent way of meeting his needs. The wealth of materials now available makes it possible to enrich the learning of the talented by a variety of activities such as the following:

1. Solve challenging mathematical problems like those found in periodicals such as *The Mathematics Student Journal* and *School Science and Mathematics* or in books such as *Mathematical Puzzles for the Connoisseur* or *Chips from Mathematical Logs.*

2. Read about exciting mathematical topics in pamphlets and books such as *Exploring Mathematics on Your Own* and *Enrichment Mathematics for High School.*

3. Learn new mathematical ideas from books such as *Mathematics and the Imagination, The Number of Things,* or *The Education of T. C. Mits.*

4. Study advanced topics such as limits, infinity, non-euclidean geometries, finite mathematical systems, computer programming, symbolic logic, or game theory.

5. Write creatively by preparing scripts, research reports, poems, plays, or essays.

6. Enjoy recreational reading of science fiction based on mathematical ideas, as found in *Fantasia Mathematica* or *Mathematical Magpie.*

7. Learn to perform tricks, solve puzzles, analyze paradoxes as described in books such as *Mathemagic, Mathematical Magic,* or *Mathematical Puzzles and Diversions.*

8. Participate in out-of-class activities such as mathematics clubs, seminars, contests, and fairs.

9. Build models such as logic machines or tesseracts to represent mathematical ideas.

10. Find applications of mathematics in science, economics, industry, government, music, or art, as described in *Mathematics in Western Culture* or *Math and Aftermath.*

11. Collect information about opportunities in mathematics and the work of contemporary mathematicians, as described in *Careers in Mathematics* or *Mathematics* (by Bergami).

12. Study more intensively and deeply the standard topics included in the accelerated course.

13. Investigate the history of mathematics and biographies of mathematicians, as found in *The Mainstream of Mathematics* or *Men of Mathematics.*

14. Prepare lessons or reports on unusual topics such as topology, transformations, symmetry, or space travel.

15. Perform laboratory activities such as forming pendulum patterns, determining probabilities, or measuring indirectly the diameter of the sun.

16. Create an exhibit on a mathematical topic: mathematics in nature or the Moebius strip.

17. Tutor students who need remedial instruction or who are culturally deprived. (This activity should increase the talented student's sense of responsibility and give him experience in communication. It forces him to reexamine content in a different light, aids his judgment, maintains a good relationship with weaker students, and gives him more appreciation for and perspective on his own gifts.)

18. Act as an assistant in the mathematics laboratory or in the mathematics class. (The activities assigned should be those that develop the initiative and leadership of the talented. Care must be taken so that this type of assignment does not cause the student to lose status with his peers.)

From the ideas listed above, it is apparent that enrichment requires an extensive library of materials other than mathematics textbooks. If students are to participate in these enrichment activities, they must also be provided with the necessary school time and not expected to do all their reading outside of school. Of course, the extra work done by the student should be given credit toward his mark, and the work should be recognized as a job well done.

ACCELERATION OF THE TALENTED

Most new ideas in mathematics and science have been created by young people before they reach the age of 26. If we are to help get our talented mathematics students to a level where they too may be able to create new mathematics while they are young, we must accelerate their education.

An easy means of acceleration is the assignment of the talented student to a class one level or more above his own grade. This may be especially appropriate for a small school but even then care must be taken to see that the accelerated student is placed in a class where he is accepted by the rest of the students.

A better method of acceleration consists in the selection of enough able students to form a class. When possible, this should be done at the seventh-grade level so that a complete secondary sequence is available. A possible sequence for acceleration is outlined below:

1. In grades 7 and 8, the content is that of the modern three-year junior high school mathematics course.

2. In grade 9, the course content includes plane, solid, and coordinate geometry as well as work with transformations and vectors.[1]

3. In grade 10, the course is a second year of algebra with emphasis on deduction, proof, and structure.

4. In grade 11, the course emphasis is on functions, including trigonometric and polynomial functions as well as matrices, vectors, sequences, limits, permutations, and probability.

5. In grade 12 there are a number of alternatives:

   a. A course in analytical geometry and calculus (usually the College Entrance Examination Board Advanced Placement course).

   b. A course in modern mathematics (e.g., linear programming, game theory, probability and statistics, geometric transformations, and computer problem solving).

   c. An integrated science-mathematics course.

   d. A selection of semester offerings (e.g., analytic geometry, probability and statistics, and modern algebra), from which the student may elect one, two, or even more.

Some schools include among the electives listed in (d) a course geared toward the specific interests of one or two teachers, the concentration being not on the content as such but on student exploration and the development of interest. Such a course might concentrate on inequalities, continued fractions, or computer programming. Several publishers are offering monographs that would be useful in such courses.

Many high schools today do not have mathematics teachers with adequate mathematical backgrounds to teach these twelfth-grade courses. Hence, teachers and administrators may wish to explore the possibilities of correspondence courses, a televised course, a course arranged cooperatively with one or more neighboring schools, a local college course, or a programmed text for independent study.

Although acceleration is a good way to provide stimulating courses for the talented, it is not appropriate to accelerate students at the expense of depth of treatment and enrichment. Note that in the program suggested, the content in grades 9 through 11 comprises enriched versions of standard courses. This seems the best course of action at all grade levels.

[1] The algebra-geometry-algebra sequence is suggested in the light of current textual materials. Most second-year algebra texts demand fairly extensive knowledge of geometry for the study of coordinate systems.

SPECIFIC TECHNIQUES FOR TEACHING THE TALENTED IN MATHEMATICS

Since the teaching of the talented is of such high significance, it is essential that it be appropriate. Too often it is assumed that the talented will learn even though the instruction is poor. In some schools the poorest instructor may be assigned to this group. This is a practice that cannot be condoned. There are some necessary teaching activities:

1. *Know each talented student.* Collect information about his ability, interests, hobbies, home environment, school activities, and summer activities. Expect differences among students even when they are grouped according to ability. It should be kept in mind that ability differences in high and low sections will be greater than in average ability classes.

2. *Know your subject.* Present challenging material at an appropriate rate. Select thought-provoking questions and problems that are stimulating. Present mathematics as a subject that is fascinating and of the greatest significance. Be ready to explore unexpected avenues when students initiate unexpected digressions.

3. *Provide time, resources, and stimulation* for independent work on topics of special interest to individual pupils.

4. *Make available and encourage the use of a variety of enrichment material*—books, pamphlets, periodicals, supplementary texts.

5. *Arrange opportunities for out-of-class activities* such as mathematics clubs, contests, fairs, seminars, camps, summer enrichment courses, mathematics bulletins, or mathematics teams.

6. *Encourage leadership and communication skills* by having student demonstrations, reports, lessons, exhibits, projects, and research papers. Provide opportunities for the talented to teach topics or give demonstrations to his class.

7. *Enrich your instruction* with new topics, historical incidents, biographical sketches, unique problems, current applications, or elegant proofs found in library books.

8. *Share original ideas, elegant solutions, superior achievement of individuals with the class.* Provide an environment in which intellectual achievement is valued. Keep the school, community, and parents informed of the program for the talented and of special attainments. The bulletin board is one resource to be used for the display of superior work.

9. *Have frequent conferences with individual pupils.* Explore vocational plans, interests, difficulties, needs, and emotional problems. Help the pupil accept responsibility for the maximum use of his talents without conceit. Explore future plans, courses, and scholarships. Investigate the total work load of the pupil and his progress in other areas.

10. *Encourage creative activities* such as creative writing, independent and group projects, and class reports.

11. *Provide an emotional climate in the classroom that stimulates interest, curiosity, participation, and security.* Evaluate achievement by marks that indicate the standing in an appropriate comparison group.

12. *Communicate with the parents.* Inform them of their child's potential and actual achievement and recommend appropriate ways of developing the potential of their talented child. Some parents put too much pressure on their children while others do not understand the talents of their children.

13. *Capitalize on community resources.* Local engineers, computing centers, industries, colleges, or research laboratories may have opportunities for work experience, projects, or seminars.

14. *Be receptive to the off-beat questions and suggestions* of the creative pupil. Expect the talented to know things that you may not know and to solve problems that you cannot solve.

15. *Require clear, precise statements and neat, correct, well-organized written work.* Since talented pupils see results quickly, they sometimes become lazy and slipshod in their work.

16. *Enjoy your association with these students.* Show them that you support them in efforts to use their gifts in positive directions. Give them support in dealing with teachers and other students.

These proposals for a program for the talented mathematics student are based on the following assumptions:

1. Intellectual talent is our *most precious resource.* Intellectual leadership, insight, and creativeness are indispensable in our current society.

2. It is possible for the talented to *learn* mathematics *rapidly* and to *be creative at an early age.*

3. For maximum development of talent, the talented pupil needs *the opportunity, the challenge, and the materials* for learning.

4. Allow *the talented student to work independently* in his fields of special interest.

5. It is essential that *the teacher of the talented be a specialist* who is talented in mathematics and in teaching.

6. It is appropriate that the talented have *courses, materials, instruction, and opportunities that are different* from those for the average or slow learner.

7. It is important that *adequate recognition be given* to the superior achievement and contributions of the talented.

LEARNING ACTIVITIES

1. Select an appropriate topic for enrichment reading. Identify a set of appropriate references for this topic.
2. Make a collection of challenging problems for talented students.
3. Write a unit for a supplementary topic—e.g., non-euclidean geometry—specifically designed for the talented student.
4. Present a demonstration lesson on an enrichment topic such as topology.
5. Write a script for a play or an essay on some historical event related to discovering mathematics.
6. Make a collection of paradoxes, tricks, or puzzles for talented students.

7. Select the library books and equipment needed for the talented students of a given school.

8. Plan a sequence of courses for the talented students of your school.

9. Establish a program for the identification of the gifted in your school.

10. Review a research study of the effectiveness of different programs for the talented.

11. Plan a mathematics club for a school. Describe its purpose, membership, and activities.

12. What are the advantages and disadvantages of a mathematics contest based on a mathematics test?

part four

use
of classroom
equipment

16

the role
of models

Modern man makes extensive use of models to clarify his thought. The geologist uses maps and charts to locate a new oil field. The chemist uses a Tinker-Toy model to represent a molecular structure. The architect makes a scale drawing of a building design. The physicist or chemist uses a formula to predict the results of an experiment. The economist uses the graphs of inequalities to estimate the most efficient production process. The psychologist uses a flow chart to diagram processes in learning concepts. All of these models are constructed to clarify problems.

Most of the great mathematical ideas arose when someone sought a way of dealing with a physical situation. Consider major concepts such as counting numbers, rational numbers, irrational numbers, location, direction, congruence, similarity, symmetry, vectors, probability. All of these originated from problems involving objects or situations in man's environment. Hence, it seems logical that if physical situations made it possible for man to invent mathematical ideas, then related physical representation will enhance the learning of these ideas. For example, tossing dice and systematically recording possible results makes the idea of a sample space and a sample point meaningful. Physical representations also are needed to test theories or to provide examples. Thus, for instance, a slated sphere is used for the representation of spherical triangles.

The effective mathematics teacher uses models to help his students think. These models, which may be sketches on paper and chalkboard, concrete devices, or mathematical formulas, furnish the basis for solving a problem, discovering a new idea, or creating a new product. These models are links between the thought processes of man and the reality of nature. They help make transitions from one level of abstraction to another and are a means for expressing ideas and providing stepping stones to new relationships. They add reality to abstract ideas and facilitate creative thinking. They are a means of relating past experience to a new situation.

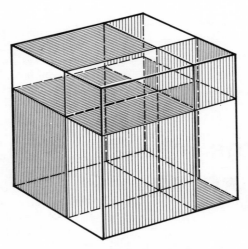

Fig. 16–1.   Model of $(a + b)^3$.

At the same time, there are inherent dangers in the use of physical models to represent abstract ideas. The concrete representation adds qualities that are not mathematical and by so doing may lead to misconceptions. Compare, for example, "wheel" and "circle." A circle is a mathematical conception. The abstraction cannot be accurately represented by a concrete model, for it is a set of dimensionless points. Even a representation of a circle as the boundary of a disc carries with it certain difficulties in interpretation, and such pictures of circles are certainly difficult to manipulate anyway. The wheel can be manipulated as it can be seen as well as felt, rolled, and measured. While the wheel may clarify certain ideas about circles, it may also mislead the student into thinking of a circle as a disc or a circular region. When teachers utilize models, they must be constantly alert to the dangers of misleading students by false constructions. The model lays the foundation for learning an abstract concept, but the concrete representation does not give a complete conception or definition of the abstract idea.

In this chapter we restrict the word *model* to include only those concrete devices utilized by teachers and students to demonstrate mathematical concepts. Thus, although an equation is a mathematical model of a genus of scientific problems, such models are not the subject of this chapter. We are concerned rather with dynamic devices and demonstration equipment for classroom use.

We think of models as three-dimensional, but the mathematics teacher commonly utilizes models that are essentially two-dimensional (linkages or the diagrams accompanying plane geometry proofs) and even one-dimensional (a slide rule or number line). In fact, the teacher may utilize three-dimensional representation of four-dimensional figures, such as the

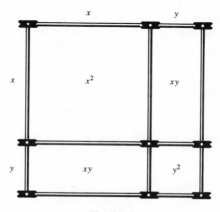

Fig. 16–2

tesseract or pseudosphere, to provide insights into non-euclidean geometries and geometries of higher dimensions.

The use of such concrete representations of mathematical ideas to teach is far from new. In the first English translation of Euclid's *Elements,* published in 1570, pop-up models similar to those in children's storybooks of today were included to illustrate three-dimensional concepts. These and other early models are described by L. G. Simons in *Historical Material on Models and Other Teaching Aids in Mathematics.* The longstanding and continuing concern for the use of models in the past is also illustrated by the eighteenth yearbook of the National Council of Teachers of Mathematics, *Multi-Sensory Aids in the Teaching of Mathematics.*

Models are, of course, of special value in the study of geometry, where spatial relationships are the basic concern. However, teachers should not restrict their thinking about models to this area, since models of algebraic and arithmetic relationships can provide students with bases for understanding concepts in these subjects. A good example of the use of a model in algebra is in exploring the terms of the square of a binomial made out of Tinker-Toy parts. In Fig. 16–2 it is easy for the student to see that $(x + y)^2$ gives the area of a square. This square is made up of regions whose areas are x^2, xy, xy, and y^2. Consequently $(x + y)^2 = x^2 +$

$2xy + y^2$. This is a simple example of how a model adds reality and meaning to an abstract, symbolic representation.

One other aspect of the use of models in the classroom should be emphasized: models facilitate one of the central goals of modern mathematics teaching—student discovery. This facet of mathematics instruction, balancing the modern concern with structure and abstraction, is strongly supported by teaching with concrete aids. Successful discoveries prompted by observing, manipulating, or even contemplating physical models give students a sense of individual achievement, a feeling of active participation, and the exhilaration of independent discovery. Through a student's independent exploration, his positive attitudes and intellectual curiosity are stimulated.

MODELS FOR CREATING MATHEMATICS

The invention of topology is a typical example of the development of a mathematical topic beginning with a physical situation. The problem that initiated the study of topology involved the seven bridges of Koenigsberg. The problem posed was "How can one walk through Koenigsberg from a given starting point and cross all of its seven bridges once and only once?"

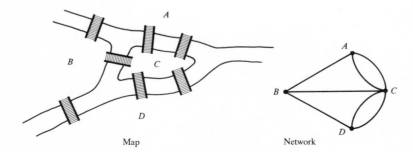

Map   Network

Fig. 16–3

No one could find a route that would satisfy the conditions of the problem. To save time someone tried the problem by drawing a sketch of the town and tracing possible walks; but still the problem remained unsolved.

The mathematician Euler was requested to solve the problem. He changed the physical problem to a sketch called a network. He called each bridge an arc and each region of land a vertex. From an analysis of this network, he found generalizations that apply to all networks.

This analysis was extended to a consideration of regions, arcs, and vertices that had no physical counterpart. Today, topology has been extended far beyond this simple beginning into a highly structured discipline.

Similarly, it is presumed that when man invented the concept of number, he first represented this idea with physical objects, such as pebbles. Later, he used marks in the sand or notches on a stick. With the invention of writing, he used tally marks; still later, digits with place value. Soon he learned to use a number line, which visualized the order and magnitude of number. Today, these primitive representations of number have been refined and extended to number systems with properties such as closure and identity elements. And new numbers (such as quaternions) have been invented, numbers that seem to have no application to a concrete situation. This sequence from the physical to the operational to the abstract illustrates the typical sequence of mathematical development and the ideal sequence for learning mathematics.

A LESSON BASED ON MODELS

A description of a lesson on Euler's formula for polyhedra illustrates the role of models and visualization in the teaching and learning of a mathematical concept. The teacher begins by having each student draw a variety of polygons, concave as well as convex. After making sure that every student knows the meaning of *vertices, edges,* and *regions,* the teacher asks each student to count and record the number of vertices,

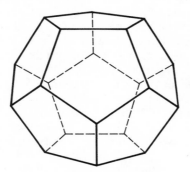

Fig. 16–4.   Dodecahedron.

edges, and regions. Each count is checked by a second student and some of the results tabulated on the chalkboard. As the results are tabulated, students are asked to record what they conjecture are the formulas describing the relationship between vertices (V), edges (E), and regions (R). As soon as a formula is suggested, students are asked to check it with their data. After a short period of exploration, a relationship is discovered and expressed by the formula $V + R = E + 2$ (for simple closed curves $R = 2$).

The teacher then asks whether the formula applies to compound figures or networks. The formula is found to satisfy all conditions the students can think of. The teacher then raises a further question: How can this formula be extended to a more complex situation? A student may suggest the formula for polyhedra.

At this stage the teacher distributes models of polyhedra. These can be commercial plastic models, homemade cardboard models, or models constructed by the class out of soda straws and elastic thread. Again the students count and record the number of edges, vertices, and faces of each polyhedron. The formula is verified by each of these models. Even so, the formula is only a conjecture arrived at by scientific (as opposed to mathematical) induction. The students explore the formula further by applying it to a variety of objects in the classroom. The next step is for the teacher to guide the students to an abstract proof of their conjecture. The proof is based on systematic dissection of the polyhedron.[1]

The students are now sure that their discovery is correct. A new model is now presented, still a polyhedron model but different from the others in that it has a hole through it. A count of faces, vertices, and edges leads to a contradiction of the "proved" relationship. This creates a lively discussion. Is it possible that the same statement can be proved and disproved? The students eventually come to recognize that their formula is true under certain conditions but is only a special case of a more general formula. Their formula is true only for polyhedra without holes—that is, topologically equivalent to (or distortable into) a sphere.

In this discovery lesson, students have shifted back and forth between abstract ideas and concrete representations. They have carried out activities which are similar to the scientific method in their structure. At every stage the students' abstractions have been tested against the data obtained from the concrete representations available to them. When their tests failed, they were forced to reexamine previously established conclusions and then to derive new ideas to fit varied conditions.

In fact, the students saw in operation a scientific research activity. Faced with a contradiction, they had three avenues open to them: (1) reject their entire effort; (2) limit their theorem in order to exclude the contradiction; (3) extend their theorem in some way in order to include the contradictory case. The first is not very satisfying, especially in the light of what had seemed to be a correct proof. The second is possible. Students should see that the proof they have developed fails when there is a hole in the original polyhedron. The dissection cannot be carried out. They then may correct the theorem by stating it for polyhedra without holes.

Finally, a much more satisfying exploration will show that the formula $R + V = E + 2 - 2H$, where H is the number of holes, takes the additional cases into account. When $H = 0$, the formula reduces to the original form.

The foregoing lesson is an illustration of the role of models in teaching. The model, whether a drawing or a three-dimensional model, helps to make the problem realistic. The models then become the source for data. By exploring the pattern of the data, students receive various clues, which lead eventually to the forming of a generalization. The generalization is checked against a variety of different situations. In addition, the relationship can be applied to everyday situations to increase familiarity. Finally, the generalization is established by a mathematical proof which is independent of the

---

[1] See Richard Courant and Herbert Robbins, *What Is Mathematics?* (New York: Oxford University Press, 1941), pp. 236–240, 258–259.

model. The objective is the establishment of the mathematical concept at the abstract level. The models used are tools for achieving that objective. It would be difficult to envision a lesson on Euler's formula without the use of models, drawings, and experimentation.

THE MODEL IN THE CLASSROOM

Each time a model is used in the classroom, it should play a positive role in providing deeper student understanding of mathematics. The model may illustrate a specific concept (a wooden conic section); it may provide the basis for a development (unit cubes for building solids); it may be used as a vehicle for a student discovery (polyhedra for Euler's formula); in each case the teacher should know the purpose and appropriate use of the model.

The primary purpose of a model is to provide a concrete visualization for thinking about and discussing an idea. For example, a model that allows a student to transform a rectangle physically into a triangle provides a basis for developing the formula for the area of a triangle. The model provides experiences which can then be used for thinking about an idea by providing a frame of reference for sense perceptions and experiences.

Such transformations, from the concrete to the abstract, are often difficult to achieve. They must be supported at all stages by thoughtful teaching. The teacher must recognize and anticipate the level of insights that occur to individual students as a result of experiences with physical models. As rapidly as possible, these students should be weaned away from the concrete model and be made to understand the conceptual model. At the same time, the teacher should recognize a student's need for additional work with a concrete model and should seek to provide him with that assistance. A slower student may be encouraged to work with the model at his desk, for the sense of touch may provide him with the needed bridge to the conceptual level. And, finally, the model should be kept available to reinforce the concept if and when students regress in understanding.

A linkage, sometimes called a Trigtracker (see Fig. 16–5), may be used to explore the trigonometric ratios for a unit circle. This device can be made out of cardboard, or a commercial demonstrator may be purchased. By forming different right triangles with the linkage, one can get approximations for the sine, cosine, and tangent of various angles. These approximations show such things as how the values of these ratios increase and decrease with the size of the associated angle and how the maximum and minimum values for the sine and cosine are $^{+}1$ and $^{-}1$. This device is useful for building a table of values for trigonometric ratios. Keeping them available helps to remind students of the relationships examined in the original demonstration.

Many teachers fail to take into account the later uses of models in supporting the initial demonstration. Since the teacher understands the abstractions, he often moves too quickly to the abstract level, carrying with him only the brightest students. In this regard consider this example: a

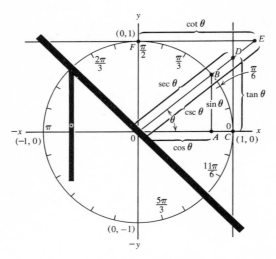

Fig. 16–5.   Trigtracker.

seventh-grade teacher of remedial arithmetic has used felt pie cutouts for
several days to illustrate fraction concepts. Students have had experience
constructing these models and using them to demonstrate addition problems involving fractions. Presently, the students, most of whom have progressed to the abstract level, are computing sums involving fractions. The
teacher tours the room, occasionally asking a student to return to the
flannel board to check his computation. The teacher is spotting weaknesses
and allowing regression to the use of the concrete devices by students who
still need this assistance, thus giving students additional security in dealing
with a complicated algorithm.

A description of a lesson on circles may illustrate other aspects of the
use of models. This lesson is concerned with the relationship between the
measures of the angles formed by intersecting lines and the measures of the
intercepted arcs of circles. The class was first requested to make drawings
to illustrate all the possible ways in which two intersecting lines could be
related to a given circle. From these results, a selection was made of all
situations in which each of the two intersecting lines intersects the circle in
at least two points (see Fig. 16–6).

The teacher then distributed a device for experimenting and collecting
data of the measures of angles and arcs. This device has a circle on its base
with marks on the circumference indicating degrees of arc. Two plastic
strips are marked off into unit lengths for reading measures of length. The
strips intersect at a point which may be placed at the center of the circle,
within the circle, on the circumference of the circle, or outside the circle. A
protractor measures the angle between the lines represented by the strips.
In the different positions the strips may represent radii, chords, secants, or
tangents.

The students were then asked to make three different settings for each

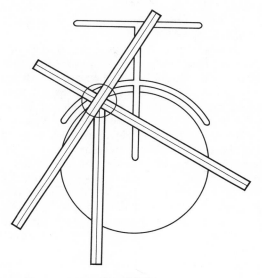

Fig. 16–6

different type of intersection. They were asked to record the measures of the angles formed by the intersecting lines and the measures of the intercepted arcs for each setting. Each setting was checked by a second student.

For this laboratory lesson some teachers would provide the students with a laboratory guide sheet. This guide sheet might tell the student how to manipulate the device and what measurements to make; in addition, it might suggest sketches of each type of intersection, provide a table for the collected data, and give some hints about the generalization to be discovered. Other teachers would prefer to have the students experiment in a completely unstructured manner, or have students work in groups and permit each group to complete the generalization. Another method would be to make the experiment a class activity in which the data collected would be recorded on the chalkboard.

No matter what method is used, the goal of the lesson is to lead students to discover the formulas which describe the relationship between the measures of angles formed by intersecting lines and measures of intercepted arcs of a given circle. After each of these is formulated, the teacher asks whether any one generalization will describe all possible results. (The measure of the angle in degrees is equal to the algebraic sum of the measures of the intercepted arcs.) For practice, the class tests the generalization by applying it to a variety of exercises.

The discoveries at this stage provide only *a conjecture*. Once this conjecture is arrived at, students are asked, "Are there any conditions under which the formula does not apply?" Further exploration is encouraged to try to find contradictions. When none is found, the students can go on, in the next lesson, to finding a deductive proof for the generalization.

In this lesson the primary goal is the development of a generalization. The end activity establishes the generalization by a proof. The models are used as a means for adding meaning to the relationship—as a vehicle for the students to discover the relationship.

Of course, such a lesson takes more time than it does to look at a drawing and read the theorems that apply. Most often these theorems are proved as outlined in the textbook and then applied in a set of provided exercises. But such a short lesson is not likely to produce retention, understanding, or interest. Such essentially sterile teaching presents mathematics as a rigid, completely formulated subject. In this type of lesson students participate by memorizing material developed by others. On the other hand, when he studies models and the development of ideas, the learner is more likely to feel—as he should feel—that he is a creative mathematician.

Note that in each of the previous examples, the model plays an important but *secondary* role to the mathematical concepts at the abstract level. In both cases, efficient advance to the abstract level is the goal: the model is a tool to achieve that goal. The additional expenditure of time in using models is amply compensated by the student's ability to retain the concept and to recognize its utility.

Models are not necessary for all students—some talented students are capable of and even enjoy discovering generalizations through reflective thinking with abstract representations. For other students, even the models are meaningless and fail to help them build an understanding of a concept. It is the responsibility of the teacher to decide *when* models are needed, *what* models are effective, and *how* the model should be used for a given class.

TYPES OF ACTIVITIES USING MODELS

The following examples do not exhaust the uses of models in the classroom. Rather, they point up the variety of activities that the use of models can provide:

1. Models may be a *demonstration aid* to add meaning to a mathematical concept: an area demonstration device adds meaning to area formulas; a large demonstration rule helps one to read the slide-rule scale; insight into concepts of the fourth dimension may be achieved by reference to a tesseract; plastic models illustrate conic sections; Tinker-Toy models demonstrate the terms of polynomial products.

2. Models are useful *laboratory equipment* to provide a means for discovering new ideas and relationships. For example, a quadrilateral device like the Welch quadrilateral is useful in discovering the relationships between measures of segments and angles. A graphing board may be a means of investigating the periodicity of trigonometric functions; a probability kit can furnish the equipment for sampling experiments.

3. Models may be used as *practice devices* with which the student builds accuracy, understanding, and efficiency. For example, folding paper provides exercises useful in illustrating relationships between lines; nomo-

graphs provide a simple device for checking computations; a percent computer may be a device for showing the relationship between certain ratios as well as for solving percentage problems.

4. Models may be used as *measuring instruments* for studying mathematical applications within or outside the classroom. A transit can be used to measure indirectly the height of a building; an angle mirror will locate points for measuring an inaccessible line segment; a stadimeter measures distances by means of trigonometric ratios and a reference object; area linkages may be used to measure area relationships; the volumes of polyhedron models can be measured by liquid displacement; the Pythagorean theorem can be discovered by various models which compare the areas of squares.

Fig. 16–7. Angle mirror.

5. Models may be *projects* for independent student work. A student may plan, construct, and demonstrate a model such as a logic machine to generate truth values for various logical connectives, or the dual regular polyhedra—those regular polyhedra (such as the icosahedrons and dodecahedrons) which have the correspondence Faces ↔ Vertices.

6. Models may be used as *enrichment devices* when they present ideas which are not in the textbook. Moebius strips or hexaflexagons suggest some of the curiosities of topology; the Galton probability board relates the normal curve to binomial expansions; polyhedron models made out of balsa strips may illustrate a finite geometry.

MODELS AS LEARNING AIDS

Teachers who use models are enthusiastic about the contributions they make. They suggest, in summary, that models are effective because they perform the following functions:

1. They give concrete representation to abstract ideas.

2. They relate new ideas to previous experience or previously learned ideas.

3. They enhance active participation of the learner in the learning

activity, and thus provide additional motivation for the learning of mathematics.

4. They concentrate attention on the concepts involved and stimulate interest in these concepts.

5. They teach how to solve problems and how to explore new ideas.

6. They speed up communication.

7. They consolidate details that are related to the generalizations being sought, and thus enhance retention.

8. They lend variety to classroom activities and provide a useful change of pace.

9. They provide a program of enrichment and acceleration for individual students.

10. They provide successful, meaningful activities for the slow learner.

11. They encourage the participation of many practical-minded students, who need this continuing contact with the concrete world.

If, through the use of models, only some of these goals are attained, it is hard to understand why mathematics teachers do not use them more extensively.

MISUSES OF MODELS

Of course, models are sometimes misused or used at inappropriate times. Some of the principal abuses and misuses of models are:

1. Excessive and indiscriminate use merely for the purpose of using a model. A model is used only where it does something which cannot be done as well without it.

2. Failure to transfer from the concrete representation to a generalization or abstract representation. The goal in mathematics is to use symbols and abstractions. Mathematical ideas themselves are independent of physical representation or application.

3. Failure to use the right model at the right time or for a sufficient length of time to establish the concept involved.

4. Use of an inadequate model—a model that is too small, too crude, or—at the opposite extreme—too complex.

5. Failure to adapt the model to the needs of the student or to the objectives involved. Some students do not need an intuitive approach and some ideas do not need visualization. At the same time, it should be noted that the most frequent misuse of models is failure to use them at all.

MODELS AS PROJECTS FOR STUDENTS

One way to encourage discovery activities in mathematics is through the construction and demonstration of a model or the preparation of a science-fair exhibit. It is usually an individual, out-of-class activity. However, it is appropriate for group work and as a part of the regular classroom activity. In any case, it should contribute to the attainment of the objectives of the mathematics class.

The construction of a model provides an opportunity for independent exploration of ideas usually beyond the scope of the typical textbook. It places major emphasis on creativeness, originality, and craftsmanship. It supplements the usual classroom activities with activities that develop the desire and capacity to think independently.

Projects which result in student-made models serve a variety of important functions, such as the following:

1. Providing an opportunity for teacher-student planning.

2. Providing an opportunity for parent-student activity.

3. Providing a means for creative, original, independent work.

4. Providing a basis for discovery of new ideas or devices.

5. Enriching the learning of mathematics by opening new fields, new applications, and new methods.

6. Providing a means for publicizing the many aspects of mathematics through exhibits in school and in store windows.

7. Providing a means for identifying, recognizing, and encouraging gifted students.

To be successful, project activity needs careful planning and adequate resources. To plan models, the teacher needs ideas for possible projects, and he needs resources such as reference books and construction materials. One convenient way to have model ideas available is to make a list of possible projects and include them in the Instructional Techniques File. These cards should contain such information as a description of the model, drawings, references, difficulties, and the mathematical principles involved.

The student's first step is the selection of an appropriate model. This choice should be a joint decision of the student and the teacher, with student interest, experience, and aptitude as major considerations. After a choice of model has been made, the teacher furnishes the student with references, materials, and a few specific suggestions. However, the teacher should not give too many hints or suggestions; if he does, the student's opportunity to discover an idea or invent a model may be lost. The student should be allowed—and encouraged—to try out his own ideas. It is advisable to set up a schedule for the completion of the model to avoid wasting time. Additional conferences may be needed to check up on the student and to give added suggestions and encouragement. Don't be too rigid in your requirements.

Some teachers require a model or project from all pupils. Others require a project such as a research report, classroom demonstration, or science-fair exhibit in order to qualify for an A or B grade. In all cases, the completed project should be evaluated carefully and recorded for grading purposes. Projects should be evaluated for originality, completeness, crafts-

manship, accuracy, and organization. Of prime importance is the mathematical learning which the student demonstrates as he presents his model or
project to the class. Recognition of excellence in project work might be
given in a letter to the parent, by a description in the school newspaper or
by an exhibition in the school. Exhibits should always be labeled so that the
person who completed the project is given the credit due him. These
exhibits should also be properly titled so that the mathematics involved is
communicated to the viewer. The informal examination and manipulation
of these projects invariably builds curiosity and interest on the part of other
students and teachers. Display in store windows or at PTA meetings gives
excellent publicity to the work of the students.

A variety of models for laboratory activities may be made in an
ordinary classroom. For more extensive laboratory work, materials and
work space (such as those discussed in Chapter 22) are needed.

The following are suggestions for student projects:

1. Display the best models of previous years to suggest possibilities
and stimulate good work.

2. Use student-made models in the classroom presentation of mathematics.

3. Provide a guide sheet with suggested models, procedure, time schedule, and references.

4. Suggest the type, source and cost of appropriate materials. Wherever
possible the school should supply the material.

5. Place major emphasis on the mathematical principles involved
rather than the entertainment value.

6. Encourage students to make models attractive by good craftsmanship.

7. Have the builder demonstrate his model to the class. The demonstration or discussion of the model will give desirable leadership experience
to the student demonstrator and will also give the class a proper introduction to the topic.

8. Encourage the use of simple material and simple devices so that
construction time is kept to a minimum.

EXAMPLES OF DISCOVERY LESSONS USING MODELS

Here are some of the concepts, relationships, or structures which can
be discovered by using models. The suggestions are appropriate for students in grades 7 through 10:

SEVENTH- AND EIGHTH-GRADE MODELS

1. The area of triangles and quadrilaterals as related to the area of a
rectangle by the use of area boards.

2. The meaning of *regrouping, carrying,* and *borrowing* by a base five or binary abacus.

3. The sums and differences of numbers written in bases other than ten, derived by means of nomographs, Napier's bones, or slide rules.

4. The properties and operations in a finite modular arithmetic, determined by use of a circular number line or dial.

5. The sums of the measures of angles of polygons, found by means of polygon models.

6. The relationship between the squares on sides of right triangles, seen by use of cardboard or graphical models.

7. The formula for the circumference and area of a circle, discovered through use of a circle demonstration board.

8. The probabilities of events, determined by the spinning of dials or the tossing of thumb tacks, coins, or dice.

9. The sample space for the events resulting from tossing two dice.

10. The symmetries of geometric figures with two- and three-dimensional models.

11. The computation of any one of the three variables in a percentage problem by a percentage computation model.

12. The illustration of the actual conditions in verbal problems by terrain models made of papier-mâché, clay, sponges, and toys.

13. The program for a computer solution to a problem with a computer trainer.

14. The practice of computational skills with games.

15. An indirect measurement of an inaccessible distance with a hypsometer.

16. The properties of optical illusions in two- and three-dimensional objects.

17. The properties of polyhedra in crystals with cardboard models.

18. The comparison of perimeter and area of various-shaped figures by forming different shapes on a pegboard.

19. The comparison of volumes of prisms, cylinders, cones, and spheres by measuring capacity of models with sand or salt.

20. The properties of similar figures drawn with a pantograph or by graphing patterns on a grid.

21. The discovery of the Pythagorean theorem by use of a model.

22. The transformation of geometric figures from one shape to another shape with equivalent area.

23. The development of formulas by the analysis of puzzles.

24. The computational algorithms used by a calculator.

25. The drawing of original designs and patterns with ruler and compass.

26. The operation of an electric quiz board for mastering concepts.

27. The representation of units of measure (such as cubic foot) by cardboard models.

28. The application of units of measure to measuring packing boxes such as those for cereal.

29. The comparison of rational numbers by sectors of circles.

30. The comparison of percents by a 100 board, pegboard, graph paper, or objects.

ALGEBRA

1. The difference between first-, second-, and third-degree algebraic phrases by models made out of balsa strips, cardboard, or Tinker-Toy dowels.

2. The properties of graphs of linear equations by models using elastic thread between golf tees on acoustical tiles or pegboard.

3. The binomial distribution and Pascal's triangle with a probability board.

4. Practice in finding sums of positive and negative numbers by tossing dice of two colors.

5. The sums and differences of positive and negative numbers with a slide rule.

6. The meaning of formulas such as $V = lwh$ or $S = rt$ by mock-ups.

7. The setting for verbal problems by mock-ups using toys or cardboard models.

8. The application of proportions and variation by using gears, levels, springs, and pendulums.

9. The solutions of quadratic equations by a quadratic slide rule.

10. The setting for quadratic equations by mock-ups (e.g., a basketball player "shooting" a basket).

11. The drawing of conic sections by linkages or paper folding.

12. The terms of a binomial expression such as $(a + b)^3$ by a sectioned cube and $(a + b)^4$ by a tesseract.

13. The terms of a geometric series by a model which measures the bounces of a "super" rubber ball.

14. The sums of arithmetic progressions by cardboard cartoons.

15. The use of the slide rule by student-made rules using logarithmic graph paper.

16. The meaning of the complex roots of a quadratic equation with a three-dimensional graph.

17. The graphs of equations with three variables by using heavy

screening for the grids and elastic thread for lines and plastic sheets for planes.

18. The properties of curves such as parabolas, ellipses, and hyperbolas demonstrated by models, drawings, or paper folding.

19. The properties of surfaces such as the hyperbolic-paraboloid by curve stitching.

20. The applications of conic sections by bridge arches, buildings, and space orbits.

21. The permutations and combinations of objects such as cards or blocks.

22. The periodicity of functions by a model of the wrapping function.

23. The values of trigonometric function demonstrated by a trig-tracker.

24. The relationship of different number systems by models of venn diagrams.

25. The meaning of inverse variation by the use of a gear chain.

GEOMETRY

1. The properties of triangles by linkages that form various types of triangles.

2. The properties of quadrilaterals by linkages that form various types of quadrilaterals.

3. The properties of polygons by using elastic thread, golf tees, and protractors mounted on a pegboard.

4. The properties of a finite geometry by constructing models out of sticks or soda straws and elastic thread.

5. The meaning of the fourth dimension by a series of zero-, one-, two-, three-, and four-dimensional models.

6. The use of congruence in indirect measurement in surveying.

7. The use of similar triangles for indirect measurement of inaccessible distances.

8. The Pythagorean theorem and different ways of proving it.

9. The approximate value of irrational numbers by drawing successive right triangles with sides $(1, 1, \sqrt{2})$, $(\sqrt{2}, 1, \sqrt{3})$, $(\sqrt{3}, 1, \sqrt{4})$, $(\sqrt{4}, 1, \sqrt{5})$, and so on.

10. The properties of parallelograms by a linkage model.

11. The meaning of loci and the intersection of loci by combining plastic models.

12. The relationship between the measure of angles formed by radii, chords, secants, and tangents, and the measure of the intercepted arcs of the circle by a dynamic geometry device.

13. The Euler formula and properties of regular polyhedra by cardboard or plastic models of polyhedra.

14. The truth values as found in truth tables verified by simple electric circuits.

15. The projections of three-dimensional objects on a plane by a projection model or mock-up.

16. The transformations and symmetries of reflections by the use of mirrors and kaleidoscope.

17. The properties of non-euclidean geometry by a slated sphere and a model of a pseudosphere.

18. The properties of curves (such as the cycloid, spiral, catenary, and cardiod) formed by moving points of light or by curve stitching or paper folding or drawing.

19. The possibility of trisecting an angle with a trisection device.

20. The properties of minimum surface and maximum volume of soap bubbles, honeycombs, and other objects in nature.

21. The properties of three-dimensional symmetries by wire and string models.

22. The combination of vectors by demonstrations with a vector board.

23. The properties of spherical triangles by drawings on a slated sphere.

24. The determination of the diameter of a sphere with a spherometer.

25. The relationship of lines and planes shown by models out of cardboard and balsa strips or a commercial solid-geometry device.

26. The applications of geometry in the home, highway construction, nature, art, advertising, sports, architecture, carpentry, navigation, maps, photography, and machinery.

COMMERCIAL OR HOMEMADE MODELS?

The variety of commercial models currently available for the mathematics teacher has multiplied tremendously. Some of this increase is due to the emphasis on the discovery method, some of it is due to the support of NDEA funds, and some of it is due to the normal invention and development of new devices. Therefore, the individual mathematics teacher and the mathematics department head or supervisor will need to render professional judgment in the selection and use of these teaching aids. It is the responsibility of the teacher to know what materials are available, how to select appropriate models, and once selected how the models can contribute best to the learning of mathematics. In order to be informed about available materials, the teacher should send for the catalogs of companies which specialize in mathematical devices (see listing in Appendix B).

In addition, current issues of professional journals should be searched for reviews, announcements, and advertisements of new models.

When a model is needed, it is necessary to decide whether the school should purchase a commercial product or whether a teacher or student should construct it. In constructing a model, the student or teacher may discover some aspects of the ideas involved which he had not thought of before; and constructing a model may also give some experience in creativeness and craftsmanship. However, it is usually better to use a commercial device whenever a good one is available, for the commercial model is likely to be better constructed than a homemade model. Commercial products are usually designed by experts, produced by specialized machines and finished in an attractive manner. In addition, manufacturers usually modify commercial models on the basis of classroom trial.

The usual argument against commercial models is that they are expensive. This is often true, but the mathematics teacher's time is extremely valuable, and when the time it takes to construct a model is considered, the homemade model usually proves to be more expensive. When a desired model is not available commercially, it should be made locally. Frequently, the industrial arts department of the school will cooperate in its production.

TYPES OF HOMEMADE MODELS

A variety of models for laboratory work or demonstrations can be made by students or teachers. These models are usually made of simple materials, such as cardboard, balsa wood, soda straws, plywood, plastic, or pegboard. The selecting, planning, making, and using of these models can be a learning experience that justifies the time it takes. A number of the books listed in Appendix C are good sources for ideas about the actual construction of such models. Below are the instructions for sample models which can be constructed in the classroom.

A PERCENT COMPUTER

This device can be used to compute the answer for all three types of percentage problems. The simple materials consist of a piece of string, a sheet of graph paper, and a piece of stiff cardboard. The best graph paper to use is one with ten squares to the inch.

Mount the graph paper on the cardboard. Draw a horizontal line, $\overline{AB}$, at the bottom of the graph paper 100 units long. This line represents a percent scale and should be labeled in convenient units from 0 at the left to 100 at the right. At A (the 0 point) draw the perpendicular to $\overline{AB}$. Locate C on this perpendicular so that $\overline{AC}$ is 100 units long. Punch a hole at C and attach a string slightly longer than the diagonal of the sheet. Draw $\overline{BC}$. Draw lines parallel to $\overline{AB}$ at 10 unit intervals such that the segments between $\overline{AC}$ and $\overline{BC}$ will be 10 units long or multiples of 10. Label these lines at each end according to their length. The computer is now ready for use.

To find what percent 8 is of 40, find the horizontal line between $\overline{AC}$ and $\overline{BC}$ that is 40 units long. Locate the point that is 8 units to the right of $\overline{AC}$ on this line and place a pin at this point. Hold the string taut to form the straight line that passes through C and the pin point. The percent is then found where the string crosses $\overline{AB}$ the percent scale.

To find 20 percent of 40 hold the string taut across the 20 point on the percent scale. The point where it crosses the horizontal line that is 40 units long between $\overline{AC}$ and $\overline{BC}$ will be the answer, 8.

To find the number if 8 is 20 percent of it, hold the taut string across the 20 point on the percent scale. Locate the line which the string crosses exactly 8 units to the right of $\overline{AC}$. The length of this line between $\overline{AC}$ and $\overline{BC}$ is the answer, 40.

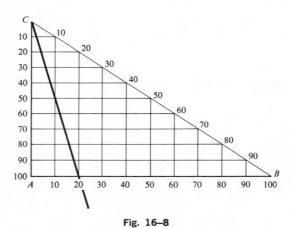

Fig. 16–8

For numbers above 100, it is necessary to increase the horizontal number scales while keeping the percent scale the same. For example, if the scale is doubled, the 10 line becomes a 20 line and each square will represent 2 units. The device will then represent numbers from 0 to 200. Other multiples may likewise be used to extend the scale. Another method of extending the scale is to cut strips of graph paper representing different scales and insert them on the scale at the appropriate place depending on the problem.

THE SPHEROMETER

A spherometer is a device for determining the diameter of a sphere. It may consist of a cylinder open at one end such as a tin can with a dowel as

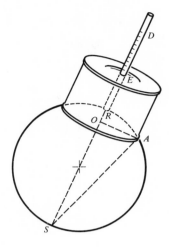

Fig. 16–9

a measuring rod at its center. When the open end of the cylinder is placed on a sphere the measuring rod indicates the height of the sphere inside the cylinder. In Fig. 16–9, OR, the height of the sphere in the cylinder, is measured on the measuring rod by the distance DE. The radius of the tin can, OA, is known. The diameter of the sphere, RS, can be computed with the proportion $OS/OA = OA/OR$. What is the basis for this proportion?

The measuring rod is usually calibrated by many measurements like the one above. Then points such as E are labeled according to the diameter of the sphere being measured, so that the diameter can be read without computation.

THE TOMAHAWK ANGLE TRISECTOR

A simple angle trisector can be cut out of cardboard, plywood, or plastic. The device has the shape shown in Fig. 16–10. It is somewhat similar to a carpenter's square. A circle is drawn with the center at T and radius r. Then DR is tangent to the circle at D and thus is perpendicular to the diameter FTD. A convenient length for $\overline{DR}$ is 7 times the length of the radius. The diameter is extended the length of the radius to E. The device is cut along arbitrary curves GH and RE to lend support to it.

The use of this device is shown in Fig. 16–11. Place point E on one side of the angle to be trisected. Slide the device until the circle is tangent to the other side of the angle and RD is coincident with the vertex of the angle. Then the points C and D locate points of the trisection lines. The proof of the trisection is based on congruent right triangles, $\triangle OAC \cong \triangle ODC \cong \triangle ODE$.

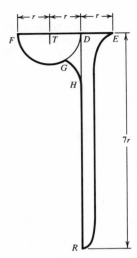

Fig. 16–10

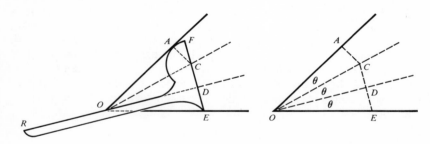

Fig. 16–11

SELECTION OF A MODEL

In selecting a model for purchase or construction, the teacher should keep in mind the objective he wishes to attain and the concepts he wishes to represent.

In evaluating a specific model, one should ask the following questions:

Does the model promote the discovery of an idea?

Does the model present the idea correctly?

Does the model permit the idea to be transferred from the concrete to the abstract?

Does the model add interest to an idea?

Can the model be easily stored, maintained, and repaired?

Is the cost of the model in time or money commensurate with its contribution?

Is the model designed for handling by the students?

Is the model large enough so that its important parts are clearly visible?

Is the idea which the student derives from the model significant?

Does the model do something which cannot be done as well as or better than something else?

Mathematics teachers should develop an almost instinctive feel for the use of models—in planning instruction or in answering student questions. When the conditions of a problem are not clear, the teacher should illustrate it concretely with the objects involved. When the relationship between factors, products, and terms of an algebraic expression are not clear, use a model. When a theorem about lines and planes seems difficult, have the students make a model of it. If an application of a quadratic equation does not seem real, toss a chalkboard eraser to a student and ask for the mathematical description of the eraser's path. When inequalities seem dull, set up a linear program for the production of the model toys displayed. In fact, use yourself as a model when you attack a new problem before the class. In these and in hundreds of other ways, models can be used to communicate mathematical ideas in an exciting, understandable way.

LEARNING EXERCISES

1. Use a commercial model to demonstrate a mathematical concept.
2. Use the criteria listed in this chapter to evaluate a commercial model.
3. Invent and make an original model to add meaning to a mathematical concept.
4. Review a research study of the effectiveness of models in teaching mathematics.
5. Make a selection of the models you would like to have available for your course. Find the current cost of these models.
6. Plan a laboratory lesson based on the use of a set of commercial models.
7. Write a set of ten performance-type test questions, each based on the use of a model.
8. Review the articles on models and manipulative devices found in the literature during the past year.

17

the role of audio-visual aids

Audio-visual aids are as essential for the mathematics teacher as spices are for the chef. They add the variety, the depth, and the breadth which make the learning process pleasant and meaningful.

The use of visual aids in learning mathematics is not new. Since primitive man first drew pictures on cave walls to communicate the number of animals he had seen, some form of visual referent has been used to represent mathematical ideas. Today, new concepts of learning and new materials have put renewed emphasis on the role of audio-visual aids in mathematics teaching.

The successful, dynamic teacher is always searching for ways to make his instruction more meaningful. He knows that through the proper use of audio-visual materials he may help build in students the number sense, the space perceptions, and the imagination needed to master mathematical ideas.

Although audio-visual materials are a necessary part in the curriculum of mathematics, they are not magic: teachers still have to teach, and students still have to study. But the teacher using audio-visual aids will be teaching in an atmosphere where meanings become clearer and where what the student learns will be more helpful in solving his future problems.

Mathematics by its very nature tends to be abstract, even though some areas, such as geometry, are based largely on visual representation. Despite the fact that the social functions of mathematics have increased in our society, the applications of mathematics are often far removed from the classroom topics. This creates problems of student motivation and learning that may be partially solved by the use of the right audio-visual material, at the right time, in the right way. If audio-visual materials and equipment are used properly, the result should be more correct and richer learning, an economy of time, and improved student retention.

Visual and audio materials, however, can be a waste of time and money if they are not used effectively. The question we must ask when selecting material is, "What *unique* contribution will this particular aid make toward better learning?" Aids should not be used just because they are fashionable, or because they are available, or because they fill in a time gap in a class period. Every teacher needs to recognize the unique contributions that audio-visual equipment and devices can make and on this basis select and use those most suitable in accomplishing aims.

THE FUNCTION OF AUDIO-VISUAL AIDS

Mathematics teachers use films, television, filmstrips, tapes, charts, pictures, projections, bulletin board displays, and sketches to attain the following goals:

1. *Visualize abstract ideas so that they have meaning.* The meaning of a number such as π, a word such as *probability,* a process such as division, a theorem such as the right-triangle relationship may be enriched by visual representations. Typical films that serve this purpose are *The Meaning of Pi, Meaning of Long Division, How's Chances?,* and *Possibly So, Pythagoras,* and the filmstrip *Thinking in Symbols.*

2. *Illustrate applications of mathematics in our world.* Although field trips are best for seeing mathematics in action, they require time and community resources that are not always available. Typical materials which add interest to mathematical ideas by emphasizing applications include the following: the film *Mathematics of the Honeycomb,* the filmstrip *Indirect Measurement,* the chart *Life Insurance,* and the graph *Population Growth.*

3. *Bring to the school and the classroom important firsthand accounts of new activities in mathematics and mathematics education.* By tape recording (or obtaining the tapes of) speeches at state and national conferences, the teacher can bring the thoughts of others, expressed in their own words, to the classroom. Films such as those of the Mathematical Association of America Series bring students into contact with great living mathematicians, such as Richard Courant and George Polya.

4. *Build favorable attitudes toward and interest in mathematics.* The uniqueness of mathematics—its power, its elegance, its artistic side—is seldom dealt with in textbooks. Visual materials may be unusually dramatic or attractive as presented in films such as *Donald in Mathmagic Land,*

filmstrips such as *Optical Illusions,* or charts such as the *Tree of Knowledge.*

5. *Present the history of mathematics and other enrichment topics.* Many topics and historical incidents can be used to enrich the learning of mathematics. Especially appropriate for enrichment are the films *Historical Introduction to Algebra, Koenigsberg Bridges, Stretching Imagination,* and *How Man Learned to Count,* as well as the chart *Mathematics Calendar.*

6. *Illustrate the discovery of relationships or principles.* We learn best those things which we discover through our own experiences. Films often show how relationships can be discovered. See, for instance, *Patterns in Mathematics; How to Multiply Fractions;* and *Volumes of Cubes, Prisms, Cylinders.* Audio tapes or overhead projectuals with worksheets are also useful for presenting these experiences because they provide activities for the student.

7. *Present dynamic ideas that depend on motion.* Motion pictures which use animation or slow motion can give dramatic illustrations of mathematical ideas. Examples of such films are *Locus, A Mathematician and a River,* and *Slide Rule.*

8. *Correlate mathematics with other subjects by presenting supplementary materials.* Topics presented in the mathematics textbook are usually limited to definite mathematical principles. A film such as *Global Concepts in Maps,* a filmstrip such as *Vectors,* a chart such as *Math at General Electric* have mathematical aspects interwoven with the topic involved.

9. *Provide complex drawings of three-dimensional effects.* Visualization and spatial relationships are often difficult to achieve with textbook or blackboard drawings. Three-dimensional stereographs such as *Solid Geometry;* films such as *Rectilinear Coordinates, Global Concepts in Maps,* and *Triple Integration;* charts such as *Polyhedrons* are highly realistic in portraying three dimensions.

10. *Teach how to solve problems.* Since it is extremely difficult to teach problem solving, any supplementary aid should be welcomed. Examples of films which deal with this skill are *Let Us Teach Guessing, Variations: A Lesson in Reading,* and *The Language of Mathematics.*

11. *Introduce a new subject or unit.* The beginning of a new course often sets the pattern for the year. Films such as *Mysterious X* and *Language of Algebra* and the filmstrip *Introduction to Plane Geometry* give a broad picture of the nature and use of the subject.

12. *Summarize or review units within a course.* At the end of a unit a new view of the entire unit may be possible with a film such as *Measurement* or a filmstrip such as *Deductive Thinking* or a chart such as *Number Systems.*

13. *Show how to teach a topic.* Many visual materials picture objects that would have greater meaning if the student could handle the object pictured himself. These materials, though, are useful to teachers in providing teaching hints. For example, the film *What Are Fractions?* shows how one can clarify the meaning of fractions by the manipulation and cutting of objects. Audio tapes or, when available, the much more expensive video tapes of classroom presentations provide the teacher with a wider range of effective teaching techniques and ideas for better instruction.

SOME AVAILABLE AUDIO-VISUAL AIDS

The support of federal funds for the purchase of teaching aids and the modern emphasis on audio and visual experiences have resulted in the growth of available visual materials for mathematics. These new aids include:

1. *Motion picture films.* The great number of mathematics films available is indicated by the bibliography in the December 1963 issue of *The Mathematics Teacher,* which lists more than 150 titles. Since that time a great number of new films have been produced. Current films are reviewed in *The Mathematics Teacher* and other professional journals. These films are able to show reenacted events, use animation, and present situations which cannot be presented through text material alone. Hence, films should be a unique means of bringing historical events, dynamic variation of conditions, demonstration lessons, or applications of mathematics into the classroom.

2. *Filmstrips.* Filmstrips are inexpensive and can be used with great flexibility. The frames may be shown at any desired speed, allowing for appropriate class discussion. Filmstrips are effective in presenting ideas that do not require motion. They seem most effective when they present material in a modified programmed format so that the viewers respond to questions posed by individual frames. Some filmstrip series have been prepared to accompany a specific mathematics text. Individual slides (2 inches × 2 inches in size) allow greater flexibility than do filmstrips, but they must be prepared by the teacher (see Appendix B).

3. *Pictures.* Collections of pictures on almost any topic can be gathered quickly from current magazines. Having them mounted and filed makes them readily available for use on bulletin boards or for opaque projections. Students should participate actively in adding to the collection. Writing appropriate captions for each picture adds to their effectiveness.

4. *Charts, Maps, Graphs.* These materials are usually available free or at very low cost from commercial companies or governmental agencies. The weekly graphs of current statistics issued by the Conference Board of New York are available to teachers upon request. Large corporations such as the Ford Motor Company, General Motors, General Electric, Chrysler Motors, and IBM have frequently published free mathematics charts (see Appendix C).

5. *Stereographs.* To add a three-dimensional effect to a picture, several techniques are possible. Duplicate pictures are taken by two cameras whose lenses are as far apart as our eyes. Then these pictures are printed in different colors or by polarizing the light. When the pictures are viewed through the proper equipment, called a stereoscope, they give the appearance of depth that we perceive when viewing the actual situation. This technique seems especially appropriate in learning to "see" three dimensions in a geometric figure or in learning to represent a three-dimensional object with a two-dimensional drawing. Some new geometry texts furnish views of this type to assist the learner in visualizing space geometry.

6. *Television.* Individual commercial or educational television pro-

grams occasionally provide an opportunity for students to see good mathematics developed by expert teachers. Closed-circuit television provides an opportunity for the school system to make available unique lessons or courses to many students. Video tape recording of classes, demonstrations, or events extends this use of television.

7. *Tape recorders.* Tapes of lessons may provide review material for weak students or original lessons for students who have been absent. The best use of tape is the planned lesson. For this a student is provided with work sheets geared to the specific tape. Earphones allow individualization of lessons even in a crowded classroom, and tape tables—tables seating four to twenty students with earphones provided at each station—allow the teacher to carry on two lessons in the classroom at once: taped lessons for some students; for others, direct work with the teacher.

Preparation of taped lessons requires considerable skill and practice on the part of the teacher. It is usually best for the teacher to outline in detail what he wishes to cover in such a lesson, to develop a worksheet from the outline, and to record his instructions as he works the worksheet problems for himself. In this way he can pace his material. The teacher should not be afraid of silent periods (when students are working problems), and he should often provide answers so that students can see their mistakes as soon as possible. Finally, the teacher should personalize his lessons by injecting humor into them just as he would in the classroom.

You need only use a taped lesson once to find how effective it can be. Student interest is concentrated, distracting sounds are shut out by the earphones, and neighboring students are not bothered. And, best of all, each student is working in a one-to-one relationship with the teacher. Taped lessons can extend the individual grouping used so successfully at the elementary school level but essentially lost in secondary schools.

8. *Television tapes and individual film-loop motion pictures.* The previous comments about sound-taped lessons extend to the use of such individualizing materials as video television tapes and 8-millimeter film loops. Each of these allows a student to view a lesson as many times as is necessary to understand the content. Some of the modern schools with this type of equipment have special sections of the library or rooms between classrooms (supervised through windows) where such materials may be used by students. As has been the case before, mathematics is lagging far behind science in the development of films and tapes.

9. *Overhead projector.* The overhead projector is a tool almost unique among audio-visual aids in its special contribution to mathematics. Many teachers prefer it to the chalkboard. The teacher can write on blank acetate, projecting his material on the screen, or he can use previously prepared transparencies or commercial projectuals. Overlays allow sequential development of a diagram or dissection of a confusing array to show basic parts. Some teachers even use the overhead projector and chalkboard simultaneously, exposing a complete diagram but tracing on the blackboard only a key feature. Thus, when the machine is shut off, only the desired feature remains. This is an especially useful technique in proving congruency when triangles overlap.

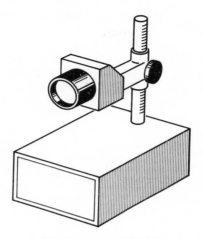

Fig. 17–1. An overhead projector.

While commercial transparencies—including plastic slide rules—are available, teachers can modify them or construct their own slides to suit their special needs.

There are four primary advantages of the overhead projector over other projected visual aids:

1. The projector is used in front of the class, so that the teacher faces and talks directly to the class. The teacher sees the material projected and, at the same time, maintains eye contact with his class.

2. The projected image is bright enough so that it can be seen under normal classroom lighting conditions.

3. The teacher operates the projector and thus maintains control of class attention. The operation of the projector requires only a flick of a switch.

4. A variety of transparencies is available since they can easily be made by the teacher or purchased from commercial producers. Complete sets of projectuals are available for almost any school mathematics topic.

The overhead projector is used in several ways. One involves the use of clear acetate and a nylon pen. The teacher writes or draws on the acetate with the pen much as he would on the chalkboard. The image of his writing is then projected in magnified size on the screen behind him. Thus, lesson development, step-by-step problem solving, or the presentation of an assignment is possible. The material can be erased with a damp cloth and the acetate sheets used for another lesson.

Another use of the overhead projector involves the presentation of material by silhouettes. The shadow of an opaque object or piece of paper will give projections of shapes such as triangles, graphs, or patterns. A variation of this shadow projection is the step-by-step presentation of prepared material by a sliding mask. A sheet of paper will mask material so that the teacher can present material in a proper sequence or direct attention to a given point.

Another major use of the overhead projector is to present transparencies prepared prior to the class session. These transparencies, called projectuals, may be prepared in several ways. Written material may be typed directly on an acetate sheet or written with a grease pencil or nylon pen. Pictures or text material may be copied by a commercial copying machine. Some of these copying devices will also duplicate material in color.

In mathematics discussions much use can be made of overlays which superimpose multiple images upon each other. These overlays consist of a series of transparent sheets attached by hinges so that they can be projected in a prearranged sequence. For example, the intersection of the graphs of a series of inequalities can be built up by first projecting the grid and axes alone, then showing one graph in a specific color, then a second graph in a different color. The final projection now shows clearly the intersection of the truth sets of the two inequalities.

The overhead projector can also demonstrate change when conditions are varied. Suppose that one transparency projects a circle and a second transparency projects an angle. By moving the second transparency over the first, one can show how an angle intercepts arcs of the circle in different positions. This technique can also be used to illustrate the relationships between loci and similar polygons, and the graphs of systems of equations.[1]

Topics for which transparencies have been found particularly useful include the following:

> Graphs of equations and inequalities.
> The number line and nomographs.
> Venn diagrams illustrating unions and intersections of sets.
> Geometric figures for two- and three-dimensional space.
> Reading slide rule scales.
> Geometric constructions and loci.
> Flow charts and computer programs.
> Conic sections—graphs, drawing with a linkage formed by paper folding.
> Systems of equations and inequalities—intersections.
> Number patterns such as the sieve of Eratosthenes.
> Curves of space travel.
> Measurement—accuracy, precision, angle measurement, areas, volumes.
> Perspective drawings of three-dimensional objects.
> The wrapping function.
> Geometric representation of algebraic expressions.
> Tables of trigonometric functions, square roots, logarithms.
> Tests and answers to test questions or assignments.
> Student papers for illustration of excellent work or common errors.

[1] For further information see the pamphlet by Stephen Krulik and Irwin Kaufman, *How to Use the Overhead Projector in Mathematics Education* (Washington, D.C.: NCTM, 1966).

10. *Opaque Projector.* The opaque projector, or stereopticon, allows projection of the colored image of a non-transparent object. Thus, this instrument allows projection of a student's paper on the screen whereas the overhead projector must utilize transparent projectuals and could not reproduce the paper without an intervening transparency reproduction process. It is especially useful in focusing class attention on student work or on material in current periodicals. Additional uses include enlarging graphs and tables, slide rules and other scales, architectural plans and pictures. Formerly a widely used classroom device, the opaque projector has been largely replaced by the currently favored overhead projector.

11. *Bulletin Boards.* A bulletin board display is one of the least expensive instructional aids available and at the same time one of the most versatile. It has one major advantage—it may present a display for several days. In view of the fact that displays are seen by all students using the room, it is important that the display be appropriate.

There are several other ways in which the bulletin board plays a unique role:

a. It involves the active, cooperative participation of students and teacher in planning and producing attractive displays.

b. It emphasizes enrichment by presenting further information about supplementary topics, historical events, famous mathematicians, unusual ideas, current applications, and challenging problems.

c. It is a means of presenting materials to attain objectives that cannot be taught directly—objectives such as values, interests, appreciations, curiosities, and study habits.

d. The preparation of a display provides a means of stimulating creativity, craftsmanship, and communication skill. By planning, organizing, and completing a display, students learn to work together, to share ideas, and to accept responsibility.

Whether a bulletin board display attains these purposes depends largely on the teacher. Displays should be an integral part of his instruction and students must be aware of their responsibility for learning from the displays. Here are some basic principles to follow in preparing displays that will attract viewers and arouse interest:

a. The display must be *attractive*. This can be accomplished through the use of color, novel pictures, unusual framing, unique titles, and tricky questions. Background material such as colored construction paper, colored corrugated cardboard, burlap, felt, or cork add color and softness to the display.

b. The display should have *simplicity, clarity, and unity.* Proper titles few key ideas, flow lines, and simple arrangements—even blank spaces—tell a story.

c. The arrangements should be *interesting*. Informal balance, striking contrasts, variations in shapes and colors add interest.

d. The display should be *timely* and changed frequently. An old display fades into the background like wallpaper.

The success of a display is highly dependent on appropriate and clever titles and captions. Titles should be brief, eye-catching, and meaningful.

These titles can be formed by commercial letters, cutout letters, stencils, or writing. Titles may be written with a brush pen, string, pipe cleaners, spray paint, or adhesive tape. Three-dimensional effects can be attained by mounting letters and pictures on pins, spools, boxes, or paper cups.

Topics for bulletin boards are many and varied. The headings and titles listed below are merely suggestive.

a. Central themes of mathematics, such as "The Number Family," "Basic Mathematical Laws," "Size, Shape, and Similarity."

b. Mathematical applications, such as "Mathematics in Nature," "Musical Mathematics," "Mathematics in the Machine Shop."

c. Habits, attitudes, or appreciations, such as "There Is Math in Your Future," "How to Make Mathematics Easy," "What's My Line?"

d. Enrichment topics, such as "Topology, the Mathematics of the Magician," "The Fourth Dimension," "How to Take a Chance."

e. Recreational exhibits, such as puzzles, problems, fallacies, or illusions.

Bulletin board materials are all around you. In addition to the usual display materials, colored paper, tacks, and pins, such materials as boxes, graph paper, balsa wood, cellophane, and many others should be considered. Usually, the art department will be ready and willing to provide ideas and support for the classroom teacher.[1]

12. *The Chalkboard.* Next to the textbook, the most commonly used aid of the mathematics teacher is the chalkboard. Mathematics teachers have traditionally used this primary tool in the same manner as Socrates and Archimedes used sketches to solve mathematics problems. The chalkboard provides an immediate and effective mode of presentation of material. Its uses are wide and varied, and teachers should consider these uses in developing and executing their plans. The chalkboard is uniquely suited to make the following contributions:

a. Provide a medium for the participation of the student in class activities.

b. Emphasize major points by outlining and summarizing. It permits a point-by-point development and a reference as the lesson progresses.

c. Present assignments, problems, or discussion questions.

d. Combine a visual and oral presentation of ideas.

Since many teachers use the chalkboard in a haphazard fashion, here are some suggestions for improved uses:

a. *Write clearly, neatly, and correctly.* Combine writing and speaking. Do not erase too quickly. Use very large figures so that all members can see them.

b. *Make all drawings simple and accurate.* Use stencils and drawing instruments to give pleasing, accurate figures. Add realism by giving attention to perspective and color. Add interest with captions and cartoons.

c. *Arrange frequent student participation in chalkboard work.* Board

---

[1] For further ideas see *Bulletin Board Displays for Mathematics* by Donovan A. Johnson and Charles Lund. Belmont, California: Dickenson Publishing Company, Inc., 1967.

work has the advantage of requiring physical and emotional involvement as well as mental activity. Select a student to act as class secretary.

   d. *Use colored chalk to identify key ideas, to add attractiveness, to emphasize common elements, contrasts, and relationships.* For example, use color to distinguish between symbols of operations and signs of positive or negative numerals. In writing numerals in different bases identify the base by the color of the numeral. In drawings use color to identify corresponding parts or measures in formulas. Color can be used to distinguish between coefficient and exponent, conditions in loci constructions, characteristic and mantissa of logarithms, factors, and terms.

   e. *Have adequate materials available.* A variety of available chalkboard tools can be used to improve board work:

> Straight edges, meter sticks, or yardstick
> Geometric figures, including triangle, rectangles, and polygons
> Stencils for perspective drawings of three-dimensional objects
> Stencils for grids for graphing
> Drawing instruments, including compasses and protractor
> T-square and linkages
> Chalkholders

   Chalkboards themselves now come in a variety of material and colors. The new materials include porcelain steel, frosted glass, formica, plastic paint on wood, linoleum, cement asbestos, and silicon carbide as well as the traditional slate. Slate continues to be preferred because of its durability, its texture, and its reflective qualities but it has the disadvantage of being available in only one drab color. Steel has the advantage of having magnets adhere to its surface.

   It is difficult to determine how much chalkboard space is adequate in a mathematics classroom. With modern duplicating facilities and the overhead projector replacing some of the functions of the chalkboard, there is less demand for board space than formerly. And space must also be provided for the wealth of material available for exhibit on bulletin boards, pegboards, book shelves, or exhibit shelves. However, there should be much chalkboard space available at the front of the room for developing daily lesson material. One way to increase the amount of board space is to use sliding panels.

   It is likely that every mathematics classroom needs a grid marked on the chalkboard for graphing. If this is painted or scratched on one section of the chalkboard, that section can't be used for other purposes. It would seem more suitable to obtain a stencil on a plastic cloth which rolls up like a window shade. When this stencil is placed on the board and dusted with chalky erasers, the chalk dust forms a usable grid. This permits the placing of grids on several sections in a very short time. These grids can then be used for class discussion, for tests, or for student board work. After being used, the grid can be erased. Some teachers prefer a painted pegboard for graphing; others use a grid drawn with semi-permanent chalk.

   f. *Use special techniques for board work.* Teachers have found a variety of ways of enhancing board work, such as the following:

(1) Use an opaque or overhead projector to give outlines for copying complex drawings from a text or picture.

(2) Draw complex illustrations before the class starts to avoid wasting class time.

(3) Erase or clean the chalkboard carefully so that old material does not distract from the material being presented.

(4) Enlarge drawings to desired size by the use of a pantograph or proportional squares or by projections.

(5) Draw semi-permanent lines, using soft chalk soaked in a saturated sugar solution. The lines will not be erased with a chalk eraser but will wipe off with a damp cloth. Use this chalk to draw coordinate axes, number lines, triangles, circles, parallelograms, or other figures used repeatedly.

(6) Use old lipstick holders as holders for colored chalk to reduce finger stains.

(7) Mount drawer knobs or empty spools to meter sticks, T-squares, or templates to facilitate holding them for board drawings.

(8) Use small suction cups to hold fixed points for drawing circles, ellipses, or spirals.

(9) Add realism to drawings representing three-dimensional objects by having the actual objects on display.

(10) Draw horizontal lines from left to right; vertical lines are drawn downward; free-hand circles are drawn with a stiff arm so that the shoulder acts as a center.

(11) Use vanishing points to establish proper perspective. Accent the nearest edge of an object with heavy solid lines. Use shading, dotted lines, overlap to accent the third dimension.

(12) Speak to the class, not to the blackboard. Combine writing and talking so that the board work has maximum interest and meaning.

(13) Use stencils, templates, drawing instruments so that your drawings are accurate and attractive.

(14) Dissolve a teaspoon of show-card colors and a tablespoon of Bon-Ami in one cup of water to get chalkboard paint that is colorful and at the same time can be removed easily. Avoid all oil or wax base colors for board work. Have students with drawing skill place colorful drawings on the board related to the season, holidays, or special events.

THE PROPER CHOICE AND USE OF AUDIO-VISUAL MATERIALS

It is obvious from the long list of available materials and equipment that one of the basic problems of the classroom teacher is that of choice. Which mode of presentation will be most effective and will best promote learning? This choice is an extremely important one. Usually there is no one best way. In fact, use of a combination of devices is occasionally appropriate. The overhead projector may be used to project a complicated geometric diagram on the chalkboard. Special parts of the diagram may then be traced in chalk directly on the blackboard. When the projector is turned off the students' attention may focus on the chalkboard display or on a mock-up of the problem at hand.

It is essential that the mathematics teacher carefully *select* the materials to be used. The excessive use of audio-visual aids may cause the students to become overdependent on physical representation and unable to work with the symbolic representation of an abstraction, a procedure so necessary in mathematics. The improper use of teaching aids may create confusion and misconception of mathematical principles. The indiscriminate use of these aids may occasionally result merely in entertainment. They should be used only when they are the most effective means available for attaining an objective. Here are some guidelines:

1. *Select the proper material or equipment to be used at a certain time to attain a specified objective.* Think carefully about supportive aids in planning units. Make yourself aware of the wide selection. Find titles in catalogs, film guides, reviews in the *Mathematics Teacher*. Select wisely.

2. *Prepare yourself for the use of the audio-visual material.* Become familiar with the content of visual material. Preview a film or filmstrip, read the teacher's guide if there is one, try transparencies on the overhead projector.

3. *Prepare the classroom.* Every modern classroom needs the facilities and equipment that make possible the optimum conditions for the frequent use of a variety of materials. Before the class meets, check to see that all needed materials are at hand and that equipment is in working order.

4. *Prepare the class.* Tell your students the purpose of the learning aid, what it will do, why it is used at this time, what they will learn from seeing it, and how they should be able to apply the information gained. Often a written guide prepared for the students increases the effectiveness of a learning aid.

5. *Present the material.* Be sure that each student hears and sees each important item. Discuss the items so that the visual or audio learning is related to the lesson at hand and to the symbolic representation that will later be used.

6. *Provide follow-up activities.* Discussions, readings, reports, projects, tests, and reshowings are needed if maximum learning is to result. Wherever possible, provide opportunity to apply the information learned.

7. *Evaluate the effectiveness of the material.* A card-file system is helpful. Over a period of time you will accumulate what are for you the best materials for each lesson. This evaluation should include remarks on the quality and content of the material as well as the response of the students to its use.

DEFICIENCIES OF VISUAL AIDS FOR MATHEMATICS

The quality of visual aids now being produced has improved greatly in the past few years. Unfortunately, many of the visual aids now available, especially the older productions, have deficiencies such as the following:

1. *Treatment of topics exactly parallels textbook treatment.* Often the

language and drawings are identical to that of a text, thus providing no new insights.

2. *Too much material is covered in a single film or filmstrip.* Many one-reel, ten-minute films cover a complete topic or unit.

3. *Applications and illustrations are lacking in interest to the student.* Installment buying applied to buying a car is more pertinent to high school students than furnishing a doctor's office.

4. *Drawings are too frequently used in place of photographs.* Photographs are hard to get for all ideas covered but are much more interesting and realistic.

5. *Commentary and situations are unrealistic.* If youths are acting in the picture, the action and language needs to be quite informal.

6. *Showing cannot be a complete substitute for concrete experience.* Observation is never as forceful as actual participation.

7. *Presentations are sometimes used as substitutes for good teaching.* Visual aids are sharp tools and require as much planning and organizing as a verbal presentation. They are not produced to replace the teacher.

8. *Available audio-visual aids are not comprehensive for any subject or topic.*

9. *Some audio-visual aids contain mathematical inaccuracies.* While such inaccuracies may not result in his rejecting an aid, the teacher should be aware of them so that they may be corrected. Many teachers like to use errors in films or texts as the basis for class discussion.

The creative teacher instinctively reaches out for an audio-visual aid to supplement verbal instruction. He knows what aids will add to his lesson so that he has them on tap when needed. The teacher who has a mature feeling for audio-visual aids and who gives careful attention to what works for him will soon learn that these aids should be part of the total approach to a lesson. While the overuse of aids is a danger, it is a far less common problem than failure to use available materials when they can add to a presentation. It is a rare mathematics lesson that cannot be improved with the use of an audio-visual aid.

LEARNING EXERCISES

1. View a mathematics film and write a critical evaluation of it. How can this film be used most effectively?
2. Prepare an overhead projectual with overlays to illustrate a mathematical concept.
3. Make a bulletin board display on a mathematical topic.
4. Make a collection of charts available from industry, government, publishing companies, or professional organizations.
5. Have a tape recording or a video tape recording made of one of your mathematics lessons. Use this recording to write a critical self-analysis of your lesson.
6. Make a list of chalkboard equipment, its cost, and source for the mathematics classroom.

7. Review a research study of the effectiveness of visual aids in teaching mathematics.
8. Write a lesson plan which coordinates the use of several different types of audio-visual aids.
9. Investigate how computer-mediated instruction uses audio-visual aids.
10. Prepare a series of overhead projectuals for a unit by copying material in several ways.

18

the role of
the textbook

The mathematics textbook is a major factor in determining what mathematics topics are taught and how they are taught. A textbook has often dictated the scope, the sequence, and even the pace of the mathematics program. Thus, the textbook is a powerful means of determining whether the new mathematics is brought into the schools or whether the old is maintained. This is all in addition to its basic function as a learning tool in the classroom. Its importance increases when instruction is inadequate. However, the mathematics curriculum should not be determined by the text; rather, the text should be selected on the basis of prior curriculum decisions.

Since the mathematics textbook is such a powerful influence in the mathematics classroom, it may be an invaluable servant or an intolerable master—depending upon the intelligence with which it is handled. Too often, it is overused. The greater variety of new textbooks available and the continuing development of new school mathematics curricula means an increasingly frequent change of textbooks.

The mathematics textbook has a unique role in the classroom. The reasons are:

1. Direct experience, visual aids and classroom instruction cannot provide all the instruction necessary. Some of this instruction must be covered by reference to a textbook.

2. Teachers have too many pupils, preparations, and extracurricular assignments to make it possible for them to plan and write complete units and daily lessons without the aid of a text.

3. Mathematics requires a sequential study treatment, and the textbook provides a useful aid to this approach.

4. For mathematics teachers with an inadequate background in mathematics and in the methods of teaching mathematics, the textbook is a substitute (*albeit a poor one*) for this inadequacy.

5. Many schools are limited in resources such as library books, concrete and visual learning aids, community resources, duplicating equipment; and so the text provides the basic and sometimes the only resource.

6. Learning mathematics depends on the mastery of concepts and skills. Students may gain this mastery by performing the exercises of the text.

7. Mathematics requires a storehouse of facts, theorems, formulas, and definitions to which reference can be frequently made. In this way, the mathematics text is as necessary as a dictionary or encyclopedia in English or social studies.

THE CONTRIBUTION OF A GOOD TEXTBOOK

The superior mathematics textbook offers the following aids to teaching and learning:

1. It provides most of the content for a course. As such, it should contain appropriate, mathematically correct topics presented in a readable and orderly fashion.

2. It presents topics in a manner that builds understanding of concepts, structure, problem solving, and computations. In other words, it is a tool to be used in attaining the objectives of the course.

3. It provides the exercises, the experiences, the directions for attaining mastery through practice, review, application, and thought-provoking questions.

4. It provides a means for independent study and, hence, is useful for assignments, make-up work, remedial instruction, and independent study.

5. It provides a means of making provision for individual differences. By giving assignments tailored to different ability, by providing suggested enrichment materials, by permitting independent acceleration, the textbook can be a source of satisfying, challenging experiences.

6. It provides a compact reference book which is useful in building the structure of mathematics. Tables, definitions, formulas, graphs, sample problems, theorems, and proofs are available to make problem solving efficient.

7. It provides a basis for achievement testing. Chapter tests, review tests, practice tests, and accompanying semester tests provide ready-made devices for evaluation of content mastery.

8. It brings directly to the student the exposition of the writer or writers, often major figures in mathematics and mathematics education or master teachers.

9. It forms the basis for classroom instruction, which may and should often follow a different but essentially parallel development. In this way the student is offered various approaches to a single topic.

THE PROPER USE OF MATHEMATICS TEXTBOOKS

Too often the text is misused, overused, or, at the other extreme, ignored. In this latter connection, many school administrators sometimes believe that they are introducing a new program by adopting a new textbook—when actually the teaching remains unchanged and the text is misused or ignored.

The following suggestions are given for the proper use of a textbook for the typical mathematics class:

1. A selection of topics to be taught should be made from the text. Only in rare circumstances should the entire content of a text be presented in a single course. Textbook authors purposely include more content than necessary so as to give a teacher the possibility of selection.

2. A decision should be made as to what topics which are not in the text should be included in the course. Every textbook needs to be supplemented by up-to-date material from sources such as library books, pamphlets, and other texts.

3. The text should be used as a resource and reference book. Rather than repeating the examples of the text or reading the text to the class, the competent teacher uses different examples and different explanations.

4. The text is used by students as well as teachers as a source for questions, exercises, reading material, and reference material. Students are expected to read the text, to answer the questions thoughtfully, to work the exercises, and to find information. At the same time the text should suggest problems, topics, or exercises related to independent study and suggest further study in other source books.

5. The students should be given instruction in how to use the textbook—for example, where to find material, how to read the narrative, how to use chapter summaries and tests, how to review, and how to solve problems.

6. The narrative or exercises of the text should be assigned with the students' differing abilities and needs in mind. The low-ability student works a greater proportion of easy problems and reviews frequently. The high-ability student works fewer and more difficult exercises, The suggested enrichment material, outside reading, references, or projects are used according to the interests of the students.

7. The assignment of textbook exercises is done carefully. The purpose of each assignment should be to improve the understanding, accuracy,

efficiency, and retention of the students. These purposes must be made clear to the student who should never think of homework as mere drudgery.

8. Answers to at least some exercises should be provided to students working exercises so that they can know what success they are having. Correct answers then reinforce correct methods while errors suggest further study of concepts and rechecking computation.

9. The textbook exposition is supplemented by instruction that provides discovery exercises, audio-visual illustrations, references, and local applications.

10. The textbook exercises also are supplemented with learning activities, reports, projects, games, and surveys.

11. The textbook tests are supplemented with other tests such as unit tests, reading tests, diagnostic tests, essay tests, performance tests, and open-book tests.

12. The resources of the text are used to enhance instruction. The projects, references, historical sidelights, and enrichment topics should be recognized to be of as great a significance as the explanations and exercises.

13. The references support teacher-requests for school purchases of additional library books and other supportive material. Additional textbooks provide the teacher with a valuable resource library to help him with planning and executing his program. They are a source of different strategies, discovery exercises, enrichment, and test items. Often texts are supplied by textbook companies as a service and in hopes of adoption. However, it is not ethical for the teacher to request "free" books purely for supplementary material. Whatever supplementary materials are needed should be purchased by the school.

WORKBOOKS AND LABORATORY MANUALS

Workbooks were very popular a generation ago. They provided the teacher with many drill exercises and saved him time in preparing material. They also saved the student time by eliminating the need to copy exercises. However, the workbooks' emphasis on rote manipulation at the expense of understanding caused them to be discarded.

Workbooks do, however, have many possible uses if they are of good quality and are used properly. Workbooks can contribute to instruction in the following ways:

1. Workbooks of different levels in a single class provide one way of meeting the problem of individual differences.

2. They permit individual work at varying rates.

3. Workbooks provide a varied testing program with progress ratings and keyed remedial exercises.

4. They supplement the textbook in building meaning as well as skills.

5. Workbooks often provide discovery activities for each student to complete. He can write his responses in specially provided places.

6. Workbooks have the advantage of being the student's own property. The student's own work is organized for him, providing him with a valuable tool for review.

7. Workbooks provide for independent work and orderliness in the overcrowded classroom.

8. They provide the teacher with duplicated material written by experts.

In the future workbook-type activities may be printed by computers. The computer would be programmed so that exercises could be tailored to previous student achievement.

Another type of workbook will probably be developed in the future. This is the laboratory manual. These manuals would provide discovery activities of the kind discussed in Chapter 22. For example, it would seem appropriate to approach the topic of probability by a series of experiments. These experiments would provide the intuitive, empirical experiences to which formulas, definitions, and abstractions would later make reference.

PROGRAMMED TEXTS

At the present time an entirely new type of textbook is provided by the programmed text. A programmed textbook is a book designed in such a way that it guides the student by a series of short steps to understand the material being presented. These short steps are in the form of brief expository statements and questions, to which the reader responds by writing the answers in spaces provided. The reader checks his answers against those supplied by the book (often hidden by a slide or presented on the following page). The questions provide the learner with immediate knowledge of his progress. In some programs, called branching programs, incorrect answers may direct the learner to remedial work, but the most important function of the question-and-answer process is the deeper involvement of the reader in the learning activity. He is virtually forced by the questions to share responsibility for learning.

These texts are being advocated because they require each student to react to each question. In this way he is "led" to discover a generalization. In addition, answers are given to each question or problem so that correct answers are reinforced and errors are corrected.

Programmed texts also are advocated because they permit independent study at whatever rate the individual wishes to establish. This seems an ideal way of providing for individual differences. The slow learner progresses at a rate appropriate to him, and the talented can be accelerated. Also, the text might be used by a student to make up work missed during an absence or for remedial instruction by the student having difficulty.

High hopes were held for these programmed texts when they were first developed. However, research on their effectiveness has shown that these texts have some negative effects. It is much too monotonous for students, especially slow learners, to work independently day after day writing answers to questions. To the superior student, the questions seem trivial and time consuming. To the slow learner, the reading is difficult and his motivation wanes. In addition, the mathematics of the early programmed texts was out of date.

This unsatisfactory experience with programmed texts does not mean that they are not useful. Rather, it means that new ways of using these texts must be devised. The texts themselves need improvement in content and format. Attempts are being made to correct these faults. Classroom discussion, experimentation, and group activities need to be combined with programmed texts. Perhaps their major role is to supplement instruction by presenting remedial work or enrichment topics. Another possible use is as a text for correspondence lessons or television courses.

As is true for all instructional aids, programmed texts do not replace the teacher. Instead they supply a new teaching tool to be used to improve instruction.

THE DANGERS OF "TEXTBOOK TEACHING"

Many teachers are strictly textbook teachers, more concerned to "cover" the text than to "uncover" ideas. Their focus is on the text rather than on the learner. Some of the following results have been noted:

1. The mathematics textbook becomes the mathematics curriculum. To bring the curriculum up to date merely means the adoption of a text with a recent copyright date.

2. The content of the text becomes the total content of the course, with rate and sequence rigidly prescribed. Some teachers even divide the number of pages of their text by the number of school days in the year to get the daily average rate. Confining the class content to that indicated by the text gives students a limited experience and increases the danger of poor attitudes and little appreciation of the elegance of mathematics.

3. The tendency of textbooks to emphasize given rules and procedures defeats the possibilities for discovery, independent thought, and intellectual curiosity. Even where discovery questions are included, the answers usually appear on the next page and students find it easier to look ahead than to discover the concept.

4. Student memorization of the language of the text and stated definitions and rules does not nourish skill in communication or the development of understanding. Students need experiences in stating generalizations in their own words even though these may lack precision.

5. The constant use of the textbook kills interest by its monotonous, formal treatment. Learning needs a variety of meaningful, interesting experiences.

6. The blind regimentation of textbook teaching loses the slow learner and bores the rapid learner. It is a discouraging experience to see teachers using the same text examples and exercises for all students in a given class.

7. The narrow emphasis on the text ignores the importance of objectives such as attitudes, problem solving, creativity, appreciations, or values.

These are the objectives which seem of greatest importance today. They are seldom attained and rarely tested by the textbook teacher.

From this discussion, it is apparent that "textbook teaching" is highly unsatisfactory. Dependence on the text and only the text is one mark of an unsuccessful teacher.

THE QUALITIES OF A GOOD MATHEMATICS TEXTBOOK

If a mathematics textbook is to serve its proper function, it must be a good text. It needs qualities such as the following:

1. *Topics:*

a. The topics are those that will attain the objectives of the course.

b. The topics allow selection to fit the sequence: building on the previous course and foreshadowing the course to follow.

c. The topics are appropriate in terms of interest, difficulty, and usefulness to the students electing the course.

d. The topics are in harmony with current curriculum emphasis.

2. *Mathematics:*

a. The mathematics is correct.

b. The structure of each topic is clear and concise.

c. The level of the rigor and precision is appropriate for the course.

d. The use of symbols is correct but reasonable, accurate, and not overly cumbersome.

3. *Language:*

a. The narrative is readable and comprehensible.

b. The abstractions and symbols are made meaningful.

c. The language is interesting and thought-provoking.

d. The definitions and explanations use only those terms which the student can be expected to understand.

4. *Pedagogy:*

a. Material is included to create interest and motivate learning.

b. Terminology and content is justified in terms the students understand so that they can see how it relates to them.

c. Material is included to make it possible to meet the needs of different levels of ability.

d. The strategies used are based on sound learning principles.

e. Concepts are introduced by providing opportunity for the student to discover ideas through reflective thinking, problem solving, experimentation, analysis, and generalization.

f. Tests for the evaluation of achievement by student and teacher are included.

5. *Mastery:*

a. Exercises emphasize reflective thinking and problem solving rather than manipulation.

b. Adequate exercises of different difficulty levels are included.

c. Review and remedial materials are included.

d. Some exercises require the student to generalize, others to consolidate concepts, and still others to improve skills or to apply what is learned to new situations.

6. *Enrichment:*

a. Enrichment topics are included in the text.

b. Suggestions are given for independent study.

c. Research topics, projects, and independent experiments are suggested.

d. References for enrichment reading are included.

7. *Aids to Learning:*

a. A teacher's manual with suggestions for teaching.

b. An answer key with worked solutions.

c. Achievement tests.

d. Overhead projectuals.

e. Accompanying workbook, laboratory manual, or programmed text.

8. *Physical Characteristics:*

a. The format of the pages is attractive and inviting.

b. The arrangement, headings, and type make the location of material convenient.

c. The use of color and illustrations is functional in terms of text content.

d. The size of the book is convenient.

The qualities listed above may be made into a checklist format and form the basis for the selection of a text. If each item is rated on a scale such as "inadequate," "satisfactory," or "excellent," information will be provided for the comparison of different texts. Each item should not be counted as equal in importance, and it is the responsibility of the teacher making the selection to determine the value of each attribute.

SELECTION OF A MATHEMATICS TEXTBOOK

Selection is not easy and should be done, ideally, by a group rather than an individual. The selection of a text should be only a part of an over-all curriculum study. Such a study should involve activities such as these:

1. The group which is to select a text should consist of teachers who are to use the text, teachers of a previous grade, teachers of a following course, a mathematician, and a curriculum coordinator.

2. The group should first decide what the contribution of mathematics is to their total educational program; that is, the text will be selected on the basis of the goals of the specific mathematics course involved.

3. They must be informed of the current trends in mathematics education. Only when the group understands the changes in school mathematics can they make an appropriate choice.

4. The text selected must be suited to the abilities and backgrounds of the students in the course. For a given grade, several texts should be selected according to the ability groupings for that grade.

5. The text selected must also be suited to the competencies of the teachers who will use the text. Often the text itself needs to be used for inservice training before it is used with students.

6. The committee members must be informed about all available texts. Then the criteria listed above should be applied to these texts.

7. The selection of a text for a specific course must be made with the program for the preceding course and the course to follow in mind. Criteria for the selection of a text series for several grades or courses are the same as for the selection of a single text.

8. If at all possible, several texts should be used on a trial basis. Only after a text is used can its strengths and weaknesses be accurately identified.

In making a textbook analysis, one will need to sample parts of the text for intensive study. Preferably, one should compare on the basis of the treatment of the same topics in each text. A checklist should be devised so that the different qualities of the texts may be compared. A value judgment will be the basis of the final choice.

Although a committee has been selected and has made its recommendations, the final decision and responsibility for a selection should probably be that of an administrator, preferably the mathematics supervisor or department head.

LEARNING EXERCISES

1. Compare a modern textbook with one of a generation ago. How do they differ?

2. Make a critical evaluation of a modern textbook in terms of the qualities listed in this chapter.

3. Observe a master teacher teach a lesson. What is the role of the textbook in his class?

4. Review a research study of the use of a programmed text.

5. Find a programmed text on a topic that is new to you. Use this text to study this topic. What are the strengths and weaknesses of this text?

6. Select a short topic. Write this topic in programmed format for inde-

pendent study. Have a class learn this topic by the independent study of your program.

7. Why isn't a textbook the basis for a mathematics curriculum? What aspects of a curriculum are provided by a textbook? What aspects are not provided?

8. What material do you need for the mathematics course you are currently teaching that is not in your text? Where can you obtain this material?

9. Make a collection of definitions from different texts to illustrate differing levels of mathematical sophistication.

10. Suppose that you were to write a textbook for the mathematics course you are now teaching or studying, how would it be different from the text you are now using?

11. Select a textbook and determine a readability score for it.

12. Make an analysis of the enrichment material of a given text. How should this material be used? For what level of ability is it most appropriate? Why?

13. Compare a modern text and an old text in terms of the percent of space devoted to exercises, explanatory material, enrichment, reviews, and tests.

19

the role of computers

One of the basic issues facing secondary school mathematics departments today relates to the role of the computer in the school program. Should mathematics courses teach computer programming? Should there be a special elective course on computers or should computer science be included in regular mathematics courses? Should the computer be used as a tool for solving problems? Should data processing be included in courses? Should the mathematics department have a computer trainer, a computer terminal, or a low-cost computer? Who should assume responsibility for teaching the role of the computer in society?

At the present time, mathematics departments are hurriedly installing computers and teaching computer science. Courses and units on computer programming are being introduced without thoughtful consideration or careful evaluation of the outcomes of this instruction. Some educators have proposed that computer programming can be a means of teaching mathematical concepts and problem-solving skills, while others propose that computers serve mainly in providing the students with a greater motivation to study mathematics. Often computer programs are developed because support is available and it is good publicity for the school to be teaching such an original field as computer science.

THE COMPUTER AND SOCIETY

The computer is causing a change in our society comparable to the change occasioned by the Industrial Revolution. Automation controlled by the computer is creating an economic upheaval in industry: data processing by the computer is making accounting and record keeping an automatic process; scientific research now has practically instantaneous analysis of data; linear programming by the computer is a means of decision making in government, education, military science, and business. Computer memories are being used to store entire courses for presentation to individual students. Medicine, law, and engineering are using information retrieval by the computer for diagnosis and decision making. And, of course, space travel and commercial plane scheduling are dependent on the computer. Linguists, psychologists, and historians are using the computer for research in their fields. Even music and poetry have been composed by the computer. In mathematics it has even been suggested that numerical analysis and the computer will make calculus, as it is presently taught, obsolete.

At the present time major computer facilities are being made available for schools through the use of computer terminals such as a teletypewriter. These terminals will make it possible for schools to use a computer for the solution of a variety of mathematical problems. At the same time, school records, schedules, research data, payrolls, and report cards can be processed by the computer. In addition, inexpensive trainers are available for instruction in computer programming. It is increasingly evident that schools must explore and utilize the capabilities of the computer to facilitate and extend educational processes.

In the near future the computer industry will need millions of trained personnel and thus will be providing vocations for today's students. The estimated market for computers and computer services is $9,000,000,000 in 1970. It is estimated that 3,000,000 people will be directly involved with electronic data processing by 1970. Therefore, at least a general knowledge of computer machines and their capabilities is a necessary part of secondary education.

Who should be teaching the role of the computer in our society? Logically, this should be the function of the social studies department. However, only the mathematics teachers are likely to have the background needed for this instruction. Hence, secondary mathematics teachers will need to teach a unit either in the social studies class or in their own mathematics class if this important aspect of current society is to be included in the secondary curriculum.

COMPUTER PROGRAMMING

Computer instruction today is usually divided into three categories: computer programming, data processing, and computer design. Teaching computer programming should be the responsibility of the mathematics department, while data processing could be taught in the business department. Computer design and maintenance should be the responsibility of the industrial arts department.

Computer programming should be part of the mathematics curriculum for several reasons:

1. The language of the computer is in terms of numeration systems with bases other than ten.

2. The logic circuits are based on truth tables and Boolean algebra.

3. Computer programs are frequently based on flow charts like those used in solving problems, so that the study of computers and the study of problem solving are mutually supportive.

4. The operations of the computer include all the operations of mathematics.

5. The code language of the computer is similar to the symbolic language of mathematics.

6. Mathematics teachers usually have the background and the interest necessary for successful instruction.

7. Knowledge of the techniques for this important tool helps to broaden the instructional base for the individual teacher.

Programming a problem for a computer is a relatively simple process, especially if a simple language such as BASIC, JOSS, or INTERCOM is used. More complex languages, such as FORTRAN, ALGOL, or COBAL, are needed for more extensive programs and more complex computers.

The first step in programming a problem consists of writing a flow chart or problem analysis similar to those illustrated in Chapter 6. A second step consists of learning the code language to be used. With these tools at hand, a problem can be programmed for computer analysis and solution.

The computer can perform many mathematical operations. It can add, subtract, multiply, divide, extract square roots, raise a number to a power, find the sine of a number, and so on. The computer performs these computations by evaluating formulas which are supplied in a program. Here are some examples in BASIC language. The typewriter symbol shown in the first column communicates the operation to the machine:

Symbol	Example	Meaning
$+$	$A + B$	Add B to A
$-$	$A - B$	Subtract B from A
$*$	$A * B$	Multiply B by A
$/$	A / B	Divide A by B
$\uparrow$	$X \uparrow 2$	Find X^2
$<>$	If $A <> B$, then	If $A \neq B$, then
INT( )	INT(A/B)	Integral value of A/B

Let us apply this language to the solution of a system of two simultaneous linear equations:

$$X + 2Y = -7$$
$$4X + 2Y = 5$$

We know that if $AX + BY = C$ and $DX + EY = F$ and $AE - BD \neq 0$, then

$$X = \frac{CE - BF}{AE - BD}, \text{ and } Y = \frac{AF - CD}{AE - BD}$$

are solutions of the system. If, however, $AE - BD = 0$, there is no unique solution.

The BASIC program for solving this problem is the following:

```
10 READ A, B, D, E
15 LET G = A * E − B * D
20 IF G = 0 THEN 65
30 READ C, F
37 LET X = (C * E − B * F) / G
42 LET Y = (A * F − C * D) / G
55 PRINT X, Y
60 GØ TØ 30
65 PRINT "NØ UNIQUE SØLUTIØN"
70 DATA 1, 2, 4, 2
80 DATA ⁻7, 5
85 DATA 1, 3, 4, ⁻7
90 END
```

Note that the program uses only capital letters, since teletype has only capitals. Also zero and the letter O are distinguished in that 0 is used for zero and Ø for the letter O. Each line of the program begins with a *line number* which identifies each statement of the program in addition to specifying the order in which the statements are to be performed by the computer. After each line number an English word denotes the type of statement.

The first statement (10) is a READ statement. It must be accompanied by one or more DATA statements. The DATA statements are 70, 80, and 85. In the program above, the computer will use statement 70 to assign 1 to A, 2 to B, 4 to D and 2 to E (as values for A, B, D, E of the given equation). With these values for A, B, D and E, the computer computes G (statement 20). If $G \neq 0$, then statement 30 reads the next entries in DATA (80): namely, -7 for C and 5 for F. Statements 37 and 42 provide the computer with instructions for carrying out the rest of the computations. The computer is now ready to solve the system.

$$X + 2Y = {}^-7$$
$$4X + 2Y = 5$$

Instruction 55 tells the computer to print the truth set. The addition of DATA in 85 gives the solution for these two additional systems.

$$
\begin{array}{lll}
X + 2Y = 1 & \text{and} & X + 2Y = 4 \\
4X + 2Y = 3 & & 4X + 2Y = {}^-7
\end{array}
$$

When these solution sets are printed, the computer has completed the program. Once the given program is printed by the typewriter, the programmer merely waits for a second or so until the computer operates the typewriter so that it prints the solutions.

The problems below illustrate other BASIC programs. The reader should be able to reconstruct the method of attack from the machine instructions.

Problem

What are the terms of the Fibonacci series and approximations to the golden ratio? (The golden ratio is approximated by the ratio of a term of the Fibonacci series to the following term.) The Fibonacci series is 1, 1, 2, 3, 5, 8, 13 ... where $F_{n+2} = F_n + F_{n+1}$ for $n \geq 1$.

Program
```
5 LET P = 0
6 LET B = 0
10 LET N = 1
11 LET X = 1
12 PRINT "THIS PRØGRAM PRINTS THE FIRST FIFTY TERMS ØF
   THE FIBØNACCI"
13 PRINT "SEQUENCE AND GIVES APPRØXIMATIØNS TØ"
14 PRINT "THE GØLDEN RATIØ"
15 PRINT
16 PRINT
17 PRINT "          RATIØ ØF TERM          RATIØ ØF TERM"
18 PRINT "          TØ PRECEDING           TØ FØLLØWING"
19 PRINT "TERM          TERM                  TERM"
20 PRINT "*****     **************      **************"
21 PRINT
22 PRINT "1                    —                      1"
23 LET B = N
24 LET X = X + B
25 LET N = X - B
26 LET G = X / N
27 LET H = N / X
28 LET P = P + 1
29 IF P = 50 THEN 35
30 PRINT N,             G,             H
31 GØ TØ 23
35 END
```

Solution
THIS PRØGRAM PRINTS THE FIRST FIFTY TERMS ØF THE FIBØNACCI SEQUENCE AND GIVES APPRØXIMATIØNS TØ THE GØLDEN RATIØ
****

TERM	RATIØ ØF TERM TØ PRECEDING TERM	RATIØ ØF TERM TØ FØLLØWING TERM
******	****************	****************
1	—	1
1	2	.5
2	1.5	.666667
3	1.66667	.6
5	1.6	.625
8	1.625	.615385
13	1.61538	.619048
21	1.61905	.617647
34	1.61765	.618182
55	1.61818	.617978
89	1.61798	.618056
144	1.61806	.618026
233	1.61803	.618037
377	1.61804	.618033
610	1.61803	.618034
987	1.61803	.618034
1597	1.61803	.618034

RAN   3 SEC.
STØP.
READY.

Problem

Print out each natural number N (for $2 \leq N \leq 100$) and the number of primes between N and $2N$. Study this output for possible patterns. Make conjectures which might then be tested with the computer.

Flow Chart

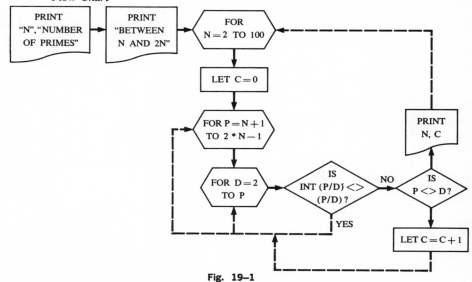

Fig. 19–1

Program

```
 10 PRINT "N," "NUMBER ØF PRIMES"
 20 PRINT "BETWEEN N AND 2N"
 30 FØR N = 2 TØ 100
 40 LET C ≤ 0
 50 FØR P = N + 1 TØ 2 * N − 1
 60 FØR D = 2 TØ P
 70 IF INT(P/D) < > P/D THEN 100
 80 IF P < > D THEN 110
 90 LET C = C + 1
100 NEXT D
110 NEXT P
120 PRINT N, C
130 NEXT N
140 END
```

Solution Printout (Partial)

N	Number of Primes Between N and 2N
2	1
3	1
4	2
5	1
6	2
7	2
8	2
9	3
10	4
11	3
12	4
13	3
14	3
15	4
16	5
17	4
18	4
19	4
20	4
21	5
22	6

Problem

Print out the pairs of inverse elements for "clock 5" addition. (Use zero as the additive identity.)

Flow Chart

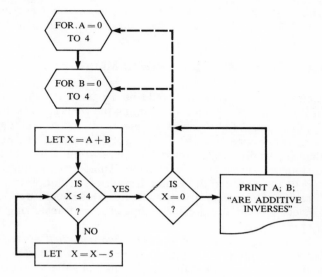

Fig. 19–2

Program
```
 10 FØR A = 0 TØ 4
 20 FØR B = 0 TØ 4
 30 LET X = A + B
 40 IF X = 4 THEN 70
 50 LET X = X − 5
 60 GØ TØ 40
 70 IF X = 0 THEN 110
 80 NEXT B
 90 NEXT A
100 GØ TØ 130
110 PRINT A; B; "ARE ADDITIVE INVERSES"
120 GØ TØ 80
130 END
```

Note: This program would be given after the development of mod 5 addition (which actually is defined by statements 10–60 of the above). Additional levels of sophistication are available:
    1. The program for mod k addition.
    2. Prefacing with the search for the identity element, mod 5.
    3. Prefacing with the search for the identity element, mod k.

Solution Printout

0	0	ARE ADDITIVE INVERSES
1	4	ARE ADDITIVE INVERSES
2	3	ARE ADDITIVE INVERSES
3	2	ARE ADDITIVE INVERSES
4	1	ARE ADDITIVE INVERSES

TIME: 1 SEC.

One difficulty beginning computer mathematics students have is understanding a statement like $N = N + 1$. Such a statement means, "Change N to $N + 1$," and, thus, is not the usual interpretation of "$=$".

GOALS FOR COMPUTER PROGRAMMING

Computer programming should be a part of the mathematics curriculum if it is an effective means of attaining the goals such as the following:

1. *Learning how to solve problems.* In programming, the problem analysis is very complete when it is set up in a flow chart. Furthermore, the problem is usually programmed in general form, which is rarely the case when students solve a specific problem. Thus, programming focuses on the method of solution and the generalization of a solution to a greater extent than traditional specific problem solving. This should develop greater skill in problem solving and greater competence in transferring the solution to other applications.

2. *Learning how to communicate mathematical ideas.* The translation of the problem conditions and operations into a program requires minute attention to the sequence, the operations, and the symbols. Writing programs and interpreting computer solutions is another means of building communication skill. It requires careful attention to order, sequence, and detail.

3. *Developing desirable attitudes, interests, and appreciations.* In view of the tremendous current interest in computers, it is difficult to imagine a more effective device for stimulating student interest. The computer is an exciting, frequently discussed device. It holds the promise of reducing tiresome computations by its instantaneous, almost magical response. Teachers who teach programming testify that students are willing to use their leisure time for computer instruction and operation. They use lunch hours, time after school, Saturdays, evenings, and even summer vacation to run the terminal or trainer. If students are willing to participate in a mathematics-related activity to this extent, it seems reasonable to provide them with the needed instruction and facilities.

4. *Teaching mathematical concepts.* In programming, a student must design algorithms and then program the algorithms for the computer. In effect, the computer does *only* the "busy" work. When a student writes programs, such as the solution of a system of equations, the solution of quadratic equations, or the properties of a finite system, he is likely to have greater mastery of these ideas than can be provided by the usual paper-and-pencil exercises. Since *sequence* is important in programming, the structure and logic of a given algorithm are emphasized. (It is worth noting that programmers must guard against degenerate cases and zero divisors.)

5. *Developing skill in computation.* Usually it is assumed that since the computer does all the calculation, computation is eliminated. While this is true, in programming the computer, the student must have considerable insight into the meaning of each step of an algorithm. Programming demands understanding—the very kind of understanding which develops

computational skill. Examples of this include programming the computation of a square root, the computation of the arithmetic average, the evaluation of a determinant, the solution of a right triangle, or calculation of an approximation of the golden ratio. At the same time, programming emphasizes the significance of units, approximations, and limits.

6. *Adapting instruction to individual abilities and interests.* Computer programming is of great interest to students of all abilities. For the slow learner, it is a new topic free of many of the frustrations and hostilities associated with topics which depend on concepts they have not yet mastered. For these students it offers relief from the grind of unsuccessful computations. For the culturally deprived, it gives a promise of new and upgraded employment opportunities. Also, problems of different degrees of sophistication are available for the enrichment of almost every topic. For the gifted, it provides a tool for probing challenging problems free of monotonous computation. To meet individual needs, computer programming has been offered as an elective course, as an extracurricular activity, and as a summer school course. If programming attains goals such as those listed above, it seems reasonable to offer it to all students as part of a regular mathematics course.

Whether computer programming actually attains the goals listed above has still to be accurately determined, and a variety of research projects are presently investigating this problem.

Two new areas of computer applications underscore the potential of the computer in the classroom. One is the use of the computer in the analysis of functions. By feeding equations or ordered pairs into the computer, the student can observe the results in graphical form on the teletype printout or on a television screen. These graphs show how lines curve, change in slope, or change in location as they represent graphs of functions.

The second area is simulation. Through simulation the computer can present the student with situations or problems as they might occur in the real world. The student is then asked to make decisions. His decision is fed back into the computer, which then presents a new set of facts. The student then makes new decisions based on the results of his previous choices. This rapid response to student decisions should be highly effective in teaching concepts and problem solving.

MATHEMATICS FOR COMPUTER PROGRAMMING

The major aspect of computer programming is the use of this process to deal with a variety of topics. Therefore, a very small part of the instruction in computer programming should be devoted to learning how to draw flow charts and to write the computer program. This should take a short time, particularly if a trainer is available and a simple language is used. Some teachers report that one week at the seventh-grade level is sufficient.

The programming is usually introduced by presentation of relatively trivial problems, such as generating the counting numbers. Next, simple equations are evaluated for several sets of values for the variables. These evaluations demonstrate the kind of analysis and formulation needed for programming, give practice in programming, and indicate the potential of the computer. To stop there (as is occasionally done) is not productive, however; additional significant problems should be explored.

Given the opportunity, teachers and students will find a great variety of problems which lend themselves to computer programs. Here are some examples:

1. *Examples for arithmetic:*
   a. Numeration systems: conversion from one base to another.
   b. Divisibility of numbers.
   c. Prime numbers.
   d. Arithmetic average.
   e. Properties of numbers.
   f. Square root.
   g. Evaluating exponential numerals.

2. *Examples for general mathematics:*
   a. Compound interest.
   b. Modular arithmetic.
   c. Mortgage tables.
   d. Salary problems.
   e. Evaluation of equations and inequalities.
   f. Graphing.
   g. Probability.

3. *Examples for algebra:*
   a. Evaluation of phrases.
   b. Systems of equations.
   c. Quadratic equations.
   d. Verbal problems.
   e. Evaluation of determinants.
   f. Coordinates, slopes, intercepts of equations.
   g. Operations with ordered pairs.
   h. Matrix addition and multiplication.
   i. Sums and limits of sequences.

4. *Examples for geometry:*
   a. Right-triangle solutions.
   b. Calculating areas and volumes.
   c. Calculating approximations to π.
   d. Finding sums of angles of polygons.

    e. Measures of triangles related to coordinates of vertices.

    f. Measures of circles.

    g. Figures formed by coordinates.

5. *Examples for trigonometry:*

    a. Solving triangles.

    b. Calculating approximations to *e*.

    c. Calculating a table of sine values from series expansion.

    d. Computing the path of a projectile.

    e. Testing validity of identities.

COMPUTER EQUIPMENT

To teach computer programming and to use it for developing mathematical ideas requires time and resources. Time should be provided in regular mathematics courses. Resources needed include a teacher with competence in computer science, computer installations or a computer trainer or terminal, and text material. All of these are now available.

Computer equipment for school programs include the following: (1) adding machines and calculators; (2) computer trainers; (3) computer terminals; (4) electronic computers.

Adding machines and calculators are inexpensive devices for beginning instruction. These machines perform most of the operations of the computer but at a slow rate. Since each operation is transmitted by keys, these machines are manually programmed. They have limited memories and cannot execute a sequence of operations automatically.

Calculators, however, can be used to show the relation of preparing a flow chart to machine solutions. For example, the flow chart for computing an arithmetic average can lead to the machine calculation of the average. Calculators can also be used to discuss various parts of a computer, such as input, control, memory, and output. The keyboard is the input. The inside gears provide the controls which perform the operation desired. One register is the memory and another register gives the output (the result of the calculation).

Each school should have one mathematics classroom or laboratory with enough calculators for an entire class. (Calculators cost from $120 to well over $1,000.) Calculators provide hands-on operation in a manner that is fascinating to students. They illustrate visually place value in base ten and often add meaning to a given operation. For example, calculators perform multiplication by repeated additions, division by repeated subtraction, recycling one place when the register passes zero. They are most appropriate for use in general mathematics classes.

The computer trainers are miniature computers, for they have the major parts of an actual computer—they are programmed by flow charts and a computer language. Also, they usually look like real computers and often use lights to show each step in a computer operation. Their primary function is to assist students in learning programming. To this end, they have the advantage of being able to be operated by students and hence become a good substitute and introduction for hands-on operation of a real computer. They are relatively inexpensive and can readily be transported from classroom to classroom or from one school to another.

The limited memory capacity of computer trainers limits the number of problems they can solve. Usually, they can deal with the same types of problems as those of a computer but exponents, coefficients, and solutions must be small integers. Trainers, therefore, are largely limited in use to teaching programming rather than providing a tool for learning mathematical concepts or solving mathematical problems. However, they can demonstrate computer processes, logic circuits, memories, and sequences in a concrete fashion that is not possible with a computer or a terminal. Currently they cost about $6,000.

The computer terminal is usually an electric typewriter connected to a computer by a telephone line or cable. The typewriter can be operated to send a program to the computer or it can cut a tape for transmission at a later time. Cutting a tape permits the examination of a program to identify errors before using valuable computer time for the program. When the computer has received the program and is finished with other work received earlier or of higher priority, it solves the problem and types the solution on the terminal typewriter. Thus, a computer terminal provides the facilities of a real computer. It is relatively inexpensive because the terminal rental is nominal and very little computer time is needed.

A computer terminal eliminates the need for a computer in the school. With a computer terminal there are no problems of computer maintenance, nor is there an investment in an expensive computer which is likely to become out-of-date in a short time. To substitute for hands-on-the-computer, the class should take a field trip to a computer center. After that, the terminal is a sufficiently realistic hands-on experience. Some very large schools or school systems may, however, justify a computer installation on the basis of multiple uses such as facilitating school business, some financial savings if guarantees of updating equipment are obtained, and insurance against the delays occasionally faced in real time terminals (that is, terminals which share the same computer).

COMPUTER-ASSISTED INSTRUCTION

A major role of the computer in the near future will be to "assist" or "mediate" instruction. It can do this because it has a memory which can store much information. This information may consist of questions, problems, proofs, answers, tests, and facts. Therefore, an entire course similar to a programmed text can be placed in the computer memory. This information can be communicated to the student by terminals, which may include a typewriter for written responses, a screen like a television screen for visual communication, and headphones for sound. The student can communicate with the computer by pressing multiple-choice keys or type-writer keys or by writing on a special screen with a "light" pencil. It is anticipated that in the future a terminal of this type will be available for each student.

The computer can act as a tutor by asking questions or presenting information. It can do this by playing a tape recording through the head-phones, by displaying a paragraph or even a photograph on the screen, or by writing with the typewriter. The screen could also present motion picture material from a video tape to accompany the verbal statements. This communication may present an explanation, a series of discovery exercises, a step-by-step development of a proof, a series of practice exercises, or thought-provoking problems.

The student may respond to the computer tutor by answering the questions, working the problems, selecting a multiple-choice response, drawing on the screen, requesting the next step in the proof or explanation, or requesting a repeat of a previous paragraph. The computer lesson is somewhat like that of programmed texts but is usually much more versatile. It can give verbal or pictorial information as requested. It can pronounce a new word or repeat an explanation. At the same time, it records the student's response. If the student responds incorrectly or too slowly, it gives the right answer and remembers to ask this question again as part of another lesson. The computer may also respond to the rapid, correct responder by giving a more sophisticated lesson in the future; the slow responder with many errors is given an easier, slower development in the next lesson.

Thus, the computer presents lessons tailored to the individual student, who is given new material as fast as he can demonstrate proficiency. The student is not bored by repetitious drill on material already mastered. He is not discouraged by new material before he has mastered the previous topic.

The computer thus frees the teacher from routine activities such as correcting assignments, reviewing, giving tests, keeping records, giving remedial instruction, selecting individualized assignments. The teacher with a computer-tutor will have time to do creative, professional work. The teacher's role will involve inspiring students, developing attitudes and values, teaching originality and application, and adding the human element in learning. The computer can teach basic facts and skills, but it cannot help the student discuss original ideas, new applications, or new ways of communicating ideas. It can teach basic concepts and provide practice, but it seems limited in developing individual interests, values and creativity.

The teacher in a computer-tutor classroom will devote his time to these professional activities.

1. *Planning.* Selecting or developing new topics, new programs, new sequences, new materials for his classes.

2. *Counseling.* With complete information supplied by the computer for every student, the teacher is now able to work with individual students in terms of their needs and abilities.

3. *Evaluating.* By analyzing student responses, reacting to student feedback, questioning individual students, the teacher will have a wider

basis than before for deciding what to teach and how to increase student achievement.

4. *Teaching.* The teacher will still conduct discussions, present new topics, make assignments, encourage independent study, direct enrichment activities. With freedom from routine, he can conduct these activities with finesse, selecting proper materials and tailoring activities to individual needs.

The computer revolution is at hand. The computer is a tool which may have multiple uses in the mathematics classroom. It may be a device for making the learning of concepts, skills, and problem solving more effective than that of traditional practice. The technology is available. The question now is, do we have the teachers and the materials for establishing computer programming in the mathematics classroom?

Computer-assisted instruction can create the ideal teaching situation— direct, individual contact between teacher and student. The implications of such improved instruction speak hopefully for the future.

LEARNING EXERCISES

1. Write a program for a lesson to be placed in a computer memory.
2. Learn a new concept from a lesson on a computer-assisted program.
3. Write the flow chart for the solution to these problems:
    a. $y = ax^2 + bx + c$
    c. $y = 1 + \frac{1}{2} + \frac{1}{4} + \frac{1}{8} + \ldots + \frac{1}{2}^n$ for $n = 1, 2, 3, \ldots 30$.
    b. $y = mx + b$
4. Write the computer programs for the flow charts of exercise 3.
5. Investigate the availability and cost of calculators, computer trainers, and terminals.
6. Visit a school with a computer program. What goals of instruction is this program attaining?
7. Review a research study on the effectiveness of a computer program.
8. Describe the hypothetical activities of a mathematics teacher of the next generation.
9. Investigate the systems-development approach. What are its implications for mathematics classes?
10. How is numerical analysis related to computer programming? How is numerical analysis related to calculus?

20

the mathematics department facilities

The mathematics department space should include offices, conference rooms, storage space, and laboratories, as well as classrooms—facilities designed to provide the best possible setting for the activities of the students, the teachers, and the department chairman. In some cases it might be appropriate to include a computer room. When the department is planned, facilities should be made adaptable to unforeseen future needs. Thus, for instance, room separations should be temporary, so that spaces can easily be rearranged for teaching machines, special programs for students of different ability levels, team teaching, programmed instruction, flexible scheduling, or computer-mediated instruction.

STAFF FACILITIES

A secondary school which has a mathematics department consisting of several teachers should have a department chairman. He should have responsibility for planning the curriculum, supervising instruction, purchasing supplies and textbooks, hiring new teachers, and conducting inservice training. To do this he will need resources such as time, finances, a private office, space for conferences, and secretarial assistance.

Teachers need a quiet, comfortable office or workroom where they can think, study, relax, and write. Here the teacher can prepare his lessons. This preparation might include the duplication of worksheets and laboratory guides, the preparation of audio-visual aids, and the building of demonstration models. Other duties outside the classroom include the preparation and grading of examinations, conferences with students, and professional self-improvement. One of the easiest ways to promote superior teaching is to provide the teacher with facilities such as duplicating equipment, type-

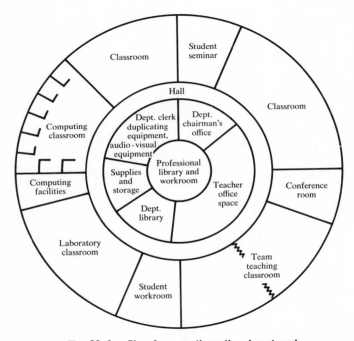

Fig. 20–1. Plan for a mathematics department.

writer, professional library, construction material, and classroom supplies in a setting that relates directly to mathematics.

At a minimum, a mathematics staff's space allotment should provide a private office for the department chairman, and a larger space for use as office–library–meeting room for the entire mathematics staff.

CLASSROOM FACILITIES

The classroom is the place where the teacher and pupil spend the major portion of their school day, where the tools of learning are available and used, and where the motivation and guidance of learning activities are concentrated. Therefore, the classroom should be planned and equipped so that it is a pleasant, stimulating, comfortable room in which teacher and student will enjoy working.

The classroom must first provide for the physical needs of the pupils: adequate light, proper acoustics, comfortable temperature and ventilation, adequate space, and furniture suited to the activities of the classroom. But this is only part of the story. As in an efficient shop, laboratory, or office, the equipment must be appropriate, adequate, and properly located. The materials and tools needed should be readily available to the teacher, so that he can put them to use with ease and convenience and with a minimum of distraction. Materials are usually used in direct proportion to their accessibility.

If the mathematics classroom is to meet the needs of modern instructional practice, provision should be made for the following types of activities:

1. *Class learning*—discussion of ideas, reading, listening, writing on the chalkboard, viewing an audio-visual presentation, correcting papers, preparing an assignment.

2. *Laboratory lessons*—performing experiments, collecting data, operating a business enterprise, making measurements, making a model, completing a drawing, making a chart.

3. *Small-group activities*—completing a bulletin board display, planning and completing a committee project, reading for enrichment, reviewing lessons, remedial instruction.

4. *Independent study*—library reading and research, completing a programmed unit, preparing a demonstration, constructing a model, having an individual conference, completing a make-up assignment or test, using a teaching machine.

5. *Computational work*—operating a slide rule or a desk calculator, participating in a practice game, programming a computer.

To meet the major problems of modern mathematics instruction, a mere rectangular space with blackboards and fixed desks is completely out of date. The modern classroom must have plenty of space that provides for a variety of seating arrangements, adequate instructional materials, and the equipment and facilities necessary for a variety of activities.

The proper size for the mathematics classroom is determined by the number of students per class and the type of activity for which the room is used. Ordinarily 1,000 square feet of space is barely adequate for conventional instruction, but much more space is needed for group work, for library work, and for preparation of displays and models.

An ideal classroom suite includes a large room for group instruction and three small rooms or partially sectioned areas for individual or group work. Folding screens, bookcases, or cabinets on casters can provide a useful and versatile means of forming these areas if it is impossible to have individual rooms. One of these small rooms or sections could be the teacher's work area. It would be the place for the teacher to keep his materials, plan his lessons, and conduct student conferences. Another small room could be used as a workroom, which would include the materials and equipment for building models, making exhibits, drawing charts, preparing projectuals, duplicating material, and completing individual projects. The third small room would be a classroom library, where books, pamphlets, periodicals, and clipping files would be available for committee work, remedial instruction, recreational activities, and individual projects. The placement of these rooms between two classrooms would make it possible for two teachers to share them. Windows with draw curtains could allow for privacy or supervision.

Team teaching also places new demands on facilities. In order to function properly in a cooperative program, teachers need classrooms that are easily modifiable to serve very large (up to 150) or very small (a half dozen or less) student groups. Such an arrangement as that described in the previous paragraph is suitable for all but the large-group activities. Separate facilities for large groups may be provided on a share basis with another department.

CLASSROOM EQUIPMENT

After the classroom space is provided, it should be properly equipped as follows:

1. Adequate desk, files, and seating for the teacher.
2. Proper tables (desks) and seating for students.
3. Equipment for demonstrations and audio-visual aids.
4. Facilities for displays, exhibits, and books.
5. Storage space for class material and students' and teacher's belongings.
6. Miscellaneous equipment such as pencil sharpener, clock, coat rack, and sink. (Since the clock is for the teacher, it should be placed in the back of the room. Likewise, classroom doors should not be at the front of the room.)

The teacher needs a large desk and a comfortable chair. Some teachers also use a movable demonstration table, which is convenient for transporting books, models, or supplies in and out of the classroom. Most mathematics teachers also use an overhead projector, which should be available at all times.

The movable demonstration table is an ideal way of providing for accessible teaching materials. Here are the various things a demonstration table may provide:

1. Space for performing experiments or displaying demonstration models.
2. A projector stand for the overhead projector, film projector, or television set.
3. Storage space for models, text, chalkboard material.

4. Storage space for student supplies, worksheets, tests.
5. Display space for library books and pamphlets.
6. A distribution area for materials for laboratory lessons.
7. Lectern for lesson plan or text.
8. Electrical outlet for projection equipment.
9. Storage for projectuals, filmstrips, films, charts.

Student desks in the mathematics classroom should have adequate writing space. Most teachers prefer tables with a formica writing surface to be used as desks. Desks and tables specifically designed for the mathematics classroom have such aids as coordinate graphing grids or tables of trigonometric functions imprinted in the formica. Before selecting these special

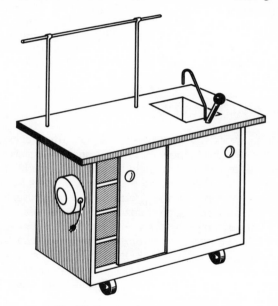

Fig. 20–2.   Demonstration table.

desks, the mathematics department should decide how they will be used and what they will contribute to the learning of mathematics.

Every mathematics classroom should be equipped with a screen for projections. Overhead projections, films, video tapes, and filmstrips are likely to be as essential as the chalkboard in the near future. Similarly, every mathematics classroom should have walls used for chalkboard, bulletin board, and display equipment. Books, pamphlets, models, and charts should be constantly on display. An exhibit case with a glass-enclosed cabinet which may be locked will permit the exhibit of materials too valuable to be handled by students. This case may be positioned in the wall between the classroom and the hall, so that it is available to both classroom and hall.

Every possible space should be utilized for storage, since the number of student supplies as well as teaching aids will undoubtedly increase in the future. Built-in storage should include spaces of different dimensions for models, charts, books, calculators, construction materials, laboratory equipment, and supplies. Some classrooms are designed to provide individual drawers for students to store their books, drawing instruments, and supplies.

It is likely that storage space for department materials will be needed in a separate room. This room should be available for storing material such as the following:

tools	models and demonstration devices
construction supplies	games
texts	chalk and chalkboard instruments
duplicating equipment	charts
calculators	measuring instruments
field instruments	laboratory equipment
tests	bulletin board exhibit materials
audio-visual equipment and supplies	drawing equipment

INSTRUCTIONAL MATERIALS

Every mathematics department should have the necessary equipment and supplies for the production of instructional materials. This means a typewriter with a keyboard that includes common mathematical symbols, duplicating devices so that written materials for class use can be easily produced, and equipment for the production of projectuals for the overhead projector. In addition, such items as tape recorders, television receivers, and movie projectors—formerly considered luxuries—are fast becoming necessities. Other potential equipment for the near future includes computers or computer terminals, calculating devices, and teaching machines. All this equipment and these supplies must be readily accessible to teachers when they wish to use them. (Specific materials for laboratory work are listed in the Chapter 22.)

SPECIAL ROOMS

Wherever possible, provision should be made for a departmental reading room or library. Sometimes this may be a separate room attached to the school library. This room should contain hundreds of books for enrichment reading and independent study, and reference material for mathematics lessons. This room might be suitable for seminar groups or committee projects. When space is limited, the room could also be used by the mathematics staff for office and meeting space, but it must be accessible to students.

In the future it is likely that mathematics departments will need additional space divided into small cubicles or carrels. In these cubicles students will be learning through the use of teaching machines. These cubicles might also have terminals connected to a central computer. These terminals may be used to communicate to the computer programs, problems, tests, or lessons. Through these terminals the computer can ask questions, correct answers, work out sample problems, complete a proof, administer tests, and perform other routine activities.

USE OF FACILITIES

In the past, many teachers have been able to excuse inadequate programs because adequate facilities have not been available. Now, however, many new schools are building the needed facilities and providing the money to purchase necessary equipment and supplies. Such facilities are sometimes misused, and therefore several suggestions pertaining to their proper use are appropriate here:

1. Students and staff should be made aware of all the facilities of the mathematics department. This may be accomplished by means of written notices, but it is better accomplished by a program of visits to special facilities with demonstrations of their use. Even an inservice education course for teachers may be needed to ensure the proper use of the many new instructional aids.

2. Staff meetings should be devoted to discussions of specific uses of specific equipment. Different teachers may take responsibility for presentations of the use of particular facilities. Opportunity should then be provided for discussion so that all teachers may contribute ideas.

3. A teacher's ability and willingness to use facilities should be taken into consideration when he is being hired. Sometimes a newcomer may provide special talents to supplement those of the current staff.

4. School or district audio-visual personnel should be invited to present ideas for using facilities and equipment to the staff. Such presentations should always be followed by discussions focusing on the general uses of such devices for special mathematics problems.

5. Individual teachers should try techniques that are new to them and report frankly on their success or failure. Such sharing of experiences not only heads off repetitions of poor experiences but also may provide better direction to the experimenter.

6. Within the framework of cooperative department activity, teachers should be frank about their hesitation to use some of the available supportive material. Such conservative attitudes are helpful in determining the worth of the new material. No facility, no equipment, should be used unless it *improves* the program for students or teachers in some way.

In planning creatively for the future, we should eliminate preconceived ideas about the shape, size, and facilities for the mathematics classroom. We should consider the elimination of stereotype furniture, the fixed time schedule, and the traditional curriculum. The acceptance of daily classes, constant time for each class and each student, and the same equipment for each classroom is no longer defensible.

LEARNING EXERCISES

1. Plan an ideal mathematics department layout for a new school. Select the materials for the department with estimated sources and costs.
2. Review a research study which involved the determination of the effectiveness of material of instruction.
3. Plan the renovation and equipment for a mathematics department located in a traditional school building.
4. Review the literature on new school buildings and classroom equipment. Use this as a basis for predicting the classroom of the future.
5. Plan the equipment which you would consider ideal for your next year. Justify the need for this purchase in a memo requesting the necessary funds from your administrator.
6. Specify a set of criteria which might be used in the selection of facilities for the mathematics department.
7. Investigate the different devices for duplicating instructional material. Select those which would be appropriate for a mathematics department and explain how each would be used.
8. Select one of the following devices and indicate what unique contributions it can make in the mathematics classroom: (1) telewriter, (2) television set, (3) tape recorder, (4) video tape recorder, (5) computer terminal.
9. Discuss the role of the "teaching machine" in the mathematics classroom.

21

field trips and excursions in indirect measurement

Vivid learning experiences are needed to add realism and pleasure to mathematics lessons. One way to do this is for the teacher to take his students on a field trip in their community or to plan an excursion in indirect measurement. These activities can be done even with limited time and resources. A field trip takes students to a local business or institution where they see mathematics at work, while a measurement excursion takes them outside the classroom to apply their learning in a realistic setting.

FIELD TRIPS

A field trip often results in better learning than other forms of educational experience. We usually recall travel experiences much more accurately and intensively than classroom learning experiences.

A carefully planned field trip is particularly well suited to attain goals such as the following:

1. Field trips *provide motivation* for the study of a unit. A trip to a factory may not only show applications of topics but also may impress the boys with the importance of competence in mathematics in order to be eligible for desirable jobs. A visit to a computing

center with its electronic computers may excite interest in the role of mathematics in the future or in the study of computer programming.

2. Field trips *enrich mathematical learnings* by relating school work to actual life situations. A visit to an insurance company will demonstrate the use of probability, mortality tables, accident rates, premiums, dividends, face policy, and loss ratios.

3. Field trips *provide specific materials* for use in the classroom. Many useful business forms and flow charts of operations can be obtained from a visit to a bank, a tax-collection office, or an architectural concern.

4. Field trips *generate realistic situations for group planning*. The class may participate in choosing a date, gathering materials for field work, making contacts to arrange the trip, scheduling a bus, sending a courtesy note. It is especially useful to have students work cooperatively with representatives of the community to make arrangements.

5. Field trips *present material in its natural setting*. In an airport the mapping of flights, the measurement of ceiling height, the interpretation of weather reports, and the locus of radio beams are matters of life or death. In a laboratory, precision measurements, analysis of data, and the use of formulas are constant activities.

6. Field trips *integrate subject matter of different courses*. At the highway office, planning the new toll road involves knowledge of weather conditions, rock and soil formation, accident causes, transportation surveys, as well as indirect measurements. At the airport aerodynamics, engine performance, weather conditions, and radar patrol are related to work in science courses.

7. Field trips *provide a means for many students and community citizens to participate in the school program*. At the place visited or in follow-up activities several people will participate as guides, demonstrators, or speakers.

PLACES TO GO FOR FIELD TRIPS

Local communities will differ greatly in the opportunities for field trips. The following list is suggestive of places where application of mathematics may be seen.

1. *Government agencies:* tax collector's office, social-security office, highway department, county surveyor's office, weather bureau, post office, military recruiting office or base, civil air patrol, forestry service, civil-service office, water or crop control office, land-reclamation office.

These government agencies will be using mathematics in a variety of ways, such as determining tax rates, completing tax forms, checking records, determining benefit payments, computing refunds, making maps, surveying land, estimating, computing areas and volumes, determining operating costs, collecting and analyzing data, determining the competence of applicants for positions.

2. *Community institutions:* museums, art centers, churches, laboratories, observatory, planetarium.

Museums may have a variety of exhibits in which the role of mathematics is important, as in, for example, map projections or ancient measuring devices. Art centers often have displays of abstract or modern art which emphasize symmetry, perspective, and proportion. Churches have stained-glass windows and architectual forms that show applied geometry. Laboratories have precise measuring devices and experimental techniques that illustrate applied mathematics. Observatories and planetariums utilize a variety of mathematics such as gear ratios, elliptical orbits, indirect astronomical measurements, temperature determinations, space navigation, large units of length, the fourth dimension, formulas related to gravitational attraction.

3. *Business enterprises:* insurance companies, banks, stock exchange, grain exchange, brokers' offices, factories, mechanical computing and recording firms, engineering offices, supermarkets, farms, architects' offices.

As is illustrated in the bank trip below, business firms are highly dependent on mathematics. Arithmetical computations such as wages, costs, depreciations, overhead, brokerage fees, market quotations, interest rates, dividends, rents are involved. Most of these enterprises collect data, prepare tables, draw graphs, predict markets, determine probability, and use a variety of statistical tools and computers. Planning buildings, laying out machine work, measuring stresses, estimating reconstruction costs require many indirect measurements. Most of these concerns use a variety of business forms and computing machines for efficient operation.

4. *Transportation centers:* airport, train station, bus depot, freight office, railway express office.

Travel by land, sea, or air involves the use of maps, schedules, rates, profit sharing, traffic control, and time zones. Air and water travel are highly dependent on principles of navigation, aerodynamics, and vectors. Measurements are made by compasses, sextants, astrolobes, and driftmeters. Radar and sonar are used every day. Research in accident control, operating efficiency, and new design is constantly being carried on.

5. *Public utilities:* telephone center, electric company, gas company, water plant.

Measurement of the amount of service used is the daily problem of public utilities. Their measurements may involve varied types of meters and units. Computing charges, bookkeeping, planning extended services, designing new equipment, planning new rates are constant activities involving mathematics at the public-utility plant.

Thus, it is apparent that mathematics is a part of many everyday activities of establishments in your community. The listing above includes topics from many fields of mathematics, from elementary arithmetic through trigonometry. Which field trip would be most appropriate for a particular course or unit must be determined by the teacher.

PLANNING THE FIELD TRIP

The success of a field trip depends on careful planning. Successful planning involves selecting an appropriate trip, making the necessary arrangements, arranging for supervision while on the visit, and providing suitable follow-up activities.

On field trips, it is important that you help students to identify or discover the mathematical aspects of what they see. These aspects should be tied in with what has been learned in the class. As an illustration, a trip was made by a general mathematics class to a bank. The mathematical aspects were outlined in a guide sheet prepared by the teacher. A flow chart was made of processing a check. Attention was called to the use of calculators and computers. Illustrations were given of interest tables and comparisons made of different types of investments. Qualifications were given for establishing credit. Questions about requirements and opportunity for employment were suggested. Without the guide sheet, the mathematics could well have been overlooked among the many processes and situations observed.

INDIRECT-MEASUREMENT EXCURSIONS

Excursions in measurement will add reality and interest to the study of measurement, geometry, and trigonometry. These excursions can be made to illustrate the historical development of geometry and trigonometry and to illustrate the measurements frequently made by civil engineers and others in technical work.

Indirect-measurement excursions are appropriate at many different grade levels. At an elementary level, scale drawings and approximations can be made with simple instruments. At a higher level, similar triangles, congruent triangles, and the Pythagorean theorem are used. At the next level, trigonometric functions are used to compute the inaccessible measurement.

Students who are taken on indirect-measurement excursions should have some background in geometry. They will need to be familiar with ideas such as angles and angle measurement, triangles, parallel lines, perpendicular lines, areas, and principles of direct measurement. They will be expected to solve formulas, equations, and proportions. In addition, a familiarity with the role of precision and accuracy in computing with measures is useful for the student on these excursions.

Another basic requirement for excursions outside the classroom is a student's sense of responsibility. Students must be willing and able to conduct independent activities without the immediate presence of the teacher.

EXCURSIONS WITH SIMPLE MATERIALS

There are a great many excursions possible with very simple materials. These are crude approximations, but the mathematical principles involved are sound. Here are some suggested problems, utilizing shadows, reflections, echoes, sticks, and a watch.

A.

1. Measure an inaccessible height, *x*, by measuring shadows. Measure $\overline{AB}$, $\overline{CB}$, and $\overline{DE}$.

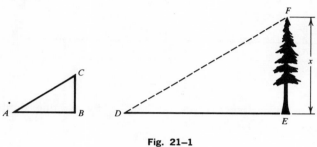

Fig. 21–1

2. Measure an inaccessible height, *x*, by a reflection at *C*. Measure $\overline{AB}$, $\overline{AC}$, and $\overline{CE}$.

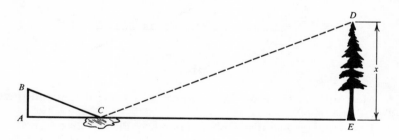

Fig. 21–2

3. Measure an inaccessible height, *x*, with a stick ($\overline{CB}$) sighting from *A*. Measure $\overline{AB}$, $\overline{CB}$, $\overline{AD}$.

Fig. 21–3

4. Measure the distance x, with a ruler ($\overline{BC}$) sighting from A. Measure $\overline{AB}$ and $\overline{BD}$. Assume $EF = 6$.

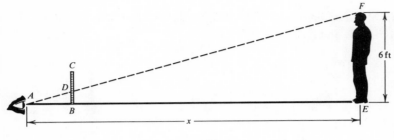

Fig. 21–4

5. Measure the distance across a river, x, by sighting similar right triangles. Measure $\overline{AC}, \overline{DC},$ and $\overline{DE}$.

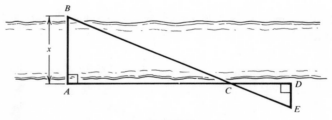

Fig. 21–5

6. Measure a distance by timing an echo. Assume that sound travels 1,100 feet per second.

7. Determine the meridian with a plumb line. Place a stick vertical to a level surface at P. Mark the tip of its shadow (A). Draw a circle with radius AP and center at P. Sometime in the afternoon the shadow of the stick will just reach the circle at B. The meridian will be the bisector of angle BPA.

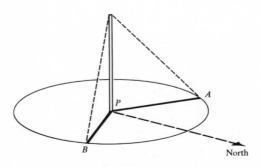

Fig. 21–6

8. Determine an east-west line with shadows. Place a stick vertically at a level spot. Mark the tip of the shadow with a small stone or peg. (A) After about 10 minutes mark the new position of the shadow tip. (B) Draw a line through the two marks ($\overline{AB}$)—this is an east-west line.

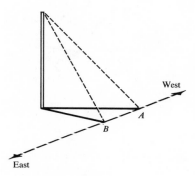

Fig. 21-7

Move the stick to the east-west line. This line is now the 6 o'clock line for a sun dial. The north-south line is the noon line. The shadow of the stick can then give an estimate of the time.

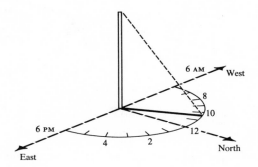

Fig. 21-8

9. Locate directions with a watch. Lay the watch on a flat surface in the sun. Place a match or stick upright against the rim of the watch. Turn the watch until the hour hand points along the shadow to the sun. The bisector of the angle formed by the hour hand and ray through 12 o'clock on the watch will give a north-south line.

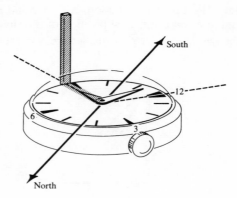

Fig. 21–9

10. Measure the distance to the moon. Tack a card to the end of a yardstick. Make a pinhole in the card. Clip a pencil onto the yardstick. Point the stick at the moon and sight the moon through the pinhole. Then slide the pencil along the yardstick until the thickness of the pencil just covers the moon. Read the distance from the pinhole to the pencil. Make several measures and average the results. Measure the width of the pencil. If the moon is 240,000 miles from the earth, how large is the moon?

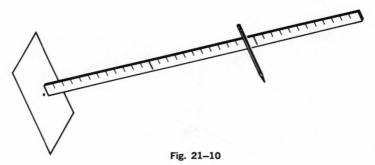

Fig. 21–10

11. Construct any angle with a steel tape. At the point at which you wish to construct the angle, draw an arc of a circle with a radius 57.3 feet long. Measure the length of arc in feet. Each foot will give an angle of one degree.

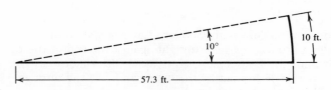

Fig. 21–11

EXCURSIONS WITH MEASURING INSTRUMENTS

When devices are available for measuring angles and distance, more sophisticated excursions are possible. Here are some possibilities (*x* represents the indirect measure):

1. Measure an inaccessible height, *x*, by measuring an angle of elevation, *CAB*, and the distance to the object, *AB*.

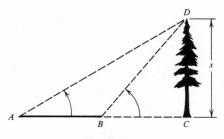

Fig. 21–12

2. Measure the height, *x*, of an inaccessible object, $\overline{CD}$, by measuring two angles of elevation ($\angle DAC$ and $\angle DBC$) at two separate points.

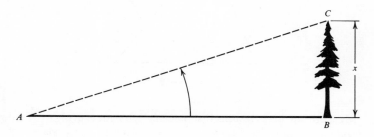

Fig. 21–13

3. Measure the inaccessible height, *x*, of an object, *EC*, by an angle mirror at *A*. Measure $\overline{AB}$ ($\cong \overline{CD}$) and $\overline{AD}$.

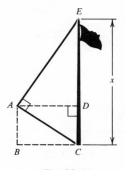

Fig. 21–14

4. Measure an inaccessible distance, $\overline{AB}$, by measuring two angles and one side of a triangle. Measure $\overline{AC}$, angle BAC, and angle BCA.

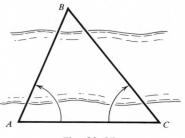

Fig. 21–15

5. Measure an inaccessible distance, $\overline{BC}$, by measuring two sides and the included angle of a triangle. Measure $\overline{AB}$ and $\overline{AC}$ and angle BAC.

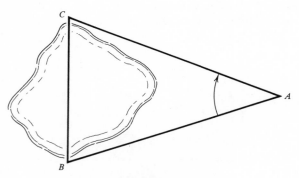

Fig. 21–16

6. Measure an inaccessible distance, $\overline{CD}$, by triangulation. Measure $\overline{AB}$, angles CAD, DAB, ABC, CBD.

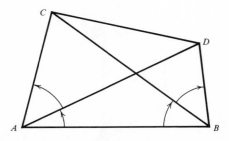

Fig. 21–17

7. Map a small region with a plane table.

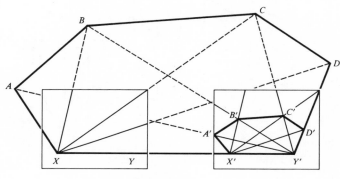

Fig. 21–18

8. Map a local park by triangulation. Measure $\overline{AB}$, angle CAB, angle CBA, angle BCD, angle CDE, and angle CED. Check by measuring $\overline{DE}$.

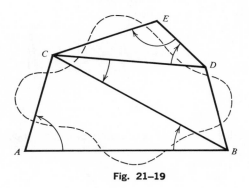

Fig. 21–19

9. Map an irregular area by offsets and determine the area. At regular intervals on $\overline{XY}$, get perpendicular offsets to poles at P_1, P_2 . . . and Q_1, Q_2 . . . and measure the offsets, $\overline{AP_1}$, $\overline{AQ_1}$ . . . Map the area by plotting the record on a section of graph paper. Compute the area by counting the squares of graph paper or by the trapezoidal rule.

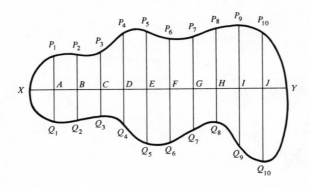

Fig. 21–20

10. Measure the horizontal distance between points on sloping ground. Sight horizontally at a leveling rod and record elevation.

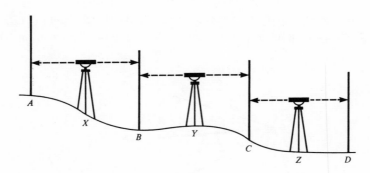

Fig. 21–21

11. Measure the levels of a series of points and draw a contour map.

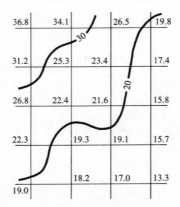

Fig. 21–22

12. Locate inaccessible points by measuring angles and compass bearings for plotting a traverse.

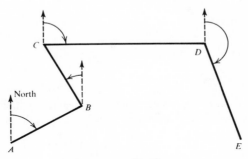

Fig. 21–23

13. Extend a straight line, $\overline{AB}$. Use the transit to measure angles at B, C, and D and length BC. Length CD must be computed to find the location of D. Find the length, CD, by a scale drawing (or the law of sines).

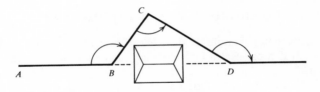

Fig. 21–24

14. Lay out a treasure hunt by establishing points through distances and lines of sight. This hunt may be laid out on a sheet of wrapping paper as a course or on the school grounds or a local park.

MATERIALS NEEDED FOR MEASUREMENT EXCURSIONS

To complete measurement excursions successfully, the mathematics department should have the following measuring and drawing instruments:

protractors	pantograph	stadia tube	micrometer
compasses	proportional	alidade	caliper
ruler	dividers	plane table	spherometer
triangles	carpenters square	yard stick	odometer
T-square	transit	meter stick	planimeter
parallel rulers	hypsometer	measuring tape	stop watch
drawing board	clinometer	ranging pole	
and drawing	level sextant	arrows	
instrument kit	angle mirror	tripod	

Many of these devices can be purchased from local engineer's supply stores or mail order stores. For more complete list of supplies, write to the following companies:

Yoder Instruments
East Palestine, Ohio

Keufel and Esser Co.
Hoboken, New Jersey

Eugene Dietzen Co.
2425 Sheffield Ave.
Chicago, Illinois

W. M. Welch Scientific Co.
1515 Sedgwich Street
Chicago, Illinois

Where commercial devices are not available, many measuring devices can be made by students. These include equipment such as the following:

hypsometer	angle mirror
proportional dividers	telemeter
sundial	range finder
pantograph	angle trisector

Here are sample instructions for making and using some simple measuring instruments.

INDIRECT MEASUREMENT WITH A HYPSOMETER

The hypsometer is a clever device for measuring angles and inaccessible heights. It is most useful in measuring angles of elevation and angles of depression.

The hypsometer is a rectangular board that has a protractor scale at the upper right corner for measuring angles from 0 to 90 degrees. A plumb line is attached at the upper right corner. The measure of an angle of elevation (or depression) is found at the point where the plumb line crosses the protractor scale. The plumb line is always vertical when hanging freely and indicates an angle of zero degrees when the hypsometer is level or horizontal. When the hypsometer is tilted for sighting, the plumb line remains vertical and indicates the angle of the tilt. Angles of elevation are measured by sighting from left to right. Angles of depression are measured by reversing the direction of sighting.

The hypsometer is mounted vertically to an upright staff so that it is free to turn. Objects are sighted through peep holes or a soda straw along the top edge of the graph.

The rectangular board is covered by graph paper that has a vertical scale on the right and a horizontal scale on the bottom. The vertical scale represents the measure of the distance from the object being sighted. The horizontal scale represents the measure of the height of the object being measured. These scales may represent any convenient unit of length, such as 1 foot, 1 yard, 1 meter, 1 pace, 10 feet. Thus, the rectangular graph provides a scale drawing of the indirect measurement being made.

To find the height of a TV-antenna, measure $\overline{AC}$ and $\overline{CD}$. Place the hypsometer at A to sight the top of the antenna as illustrated below.

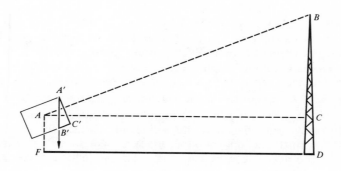

Fig. 21–25

The horizontal line of sight is represented by $\overline{AC}$. The line of sight to the top of the antenna is represented by $\overline{AB}$. The height of the antenna is $BC + CD$. On the hypsometer the scale drawing of triangle ABC is represented by triangle $A'B'C'$. Since triangles ABC and $A'B'C'$ are similar,

$$\frac{BC}{AC} = \frac{B'C'}{A'C'}$$

If $AC = 300$ feet, $A'C' = 100$, and $B'C' = 75$, then $BC/300 = 75/100$ or $BC = 225$. The height of the antenna is $[225 + CD]$ feet.

A more convenient scale drawing of this measurement may be obtained by locating C' at 30 (for 300 feet) on the vertical. Then the horizontal line ($B'C'$) is 22.5 units long, representing a measurement of 225 feet.

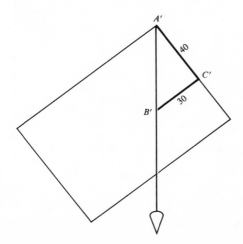

Fig. 21–26

PLANS FOR CONSTRUCTING A HYPSOMETER MODEL

Materials: Cardboard or plywood base 16″ by 12″, graph paper 10 squares to the inch, 10″ by 15″ in size, one quadrant of polar coordinate paper, soda straw, string, cellophane tape, rubber cement, fishline sinker.

Construction: Glue the graph sheet to the cardboard rectangle. Trim the polar coordinate paper and glue it, at the center (A), to the graph paper (Fig. 21–27). Label the vertical scale $\overline{AB}$ and the horizontal scale $\overline{EB}$ 10 units to the inch as indicated in Fig. 21–27. With A as center and a radius of 10 inches draw the sines and cosines arc. Attach the soda straw along line *IA* with the cellophane tape. Place a piece of string through a hole at A and tie a knot on the back side. Tie the fishline sinker to the string for a plumb line.

When the hypsometer is mounted in a vertical position to a staff with a screw at point *J,* it is ready for field work.

The hypsometer graph as shown in Fig. 21–27 has the following scales:

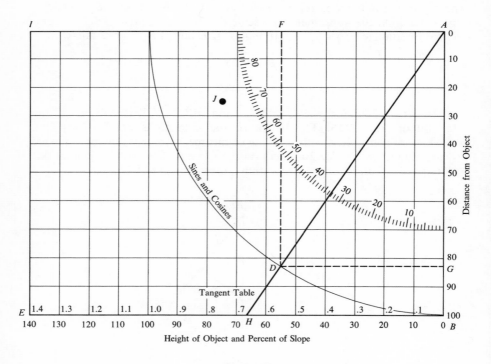

Fig. 21–27

1. *AB* represents the distance to the object being measured.

2. *EB* represents the height of the object and also the percent of slope. If this scale is divided by 10 the scale becomes a tangent scale.

3. $\overset{\frown}{MN}$ is a protractor arc indicating the angle of elevation or angle of depression.

4. $\overset{\frown}{KB}$ is a scale for finding sine and cosine values.

5. $\overset{\leftrightarrow}{AI}$ is the line of sight.

6. J is the point at which the base is mounted to a vertical staff.

Although hypsometers are available commercially at a relatively low price ($10), the construction of a cardboard model can be an excellent laboratory lesson.

If $\overline{AH}$ on Fig. 21–27 represents a plumb line for a certain sighting, the following information can be obtained:

1. The angle of elevation is 35 degrees.

2. If the object is 100 feet from the hypsometer, its height is 67 feet (HB). If the object is 30 feet away, it is 21 feet high. The height is measured by the scale $\overline{EB}$ directly below the intersection of the plumb line and the 30 mark on the distance scale. Note that this is the height above the instrument (AI).

3. The tangent of 35° is indicated on $\overline{BH}$ to be .67.

4. The sine of 35° read on the height scale ($\overline{EB}$) is .56. The value of the sine equals the scale measure of the length of $\overline{DG}$.

5. The cosine of 35° read on the distance scale ($\overline{AB}$) is .82. The value of the cosine equals the scale measure of the length of $\overline{FD}$.

6. The percent of a slope is 67, as indicated on the height scale ($\overline{EB}$).

ADDITIONAL PROBLEMS FOR THE HYPSOMETER

1. Find the height of some object (CD) that is on a slope below the hypsometer. Measure the angle of elevation and the angle of depression with the hypsometer at A. Measure the distance to the object (AB or AD) and compute BC and BD.

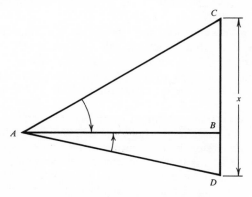

Fig. 21–28

2. Read the values of the trigonometric ratios on the hypsometer. Compare your reading with the four-place table readings.

	hypsometer readings	actual reading from table
(a) sine 30°		
(b) cosine 50°		
(c) tangent 45°		
(d) sine 27°		
(e) cosine 33°		
(f) tangent 64°		

3. Determine the length of right-triangle legs. Set the plumb line on the angles indicated. Read the missing length on the hypsometer.

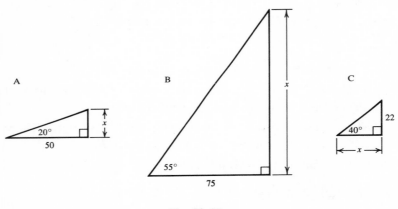

Fig. 21–29

PREPARING FOR AN EXCURSION IN INDIRECT MEASUREMENT

Before beginning an excursion, the student should know exactly what to do, how to do it, and what materials will be needed. He will need to know the mathematical ideas involved, the data to collect, and how to operate the measuring instruments to be used. In completing the report of his field work, he should make a neat drawing and label it with the known measurements.

Excursions in indirect measurement often can be done in your classroom, on the school grounds, or at home. The gymnasium has adequate space for an indoor excursion if the weather is inclement. Most measurement excursions should be made up of groups of two to four persons. Each member of the group will have a different job, such as recording and keeping records, measuring distance, operating instruments, or placing sighting poles. The equipment should be selected in advance so that each student will have everything needed. Complete written instructions should be given to the group so that the group is clear about what the necessary measurements are. Here are sample instruction sheets for students.

Lesson 1

Object
To determine the length of one's own pace.

Equipment
Steel tape.

Procedure
With the steel tape, mark off a distance of 50 feet. Placing the heel at the beginning of that distance, count each time thereafter that this same foot touches the ground. Then divide 50 by the number of paces. Do this three times and average these results for the length of your pace.

Data
Number of paces
    1. _____
    2. _____
    3. _____

Computation
50 divided by the number of paces.
    1. _____
    2. _____
    3. _____

Average length of pace _____

What is the length of your pace?

Lesson 2

Object
To estimate the length of the school.

Procedure
Pace off the length from one end of the school to the other. Then multiply the number of paces by the length of one's own pace.

Data

Number of paces	Length of pace	Length of school
1. _____	_____	_____
2. _____	_____	_____
3. _____	_____	_____

What is the approximate length of the school?

Lesson 3

Object
To measure indirectly the height of the school.

Equipment
Plane mirror and steel tape.

Procedure
Place the mirror on the ground between you and the building so that you can see the top of the building in the mirror. Mark the point on the mirror

at which you see the top of the building. Then measure the distance from where you stand to that point on the mirror and also the distance from that point on the mirror to the building. You must also find the distance from the ground to your eyes. Then, using similar triangles, you will be able to find the height of the building.

Data
Distance from feet to mirror _____
Distance from mirror to building _____
Distance from feet to eyes _____

What is the approximate height of the building?

Lesson 4

Object
To measure the height of an inaccessible object (a smoke stack).

Equipment
Transit, tape, plumb bob.

Procedure
Set up the transit in a level position about 200 feet from the base of the smokestack and measure the angles of elevation and depression. Following the above line of sight, place the transit about 100 feet from the smokestack and again measure the angles of elevation and depression.

Data
Angle of elevation at first position _____
Angle of depression at first position _____
Distance from first position to second position _____
Angle of elevation at second position _____
Angle of depression at second position _____

Computation
Write the equations used in the solution.

What is the approximate height of smokestack?

LEARNING EXERCISES

1. Write a lesson for an excursion in indirect measurement.
2. Visit a local establishment and plan a field trip to it.
3. Find out how Eratosthenes measured indirectly the circumference of the earth.
4. Find out how astronauts make measurements in space.
5. Investigate what instruments are used to navigate airplanes.
6. Make a hypsometer and use it to design a series of excursions.
7. Investigate the availability and cost of commercial measuring devices. Make a selection for your school.

22

laboratory lessons

The shibboleth of today is that students should discover many ideas for themselves without being told. A mathematics teacher sets the stage and directs the teaching so that students have the experiences they need to develop insight into the nature of a new process or idea. To do this a teacher needs to become skillful in directing the student in exploring new ideas, in performing experiments, and in stating generalizations. This type of laboratory teaching is highly successful because every student participates actively.

Many students are unable to construct and abstract mathematical concepts except through relating these concepts to something real and concrete. It is the purpose of laboratory lessons to provide needed meaningful experiences. Too often, sheer drill stamps in a rote response. Instead, the teacher should guide the learner to abstract generalizations by presenting them to him in various ways. The more experience the learner has of the different ways in which a principle can be applied, the deeper will be his understanding of it. Instead of expecting students to store and retrieve information, the teacher should direct the students to build and test theories for themselves by the use of open-ended questions and experiments. Students who play it safe by waiting for the teacher to hand out knowledge become dependent learners. Even though a student may be naturally inquisitive, he doesn't want to run the risk of a rejected wrong response. The spirit of laboratory lessons includes experimentation and guessing, and a student will often learn by his failures. Such a try will create a favorable classroom atmosphere, in which curiosity and independence grow.

THE ROLE OF LABORATORY LESSONS

Because laboratory lessons give a new approach to learning mathematics, they are especially successful in the following ways:

1. They provide *success* for the learner who has not mastered the use of abstractions. In this way laboratory lessons are particularly helpful in dealing with individual differences, in reaching the culturally deprived, and in preventing dropouts.

2. The possibilities for *individual, independent work* make laboratory work appealing and profitable for the creative, talented student.

3. As a result of the relaxed independence of the laboratory, *positive attitudes* toward mathematics and the mathematics teacher are likely to be a major outcome.

4. The completion of an experiment results in an individual product or an independent discovery that gives tangible *evidence of the progress* to the student. However, do not assume that a correct student answer means that the student has attained complete understanding. Hence, accept immature statements until more experiences build greater maturity.

If a student asks, "Is this the result we are supposed to get?" reply, "If your answer is already determined, why bother to do the experiment?"

5. The similarity of the laboratory work to that of the science class or to the operation of a business ensures greater *transfer of learning* than the usual classroom procedure.

6. The laboratory lesson is most effective in getting every student to *participate actively*. Each student must do some thinking as he collects data, plays a game, or conducts an experiment. The student's active involvement is the key to his successful learning.

KINDS OF LABORATORY LESSONS

Mathematics is a study of patterns, a language for expressing relationships, and a tool for dealing with approximate data. Consequently, mathematics is uniquely suited for exploring ideas in a laboratory setting. These laboratory lessons may be of several types:

1. *Make measurements of two variables in an everyday setting to determine the relationship between them.* A typical example of this would

be the comparison of measures of the circumference and diameter of round objects.

Measure the circumference and diameters of many round objects (wheels, wastebaskets, tin cans, clock dials, lamp shades). Tabulate the data in a table like that below and compute the sum, difference, product, and quotient of each pair of measures.

Object	Circumference (C)	Diameter (D)	c + d	c − d	c × d	c ÷ d
Wheel	7	21	28	14	147	3.0
Basket	46.5	15	61.5	31.5	697.5	3.1
Can	6.2	2	8.2	4.2	12.4	3.1
Clock	10.5	3.4	13.9	7.1	35.7	3.1
Lamp	36.8	11.5	48.3	25.3	423.2	3.2

From the pattern of the data obtained in this table, it appears that $C \div d = 3.1$. From this consistent result, it is estimated that $C = 3.1\ d$, or $C = \pi\ d$.

2. *Collect data by performing an operation.* A typical example of this type is the pattern of factors of counting numbers.

n	Factors	Number of factors	Sum of factors
1	1	1	1
2	1, 2	2	3
3	1, 3	2	4
4	1, 2, 4	3	7
5	1, 5	2	6
6	1, 2, 3, 6	4	12
7	1, 7	2	8
8	1, 2, 4, 8	4	15

To determine the pattern of this data, it is helpful to ask questions such as these:

a. What numbers have exactly 2 factors? (Primes.)

b. What numbers have exactly 3 factors? (Squares of primes.)

c. What numbers have exactly 4 factors? (Cubes of primes and products of prime pairs.)

d. How does the number of factors of a number compare with the number of its prime factors? (Less than or equal to the sum of the number of prime factors.)

e. How does the sum of factors of prime numbers compare with the prime number? (One more than the prime.)

f. What formula gives the sum of factors of 2^a? ($2^a - 1$.)

3. *Find a pattern by drawings or constructions.* An example of this type of experimentation is the exploration of the formula for the maximum number of parts into which the interior of a circle can be divided by a given number of lines in the plane. The results are the following:

Number of lines (n)	Drawing	Maximum number of regions (r)	Difference in number of regions
0		1	
			1
1		2	
			2
2		4	
			3
3		7	
			4
4		11	
			5
5		16	

Since second differences are constant, the formula is quadratic. ($r = n^2/2 + n/2 + 1$.)

4. *Discover a scientific principle by performing an experiment with simple equipment.* A simple example of this type is the determination of the geometric series which represents the bounce of a "super" ball.

Form a cylindrical tube from a large sheet of clear plastic. Place this tube upright on a hard surface. Drop a ball from the top of the tube and record the height of each bounce. Repeat the experiment many times to get the average height of each bounce. The collected data will give an approximation to a geometric series.

5. *Explore a relationship by manipulating simple objects.* A simple experiment to determine the permutations of different numbers of objects can be performed by arranging a series of cards. The results can be related to factorials ($n!$) to obtain a formula $_nP_n = n!$

6. *Collect original data from a survey to determine what variables are related.* Data from students may suggest that there is a relationship between grade in mathematics and number of hours of homework, number of hours spent viewing television, or car ownership.

7. *Perform indirect measurements to determine unknown distances.* A simple experiment of this type is the determination of the height of a tree by measuring its shadow and comparing this with the shadow of a known height.

$$\frac{a}{b} = \frac{x}{c}$$

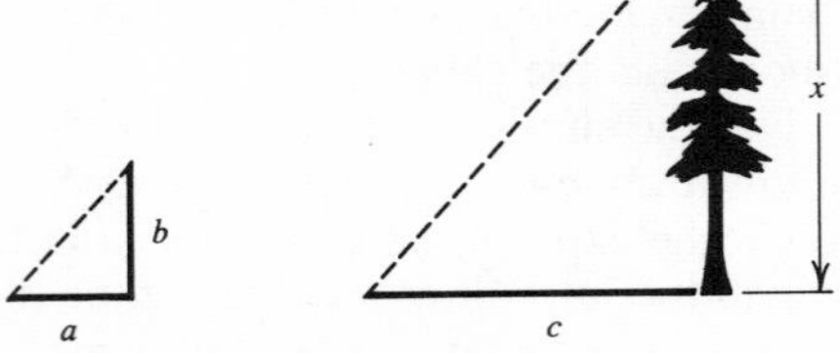

Fig. 22–1

8. *Extend the solution of a specific problem to a generalization.* Consider the problem of a drawer filled with single brown and blue socks. If one selects individual socks in the dark, how many selections are needed to guarantee two socks of one color? The easy answer is three. To generalize this problem, we can increase the number of colors and increase the number of feet needing matching socks. The analysis can be done with objects representing socks or by logically analyzing each situation. The results may be recorded in a table such as the following:

Number of feet (F)	Available colors (C)	Number of selections which may be tie result	Number of selections which guarantee matched socks (S)
1	1	—	1
1	2	—	1
1	3	—	1
2	1	—	2
2	2	2	3
2	3	3	4
3	1	—	3
3	2	4	5
3	3	6	7
4	1	—	4
4	2	6	7
4	3	9	10
5	1	—	5
5	2	8	9
5	3	12	13

The guaranteed selections are $S = C(L - 1) + 1$, where $C(L - 1)$ represents the possible tie results.

9. *Represent a mathematical idea by building a simple model.* For example, it is impossible to represent the fourth dimension by a two-dimensional model. Using balsa strips, pins, and glue, students can build a tesseract or super-prism in one class period. This model then becomes a basis for dimensional analysis and the meaning of dimensions beyond three. Tabulating data such as the following adds meaning:

Figure	No. dimensions	No. boundaries	Dimensions of boundaries	Coordinates needed to locate a point on figure	Distance formula
Point	0	0	0	0	
Line segment	1	2	0	1	$d = \sqrt{(x_1 - x_2)^2}$
Region of plane	2	4	1	2	$\sqrt{(x_1 - x_2)^2 + (y_1 - y_2)^2}$
Bounded three-space	3	6	2	3	$\sqrt{\Delta x^2 + \Delta y^2 + \Delta z^2}$
Bounded four-space	4	8	3	4	$\sqrt{\Delta x^2 + \Delta y^2 + \Delta z^2 + \Delta w^2}$

10. *Complete an individual project or report.* When time and construction materials are available, students can create original devices to demonstrate mathematical ideas. For example, a student may use balsa strips to

build a stereograph (three-dimensional graph) of data consisting of three variables.

11. *Illustrate mathematical ideas by folding paper.* For example, flexagons are fascinating devices which mathematicians have investigated as a simple new branch of mathematics. A hexaflexagon can be folded and glued together in thirty minutes. The balance of the period can be devoted to the story of its development, a study of the properties, and the extension to multisided flexagons.

12. *Build exhibits, charts, bulletin board displays.* An excellent way to build communication skill is the construction of a display. This construction requires concrete and visual representation which should add new meaning to the idea. For example, one group of students may use Tinker-Toy pieces to illustrate the meaning of algebraic expressions such as x, $3x$, x^2, $x + y$, $(x + y)^2$, and x^3.

13. *Use commercial laboratory devices to perform experiments.* There is a variety of equipment suitable for laboratory work. For example, the Welch Dynamic Geometry Circle Device is an excellent laboratory device for determining the relationship between the measures of angles and the measures of intercepted arcs of circles.

14. *Use laboratory kits for laboratory work.* There are many kits, such as the Probability Kit, which provide the necessary equipment, materials, and instruction for a whole series of laboratory experiments for determining probability empirically.

15. *Plan, make, and use mathematical games, puzzles, stunts.* A game such as Battleship can be made and played as a means of learning to locate points on a coordinate grid. A puzzle such as the Tower of Hanoi can be made with three nails, a small board, and pieces of cardboard. The solution to this puzzle may be expressed in a mathematical formula.

16. *Operate calculators and program computers.* Some laboratories largely base their solution of problems on the use of calculators. Other laboratories are computer oriented, with a computer trainer and a computer terminal. These computer devices are used to learn programming and to find solutions to programmed problems.

17. *Organize and operate a business enterprise.* The establishment of an insurance company which insures students for specific items such as breakage, textbook loss, illness, or accident can be a realistic way of teaching probability and insurance. A stock brokerage firm, bank, credit union, and a school store are other examples of possible business ventures to operate as a learning experience.

18. *Use an audio-visual aid as the basis for laboratory work.* Students may draw or take photographs for a series of stereopticon views, which can be used as a means of learning to draw two-dimensional views of a three-dimensional object. A series of overlays for the overhead projector may be prepared to demonstrate a topic or problem.

Some laboratory lessons will involve a combination of the types outlined above. At other times part of a lesson will be a laboratory session and part a practice session. Not all lessons are suitable for laboratory sessions.

But too often laboratory lessons are not used because the teacher lacks the ideas, the time, or the material to present them.

HOW TO TEACH LABORATORY LESSONS

A laboratory lesson, like any other lesson, requires careful planning to be successful. However, laboratory lessons tend to be more difficult than textbook lessons for several reasons. For one thing, there is little ready-made material for these lessons. Thus, most laboratory-lesson material must be developed by the teacher. Also, laboratory lessons require the use of a variety of materials, which need to be scheduled and prepared well in advance. In addition, the laboratory situation is naturally more permissive and unstructured and, thus, needs the teacher's constant attention to avoid undesirable disruptions. Even so, teachers who use this method find that the results are well worth the effort.

SPECIFIC PROCEDURES FOR LABORATORY LESSONS

Here are some specific procedures to follow in order to have successful laboratory lessons:

1. *Prepare guide sheets for the students so that they will know what material they need and what they are to investigate.* These guide sheets must not overstructure the lesson and leave no decisions for the student to make. At the same time, laboratory lessons should usually be completed during a regular class session; therefore, considerable efficiency will be required of both student and teacher. As in discovery teaching, laboratory guide sheets should include a series of carefully prepared questions. These questions should suggest possible variations, common properties, or patterns. Also, the questions should direct attention to interrelationships, analogies, or special cases. Replication is encouraged so that no counter example is possible. Note how the following pattern of arithmetic computation might lead one to a false conclusion.

$$2 \times 2 = 4 \qquad\qquad 2 + 2 = 4$$
$$\tfrac{3}{2} \times 3 = 4\tfrac{1}{2} \qquad\qquad \tfrac{3}{2} + 3 = 4\tfrac{1}{2}$$
$$\tfrac{4}{3} \times 4 = 5\tfrac{1}{3} \qquad\qquad \tfrac{4}{3} + 4 = 5\tfrac{1}{3}$$
$$\tfrac{5}{4} \times 5 = 6\tfrac{1}{4} \qquad\qquad \tfrac{5}{4} + 5 = 6\tfrac{1}{4}$$

The generalization that $a \times b = a + b$ can be disproved by the simple example $3 \times 3 \neq 3 + 3$.

The specific conditions under which this works are shown by these equations.

$$\left(\frac{x}{x-1}\right) x = \frac{x^2}{x-1} \qquad\qquad \frac{x}{x-1} + x = \frac{x + x^2 - x}{x-1} = \frac{x^2}{x-1}$$

The sample guide sheets below are suggestive of possible format and content.

A. Laboratory Exercise: Law of the Lever

Objectives
    a. To collect data on the weights and lengths of a lever which is balanced.
    b. To investigate whether there is a pattern in the data which can be expressed by a simple formula.

Equipment
    Meter stick, fulcrum, weights, thread.

Directions
    a. Suspend by a thread or support with a fulcrum a meter stick at its midpoint. If it does not quite balance, place a rider made of a bent piece of foil on the lighter side to establish equilibrium.
    b. At some point of the meter stick attach a weight (W) at any distance (d) to the left of the fulcrum.
    c. At some point on the other side of the fulcrum, hang another weight (R) which balances (W). Measure the distance (a) to the fulcrum. It is not necessary to wait for the lever to come to rest, for it is in equilibrium when it swings through equal distances on opposite sides of the horizontal position.
    d. Repeat at least four times, using different sets of weights and distances.
    e. Record both the weights (W and R) and their distances (d and a) from the fulcrum when the lever is balanced.

DIAGRAM

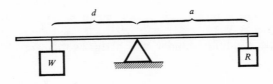

Fig. 22–2

TABLE

Trial	W	R	WR	W/R	d	a	da	d/a	a/d
1									
2									
3									
4									

Results

    a. What products or ratios above appear to be related?
    b. What formula expresses this relationship?
    c. What are some applications of this principle?
    d. Was Archimedes correct when he said, "If I had a long enough lever and a fixed point for a fulcrum, I could move the earth"? Explain your answer.

B. Laboratory Exercise: The Area of a Triangle

Use a rectangle as shown in Fig. 22–3A, and move the small triangle to the upper base of the rectangle to form a right triangle as shown in Fig. 22–3B.

What is the area of this triangle? How does the measure of the base of the triangle compare with the length of the rectangle?

How does the measure of the altitude of the triangle compare with the width of the rectangle?

Is the area of the interior of a triangle equal to the product of the base and altitude?

What number sentence expresses the relationship of the area of a triangle to the measures of the base and altitude?

(Questions such as these should lead the pupil to the conclusion: Area equals ½ base times altitude, or base times altitude/2.)

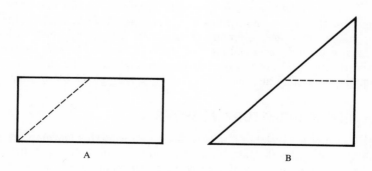

A   B

Fig. 22–3

C. Laboratory Exercise

Here is an example of how a number pattern can be developed to discover the product of two negative numbers. Study the pattern of products below:

$$^{+}12 \times {}^{+}5 = {}^{+}60$$
$$^{+}12 \times {}^{+}3 = {}^{+}36$$
$$^{+}12 \times {}^{+}2 = {}^{+}24$$
$$^{+}12 \times {}^{+}1 = {}^{+}12$$
$$^{+}12 \times \ \ 0 = \ \ \ 0$$
$$^{+}12 \times {}^{-}1 = \ \ \ ?$$

How is the change in the product related to the change in one factor? Why is it logical to expect that $12 \times {}^{-}1$ is a product less than zero?

If $12 \times {}^{-}1 = {}^{-}12$, what is $12 \times {}^{-}2$ equal to?

The results above suggest that the product of a positive number and a negative number is a _____ number.

2. *The laboratory lesson needs adequate materials.* For some lessons only paper and pencil are needed. For others, measuring instruments, graph paper, or a laboratory device is needed. These materials must be ready for use when the laboratory lesson begins.

3. *The laboratory lesson needs a classroom with some flexibility and certain special equipment.* Student stations should be tables instead of desks. Storage cabinets are needed to keep equipment at hand. Filing cabinets and book shelves are needed to store resource materials. Electrical outlets should be plentiful, and a sink with running water should be provided. At least one table should be a workbench with a vise and other tools for simple woodworking.

4. *Each student should participate in an activity in which he can have some success.* Ideally, the mathematics laboratory needs laboratory assistants as in a science laboratory. These assistants may be auxiliary workers such as teacher aides or student assistants. In any case, students in the laboratory need considerable individual attention if each one is to complete the experiments correctly and arrive at generalizations. Be sure to allow ample time for the completion of the experiment.

5. *The students must be properly prepared for the laboratory lesson.* They must accept responsibility for independent work and for the care of equipment. Sharing equipment, cleaning up debris, and being orderly must be the accepted responsibility of each student. Provide supplementary activities for the learner who completes his work far in advance of others. Sometimes he may also use this extra time to act as a laboratory assistant.

SPECIFIC LABORATORY LESSONS

The number of laboratory lessons appropriate for learning mathematics is limited only by the ingenuity of the teacher and the facilities available. Most concepts can be discovered by experimentation if time is taken to plan and devise appropriate experiments. The suggested lessons that follow indicate the wide range of possibilities. In each of the following cases the reader must extend the idea in order to make a complete laboratory lesson. This extension will often involve a search for related literature which will offer further suggestions and a more complete discussion.

NUMBERS AND CALCULATION

1. Build nomographs for computations, such as addition, subtraction, multiplication, division, squaring, square root, and the Pythagorean formula $a^2 + b^2 = c^2$.

2. Make models of Napier's bones out of cardboard. Make the bones for different bases to illustrate or check computations with numerals in bases other than ten.

3. Using a sheet of graph paper and a string, make a percentage computer.

4. Using two squares of cardboard on nails pounded into a board, make a binary abacus. A string of lights, such as those used as Christmas tree decorations, can also be used to represent the 1 and 0 of the binary system.

5. Discover the patterns of multiples of numbers by writing the multiples in a vertical column. What is the pattern of the sums of the digits? What is the pattern of the units digits? Of the tens digit?

6. Write a 10 by 10 table of numbers from 1 to 100, listing them consecutively left to right in rows. Examine the patterns in this table of multiples and primes. Cardboard templates uncovering certain multiples may be cut out to show various patterns.

7. Use dots to represent the values of counting numbers. What numbers are triangular numbers? Square numbers? How are triangular numbers related to square numbers? What numbers are pentagonal numbers? How do triangular numbers and square numbers combine to form pentagonal numbers?

8. Start Pascal's triangle. What number series are formed by numbers found in different rows, columns, and diagonals?

9. Learn to write magic squares.

10. Explore counting number games such as Nim with rules of increasing complexity and generality.

11. Discover shortcuts and explain why they are appropriate.

12. Investigate the pattern of Pythagorean triples and derive the formulas that express the relationship discovered.

13. Investigate the shapes and surfaces of soap bubbles.

14. Explore the mathematics of codes and ciphers.

STATISTICAL SURVEYS

Collect data such as the following for graphs, statistical analysis, or the study of cause and effect:

1. Scoring records or athletes' percentages at athletic contests.

2. School records, such as attendance, tardiness, registrations, illness.

3. School sales in the lunchroom, bookstore, or candy counter.

4. Daily community vital statistics, such as births, deaths, fires, accidents.

5. Student activities, such as playing games, seeing shows, watching television, listening to the radio, and reading books.

6. Marks and test grades in different courses.

7. Market quotations of stocks, bonds, grain, cattle.

8. Utility bills such as electric, gas, telephone, water.

9. Sizes, weights, heights of students.

10. Tax rates, school costs, public debt, business conditions.

11. Traffic records, such as accidents, amount of traffic, cost of automobile operation, kinds of automobiles.

PROBABILITY EXPERIMENTS

1. Toss coins to compare the predicted results with experimental results.

2. Toss thumbtacks, corks, bottle caps to determine the probability of falling in various positions.

3. Make a spin dial. Check the probability of the arrow's stopping within a given section of the dial.

4. Roll a hexagonal pencil or toss a die to find the probability of a given side turning up. Roll two pencils or toss two dice to build the sample space of events and find the probability of combinations of events.

5. Make duodecagon dice from cardboard. Determine the probability of certain tosses of one or two of these polyhedra.

6. Draw cards at random from a deck of homemade number cards or playing cards. Determine the probability of drawing certain cards.

7. Toss different numbers of coins. Compare the events with the numbers in Pascal's triangle.

8. Draw samples from bags of colored marbles or decks of cards. Predict the composition of the collection. Compare results obtained from different-sized samples.

9. Make a probability game in which players capture points by spinning a dial or by predicting events.

10. Collect data on the frequency of letters in a paragraph or the frequency of digits in telephone numbers. Predict the frequency of all paragraphs and check the results.

11. Compute a value for π by tossing sticks (or toothpicks) on parallel lines.

12. Collect data and compare results with the normal curve. Experiment with a probability board and compare results with Pascal's triangle and the normal curve.

13. Keep a record of weather predictions for several days. What is the probability that the weather forecast is correct?

14. Find the batting average of a certain baseball player, the average yards gained by a certain football player, or the average points scored per game by a certain basketball player. Use these results to predict events of the next game.

15. Record the kinds of cars either parked in a parking lot or passing over a busy street in a ten-minute time period. Use these results to approximate the number of Fords, Chevrolets, Plymouths, or Ramblers in the United States. Compare results with data in the *World Almanac*. What are some reasons why the suggested sampling may not be a proper guide?

16. Glue two dice together. Toss and collect data to illustrate dependent events.

17. Construct a probability game based on tossing a thumbtack. Each player gets 20 points if he predicts correctly whether the tack will land with its head up or down. To estimate the probability of the tack turning up or down, each player can have as many sample tosses as desired. However, one point is lost for each sample toss. How many sample tosses should a player take before he is willing to predict an event for 20 points? The answer depends on the results of the sample tosses. If the tack lands head down the first six times, he may be willing to predict "down." If the sample tosses give four down and two up, he may want more sample tosses before he predicts for 20 points.

RATIO AND PROPORTION

1. Determine the ratios of speeds and revolutions for gears and pulley trains. Use a bicycle to make this determination.

2. Use a meter stick lever to determine the law of the lever.

3. Draw geometric figures on graph paper. Determine the ratios of areas as dimensions are varied.

4. Compare the volumes of different cylinders, cones, or prisms. Determine the ratios of volumes as dimensions are varied.

5. Measure the variation in the period of a pendulum as the length of the pendulum is changed, to determine the relationship between these variables.

6. By measurement determine the ratios between the parts of an automobile in a picture, and the ratio that occurs when the automobile itself is measured.

7. Draw rectangles which represent the golden section. Investigate its occurrence in daily life and the unusual properties of the related Fibonacii series.

AREA AND VOLUME

1. Use a rectangular sheet of graph paper marked off into square inches. Cut into parts and reassemble to form a parallelogram, triangle, or rhombus. Use the dimensions of the new figure to find the appropriate formula. The commercial material called Area Aids by Judy Toy Company provides linkages for these experiments.

2. Use containers such as cylinders, cones, prisms, and pyramids with equal altitudes and bases. Compare the volumes by pouring sand or salt from one container to another.

3. Cut a circle into small equal sectors. Reassemble them into a shape which is like a parallelogram. The altitude of this pseudo-parallelogram will be the radius, and the base will be $\frac{1}{2}C$. Then the area of a circle is $\frac{1}{2}C \times r = \frac{1}{2}(2\pi r) \cdot r$ or $A = \pi r^2$.

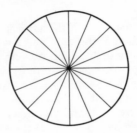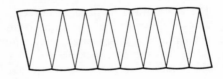

Fig. 22–4

4. Illustrate the Pythagorean theorem by comparing areas as follows:

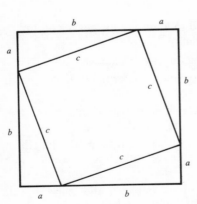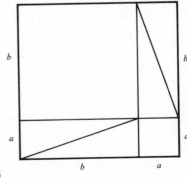

Fig. 22–5

5. Draw right triangles on graph paper. Outline the squares on each leg. Cut a square of graph paper to represent the square of the hypotenuse. Compare the areas of these squares by counting the squares of graph paper.

6. Show the relationship of area and perimeter by drawing different rectangles on graph paper or pegboard. If the perimeter is held constant, what constraints are put on the area? If the area is held constant, how may the perimeter vary? Extend these relationships to volume and surface area.

ALGEBRA

1. Use sticks or dowels to form the representation for algebraic phrases such as a, $a + b$, $3a$, ab, a^2, a^3, $(a + b)^2$.

2. Represent the graphs of linear equations by elastic thread on pegboard, acoustical tile, or on a commercial equation board. Do the same for inequalities, using colored paper or plastic to represent the regions.

3. Make drawings on graph paper so that regions represent the terms of binomial expansions and the factors of algebraic phrases.

4. Draw a spiral on graph paper to obtain lengths which represent the square root of counting numbers. Use a strip of graph paper to measure the lengths which represent the square roots. Use this means to build a table of square roots.

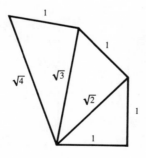

Fig. 22–6

5. Make a clock dial to illustrate a finite number system. Use this dial to establish tables for the operations and for solutions to equations. Examine the results to determine whether the system satisfies the conditions for a group or field.

6. Use paper folding to form the curves of conic sections. Cut sections of plastic foam cones to identify the formation of conic sections. Use linkages to draw these curves. Make curve stitching patterns to illustrate quadratic curves.

7. Build models which will illustrate curves such as the cycloid, catenary, cardioid, or spiral.

8. Design and make a game based on mathematical ideas, as those described in *Games for Learning Mathematics*.[1]

9. Develop the flow chart for an algorithm such as computing a square root. Write the computer program for this flow chart and check it on a computer. Find out how a calculator computes a square root.

10. Build a three-dimensional coordinate system, using three squares of coarse screen. Represent graphs of equations with elastic thread for lines and plastic sheets for planes.

11. Compare the extension of a spring to the weight which causes the extension. (a) Attach weights to the bar of a wire coat-hanger. Measure the sag for each weight. (b) Attach a meter stick over the edge of a table. Attach weights to the end of the meter stick and measure the distortion for each weight.

12. Measure the distance an object falls in space and compare with the time measured by a stop watch. Or time a marble as it rolls down an incline.

13. Establish area formulas for composite figures such as those below (Fig. 22–7).

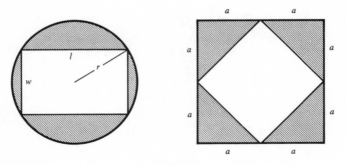

Fig. 22–7

14. Use toys or models of cars, trains, airplanes to build a concrete representation of a verbal problem. Use these models also to illustrate travel on the number line as an introduction to the addition or multiplication of directed numbers.

15. Find examples or pictures of curves and geometric patterns in nature such as the snowflake, a honeycomb, the spiral shell, crystals, and elliptical orbits.

[1] Donovan A. Johnson, *Games for Learning Mathematics* (Portland, Maine: J. Weston Walch, 1960).

GEOMETRY

1. Make simple electric circuits to represent truth tables.

2. Form regular polygons by folding paper. Perform all the usual constructions of euclidean geometry by paper folding as described in *Paper Folding for the Mathematics Class.*[2]

3. Outline regular polygons on graph paper or by elastic thread on pegboard. Measure angles and area to determine formulas.

4. Count vertices, edges, and regions of polygons and polyhedra to determine Euler's formula. Compare results of concave and convex, simple closed polyhedra, and composite figures.

5. Measure the angles and sides of parallelograms to determine equalities. Use a linkage to discover these relationships.

6. Make drawings of triangles with specified conditions. Cut them out and compare by superposition to determine conditions for congruency.

7. Draw triangles of various shapes and sizes. Determine relationships of angle bisectors, altitudes, medians, and perpendicular bisectors of the sides. This can be done with commercial instruments, by constructions, and by paper folding.

8. Use drawings on acetate film or a commercial device to find the relationship between the measures of angles between two intersecting lines and the measures of the intercepted arcs of a circle.

9. Draw figures and check the results for Desargues's theorem.

10. Make a model of a finite geometry. Use dowels mounted vertically to a base to represent points. Use colored elastic thread to form the finite set of triangles.

11. Suspend a model of a triangle from each vertex to find its center of gravity. Check to see whether this is the intersection of the medians of the triangle.

12. Use a resolution of forces board to check the addition of vectors.

13. Use reflections in a mirror to show properties of reflective symmetry. Use wire models to illustrate other transformations, such as rotations or translations. Build and use a kaleidoscope to find symmetric transformations.

14. Investigate paradoxes such as "every triangle is an isosceles triangle."

15. Use or make models of pseudospheres and spheres to illustrate non-euclidean geometry.

16. Make models for topology and investigate the properties of the Mobius strip, the hexaflexagon, and the four-color map problem on a plane, sphere, and torus.

17. Make drawings and three-dimensional models of symmetries.

[2] Donovan A. Johnson, *Paper Folding for the Mathematics Class* (Washington, D.C., National Council of Teachers of Mathematics, 1957).

18. Make a collection of optical illusions. Find the basis for the illusion, as described in *Experiments in Optical Illusion*.[3]

19. Use a semicircle to illustrate the relations between the arithmetic mean and the geometric mean.

20. Devise a system of computation based on line segments and geometric constructions.

21. Examine drawings for perspective. Make drawings based on vanishing points. Make models to demonstrate perspective.

22. Determine the basis for tesselations, mosaics, stained-glass window design, and other patterns.

23. Use pendulums of various types to trace pendulum patterns.

24. Determine projections of lines and closed curves by shadows.

25. Make models of geometric solids. Use these as a basis for developing Euler's formula and determining volume and surface-area relationships.

26. Construct two- and three-dimensional optical illusions. Use a camera to photograph staged illusions based on expected geometric relationships.

TRIGONOMETRY

1. Draw a number of right triangles on graph paper. Use the ratios of the measures of sides to build tables of sines, cosines, and tangents. Use unit lengths for the adjacent side or the opposite side so that the measure of the hypotenuse is the value of the sine or cosine.

2. Make a model to illustrate the winding or wrapping function. Use it to build a table of sines and cosines.

3. Demonstrate wave action with a rope, waves on water, alternating current on the oscilloscope.

4. Make a trigtracker out of cardboard. Use it to make a table of sine, cosine, and tangent ratios.

5. Make a three-dimensional rectangular coordinate system with three squares of cardboard or plastic. Use one of the three axes for the scale of imaginary numbers. Draw the graphs of quadratic equations on these planes extending the graph to include the complex roots.[4]

FACILITIES NEEDED FOR A MATHEMATICS LABORATORY

The classroom described in Chapter 20 will provide a proper setting for laboratory lessons. In addition, facilities, supplies, and tools are essential. For laboratory work every mathematics classroom needs the following materials:

[3] Nelson F. Beeler and Franklyn M. Branley, *Experiments in Optical Illusion* (New York: Thomas Y. Crowell, Co., 1951).

[4] For complete instructions see *Multi-Sensory Aids in the Teaching of Mathematics* (Washington, D.C.: National Council of Teachers of Mathematics, 1946).

cardboard
tackboard
fiberboard
colored corrugated cardboard
plywood
pegboard
balsawood
cork panels
plastic foam
plastic sheets (plain and colored)
felt
glue
rubber cement
adhesive wax

paint
crayons
colored chalk
spray paint
nails
thumbtacks
brads
staples
map tacks
construction paper
wax paper
drawing paper
aluminum foil
graph paper (rectangular, polar coordinate, logarithmic)

adhesive tape
masking tape
colored plastic tape
string
yarn
elastic thread
colored rubber bands
pegs
golf tees
soda straws
plastic tubes
toothpicks
letter stencils
letters for mounting
title board

beads
marbles
chips
rings
tongue depressors
pill boxes
modeling clay
powdered plaster
fishline weights
balloons
wire
sandpaper
brush pens
nylon point pens
paint brushes

To work with these materials, tools such as the following should be available:

pliers
hammers
saws
screw drivers
shears
staplers

paper punch and eyelets
soldering iron
hand drill and assorted drills
paper cutter

planer or rasp
knives
razor blades and holder
carving knife
bench vise

gluing clamps
carpenter's square
drawing set
drawing board
protractors

For laboratory lessons, the following demonstration models and commercial devices are needed:

1. *Demonstration devices*

abacus
base and place model
counting frame
binary abacus
area boards
area aids
balance
binomial cube
calculator
computer trainers
caliper, vernier
micrometer
circle device (circumference and area)
cube cylinder
cone
conic sections

data graphing board
equation board
flannel board
force table
geometry instruments (boards, pegboards)
geometric solids
graph board (peg, magnetic)
inverse squares apparatus
lines and planes models
map projections
measuring disk for determining pi
micrometer demonstrator

number base blocks
number lines
orthographic projection models
pattern dial
perimeter measurement device
polyhedra (plastic)
probability board
prisms
pyramids (dissectable)
pythagorean theorem demonstration set
reflectors (parabolic)
sand pendulum
sextant

slated globe
slide rules
solids of rotation
sphere (plastic, dissectable)
sticks
polyhedra models
string models
transit
trigonometric functions device
vector demonstrator model
vernier demonstration
volume and unit cube demonstration

2. *Drawing devices*

compass	drawing instru-	pantograph	protractor
drafting machine	ment kit	parallel rules	triangles (plastic)
drawing board	ellipse drawing	proportional	ruler
drawing board set	device	dividers	

3. *Kits*

base and place	geometric	multiplication	solid shapes
contour mapping	laboratory	and division	surveyors
curve stitching	mapping	numerative	time learning
drawing	mathematical	probability and	
geometric con-	shapes	statistics	
struction	measurement	sampling	

4. *Measurement instruments*

alidade	hypsometer	micrometer	transit
altimeter	compass—mag-	odometer	tripod
angle mirror	netic needle	plane table	steel tape
arrows	Jacob's staff	planimeter	stopwatch
caliper	level	proportional	sun dial
carpenters rule	leveling rod and	dividers	
carpenters square	target	protractor	
clinometer—	meter sticks	spherometer	

5. *Toys and puzzles:* Mek-N-Ettes, Erector Set, Tinker-Toy, Tower of Hanoi, etc.

6. *Commercial games:* Quinto, Wiff and Proof, or Equations.

7. *Science apparatus* (to be shared with science department):

balance and	lum	resolution of	wheel and axle
weights	levers	forces	spring scales
seconds pendu-	inclined plane	pulley set	

Much of the material listed above can be purchased at hardware or department stores, toy stores, lumber yards, or school-supply stores. The commercial devices are available from the companies listed in the Appendix B.

LEARNING EXERCISES

1. Find an example of a laboratory lesson in a mathematics or science textbook. Evaluate the strengths or weaknesses of the lesson.
2. Observe a laboratory lesson taught by a master teacher. What were the key factors in the success or failure of this lesson?
3. Using a set of commercial devices such as the variable quadrilateral, prepare a laboratory lesson with a guide sheet for the students.
4. Prepare a laboratory lesson based on a demonstration model such as a micrometer.
5. Prepare a laboratory lesson based on an audio-visual presentation such as the film *The Slide Rule—C and D Scale.*
6. Prepare a laboratory lesson in which the students build a model such as a tetrahedron to investigate a finite geometry of four points.
7. Design a game for students to make and play during a laboratory session.

8. Make up a performance-type test item to be used to test ability to discover ideas independently.
9. Review a research study which investigates the effectiveness of laboratory work in mathematics.
10. Make a selection of materials needed to establish a mathematics laboratory in your classroom.

part five

evaluation,
organization,
and the future

23

evaluation of achievement

Evaluation activities chart the progress of students toward the objectives outlined for them by the teacher and by themselves. Therefore evaluation is an essential aspect of instruction at all levels. It is a means whereby the quality of our mathematics programs can be constantly maintained and improved.

Evaluating a student's achievement is a teacher's constant duty. It is a time-consuming, frequently tedious activity, because of the clerical work involved. At the same time, it requires a highly technical proficiency and involves the teacher's professional value judgments. It can be discouraging to find out in evaluating students how little they have learned from what we thought was well-planned instruction. But evaluation is an indispensable task, which becomes increasingly important if we want students to achieve their optimum potential.

Evaluation involves activities such as the following:

1. Constructing and administering, marking and evaluating tests, examinations, checklists, and questionnaires.

2. Observing, recording, evaluating student activities.

3. Assigning, directing, and evaluating student projects, reports, written work.

4. Recording evaluations, interpreting the records, and assigning grades.

5. Conferring with parents, students, counselors, and employers.

6. Writing recommendations for colleges, the government, or employers.

No wonder teachers need time and clerical help for evaluation activities. And, for the following reasons, it is likely that future evaluation activities will increase.

1. The teacher is required to supply a great deal of information relative to the selection of students for colleges, vocations, and military service.

2. More accurate information is needed for the assignment of students to classes according to ability, achievement, and motivation.

3. The recent plethora of published tests available and the federal funds that can be used to purchase them require the teacher to expend a great deal of time evaluating these materials.

4. New machines are now available for administering and correcting tests, recording scores, and keeping records.

5. The new emphasis on research concerning the learning process and curriculum problems requires further measures for analysis.

Thus, every mathematics teacher needs to be competent and well informed in evaluation procedures.

PURPOSES OF EVALUATION

One of the most important purposes of evaluation is to find ways of *improving the instructional program*. Through evaluation we are able to determine the effectiveness of techniques, materials, and content of our teaching. Achievement tests can locate the level of attainment at a given time and measure the amount of progress achieved in a desired direction. In this manner, evaluation can locate the strengths and weaknesses of a program, and it can provide a basis for building a better curriculum and for selecting effective teaching methods.

Evaluation also has the potential for *improving the progress of individual students*. Tests can be used to determine whether the student is ready for instruction in a given topic. For example, diagnostic tests can be used to locate his weaknesses, sources of difficulty, mental processes, and special talent. When a student's talent and achievement are known, the teacher can guide him into courses and vocations suited to his aptitude and ability.

A student's preparation for a test and his participation in evaluating the test may be a *worthwhile learning experience in itself*. The preparation involves learning activities such as summarizing, organizing, and outlining. Completing the test itself is an intense learning experience for him, which may involve problem solving, reflective thinking, deductions, and computations. Giving the student an opportunity to discuss a completed test and correct errors helps him locate his areas of misunderstanding and correct wrong methods and thereby reinforces a student's correct learning procedures.

However, a word of caution is needed here. Cramming for a test often involves memorizing facts which are quickly forgotten after the test. Furthermore, intense preparation for a test makes the completion of the test, rather than learning the material, the goal of learning.

Self-evaluation activities tend to *motivate the student to learn ideas and skills*. Competition with one's own record, the class record, or national norms can be a stimulating experience. However, learning mathematics should be accepted by the student as worthy of effort regardless of the achievement mark involved.

Communicating with others is a major aspect of evaluation. It involves collecting information for reporting a student's status to him, to his parents, to counselors, to admission officers, and to employers. Evaluations which are correct and meaningful are needed by all individuals who make decisions regarding a given student.

The measurements made in evaluating may be *useful data for research projects*. Research studies analyze data obtained by measurement to study learning and to evaluate the effectiveness of methods, materials, or curricula.

SOME BASIC PRINCIPLES OF EVALUATION

The purpose of teaching mathematics is to provide experiences that help each student make progress toward the attainment of certain objectives. We measure the amount of progress each student has made in attaining a given objective by the use of instruments such as examinations. Then we use a value judgment to evaluate this measure. Thus, evaluation involves construction, interpretation, and appraisal of measures.

The meaning of achievement can be clarified if we consider achievement as a vector. This vector is described by coordinates which are measures of achievement. The measures may be scores on tests of specific objectives. A simplified model will illustrate this concept and at the same time point out some of the real difficulties of achievement measurement. Consider the achievement of two students on two tests before and after exposure to a specific instructional program as shown below.

	PRETEST		POST-TEST	
	Concepts	Skills	Concepts	Skills
Paul	7	32	13	50
Mary	19	23	43	52

In Fig. 23–1 these results are recorded on a coordinate system. The progress of each student is indicated by vectors representing the difference between the initial and final achievement vectors. Some basic questions of measurement are indicated by this model.

1. Does a scale unit have meaning?
2. Can we assume that units on the two scales are the same?
3. Would a zero vector really represent the absence of achievement?

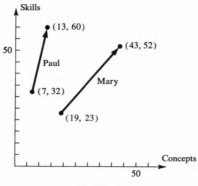

Fig. 23–1

4. How can goals be indicated on such a model?

5. Do the measurements really indicate achievement of the concepts? In fact, are they even approximations to such achievement?

6. There are so many facets to be measured that the vectors would be multi-dimensional, perhaps including even more than ten components. Would metric-space hypotheses have any application to such vectors? (For example, would the length of these *n*-dimensional vectors provide a basis for comparing achievement increments?)

Thus, achievement may be seen to be extremely difficult to pin down. The model does, however, provide a framework on which to focus thinking about achievement testing along the following lines:

1. *Achievement should be measured in terms of all the objectives of instruction.* Our goal is located by coordinates which represent measures of all objectives. Hence, we can locate our students in this coordinate space only if we have all the coordinates for each student. To arrive at these coordinates, we need devices which will measure the level of attainment of each objective. Therefore, we must know what our objectives are, so that we can measure the progress we have made toward attaining them. The evaluation of achievement in mathematics must be more than just measuring skills and knowledge, for we must also measure our students' status relative to such goals as attitudes and appreciations. We should test our students' progress in learning how to study mathematics or how to read mathematics. If we are attempting to teach how to apply mathematical learning to new situations, we need to devise tests of this ability. If we are building skill in thinking logically and building mathematical structures, we will need to build test situations or items in which the student can exhibit his ability to do these things.

2. *Achievement should be measured in terms of growth, change, progress in the attainment of our goal.* This implies that we have a pretest or achievement record which locates the student's standing at the beginning of the term. It also means that we have measuring instruments which can

determine the different levels of attainment of the concepts or skills involved. It also means that we must take into account the differences between students.

3. *Measurement should emphasize the retention of learning over a long period of time.*

4. *Measurement should emphasize ability to use the learning involved.* The coordinates of achievement should be in terms of ability to transfer knowledge to problem situations and to new applications.

5. *Measurement should emphasize understanding of structure and concepts.* The coordinates of achievement should be measures of comprehension, rather than measures of the memory of isolated facts.

STEPS IN AN EVALUATION PROGRAM

If measurement is to give coordinates in terms of objectives, several steps are necessary:

1. *The objectives of instruction must be carefully selected.* Usually these objectives are stated in terms of specific facts, formulas, principles, or theorems to be taught. Specifications of this type are necessary but not sufficient.

2. *To function as coordinates, objectives must be stated in terms of behavior patterns on the part of the learner which indicates attainment of a particular objective.* What does the student who has mastered a concept do, think, and feel? The behavioral description uses terms such as recall, state, draw, solve, analyze, describe, derive, apply, or prove. This is the format of the objectives stated in Chapter 2.

3. *Sample situations, problems, activities must be selected that will demonstrate the student behavior outlined in the objectives.* In mathematics this usually consists of a sequence of test items. However, the measurement of attitudes or creativity may involve the observation of behavior in an unstructured classroom situation or even outside the classroom. At other times the testing situation may involve the use of the text, reference books, or laboratory equipment.

4. *The situations, problems, and test items are presented to the student under optimum performance conditions.* The student is given the time, tools, and materials he needs to perform to the best of his ability.

5. *The student's responses are analyzed.* An item analysis of a test will provide information for the next step in instruction. This analysis may suggest changes in objectives, learning activities, instructional methods, or materials. It may indicate what content needs to be revised, repeated, or eliminated. Through class discussion correct answers are reinforced and errors eliminated; and individual needs are diagnosed and remedial instructions given. Questions to ask yourself regarding individual students include:

Who is having trouble?
Is he achieving as well as expected?
How can he be encouraged to improve?

Where is he having trouble?
Why is he having trouble?
What should be done to aid in improvement?

6. *The measuring instrument is evaluated and revised.* The item analysis will determine the difficulty level and discriminatory power of each item. With these data, the teacher uses value judgments to revise the test items, to eliminate poor items, and to write new items.

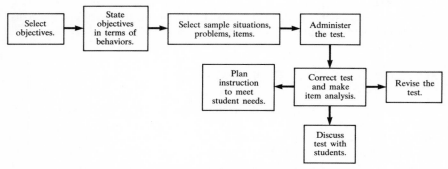

Fig. 23–2.   Evaluation flow chart.

TYPES OF TESTS FOR MEASURING ACHIEVEMENT

The type of test to select depends largely on the objective to be measured and the purpose of the test.

1. *Open-book tests.* These tests emphasize understanding, application, and use of the text. They also have the advantage of stressing the transfer of knowledge rather than the memorization of facts. A sample item is as follows: "Identify the undefined terms, definitions, assumptions, and theorems which indicate the mathematical structure of the topic Area."

2. *Reading tests.* We need to build reading skills, study skills, and the desire to learn mathematics independently. A reading test presents a paragraph of unfamiliar mathematical material and then proceeds to ask questions about the content.

3. *Performance tests.* These tests require the student to discover a relationship through measurement, manipulation, experimentation, drawing, paper folding, investigation of patterns. This is a way of measuring ability to discover a new idea, apply facts, and do productive thinking. For a performance test, each item is a separate "station" or table in the classroom. Here is a sample item.

STATION NO. 10   MATERIALS: Piece of board, 5 hooks, 18"
                                              ruler
At this station you are given a piece of board which is to be nailed to the wall in the laundry room. Various items are going to hang from the hooks, which will be screwed to the board.

————1. To the nearest ¼ inch, how long is the board?

————2. To the nearest ⅛ inch, how far is the black center line from the sides of the board?

     A. 1⅞"   B. 1¾"   C. 1⅝"   D. 1½"

————3. The five hooks are to be screwed into the board along the center line such that the distance from the edge of the board to the outside hook is equal to the distance between any two adjacent hooks along the board. What should this distance be?

4. *Essay or free-response tests.* These tests include items which emphasize integration of ideas and communication skills, and show the level of concept mastery. Here are two sample items:

> Show that the (radian) measure of an acute angle is less than the arithmetic mean of its tangent and sine.
>
> Compare the techniques of proof in coordinate geometry with those of synthetic geometry.

5. *Attitude appraisal.* Attitude tests are still in primitive form. However, rating scales, questionnaires, and anecdotes shed some light on attitudes. Here are some typical items:

> I would like to take another mathematics course like this one.
>
> My favorite subject in school is ————————.
>
> I enjoy mathematics problems as long as I get the right answer.

6. *Tests of productive thinking.* In problem solving, we should test the method of solution and the elegance of the proof rather than the answer. The planning, the organization, and the insight are significant aspects of productive thinking. A sample item is as follows:

> Jim runs around a track in 40 seconds. Mark, moving in the opposite direction, meets Jim every 15 seconds. How many seconds does it take Mark to run once around the track? Show your method of solution. If possible, find more than one method of solution.

7. *Achievement tests.* These are tests which measure the extent to which the pupil has attained the specific objectives of a course or unit of instruction. A typical item would be:

> If $(x - r)(x - s) = 0$, then
>
> A. $(x - r)$ must equal zero.
> B. $(x - s)$ must equal zero.
> C. $(x - s)$ and $(x - r)$ must both equal zero.
> D. $(x - s)$ or $(x - r)$ must equal zero.
> E. None of the above.

8. *Diagnostic tests.* This type of test is designed to discover the specific process, skill, type, or level of problem which creates difficulty for the pupil. This is useful in planning remedial instruction. Here is the beginning section of a diagnostic test. Note how the columns and rows have common difficulties.

Type	Solve for a	Solve for b	Solve for c	Solve for d	Answers
I	1. $6a = 30$	2. $32 = 4b$	3. $18c = 6$	4. $15 = 8d$	1. $a =$ 2. $b =$ 3. $c =$ 4. $d =$
II	5. $\dfrac{a}{4} = 8$	6. $12 = \dfrac{2b}{3}$	7. $\dfrac{c}{3} = \dfrac{1}{5}$	8. $3\frac{1}{4} = \dfrac{3d}{4}$	5. $a =$ 6. $b =$ 7. $c =$ 8. $d =$

9. *Practice tests.* This is a self-administered test (typically end-of-chapter tests in textbooks) designed for the pupil to check his own progress and needs. As a result, correct responses are reinforced, errors are corrected, and areas for further study are suggested.

10. *Inventory or survey or pretest or readiness tests.* These are tests designed to determine a student's readiness for new work by measuring his background of previous experience and achievement. Such tests often include questions on the content to be studied in order to provide the teacher with an indication of the pace at which the new material may be presented.

11. *Prognostic or aptitude tests.* These tests predict a student's likely success in a given course. A typical item on an algebra prognostic test is the following:

> Given: $x = y/n$. If y and n are always equal, how will x change in value if y and n increase?
> (a) Remain the same. (b) Increase. (c) Decrease. (d) Cannot tell.

12. *Contest tests.* Tests sometimes provide the basis for a contest between two mathematics teams (sometimes called *mathletes*). State or national contests also use tests which probe high level insight and mastery. The following are two sample items:

> A circular piece of metal of maximum size is cut out of a square piece, and then a square piece of maximum size is cut out of the circular piece. The total amount of metal wasted is what fraction of the original square?

> Given: the distinct points $P(a, b)$, $Q(c, d)$, $R(a + c, b + d)$, and $S(0, 0)$. Line segments $\overline{PQ}, \overline{PR}, \overline{QR}, \overline{PS}, \overline{QS},$ and $\overline{RS}$ are drawn. Depending on the location of P, Q, and R, is figure $PQRS$ I. a parallelogram? II. a trapezoid? III. a straight line?
> (a) I only. (b) II only. (c) III only. (d) I and II only. (e) All three.

Besides teacher-made appraisal instruments, we need to capitalize on the wealth of available published evaluation materials. These tests are constructed by experts, are based on extensive experimentation, and have established norms. These published tests (see list of publishers in Appendix C) include prognostic, diagnostic, unit, and long-range achievement tests. Some of them emphasize the manipulative aspects of mathematics, while others emphasize structure and logic. All these tests can be scored objectively. Some of these tests can be used to measure year-to-year progress in mathematics while others measure achievement in specific topics or subjects. Published tests usually furnish norms such as grade equivalents or percentile ranks or standard scores. Norms make possible the comparison of class or individual performance with national or state norms. However, the norms may be unsatisfactory as a standard or measure of your class because your class may be very different in aptitude from the norm sample.

On the other hand, teacher-made tests have great advantages also:

1. Teacher-made tests may be adapted to the local situation—the students, the teacher, the community, and the school.

2. Teacher-made tests can be constructed to keep pace with curriculum changes. Published tests should not be the basis for curriculum decisions, nor should they establish objectives—as they sometimes do.

3. Teacher-made tests are inexpensive as compared to published tests. However, the saving of time, the increased accuracy of measurement, and the use of answer sheets more than justifies the costs of published tests.

4. Writing a test is a wholesome learning experience for the teacher. Constructing a good test forces the writer to consider the objectives of instruction and the individual differences of his class.

Whether the test used is a published one or a teacher-made one, it should meet the following criteria:

1. The test must be *valid*. It must be a true measure of the objectives it is supposed to measure.

2. The test must be *reliable*. It must measure consistently that which it is designed to measure.

3. The test must be *fair* to the student. The statement must be clear and the answer determinable and definite. The language must be readable and correct.

4. The test must *discriminate* between the good and the poor achiever.

5. The test must be *comprehensive* so that it measures completely, not merely skimming the surface.

6. It must be easy to *administer* and *score*.

WRITING TEST ITEMS

When writing test items to measure mathematical achievement, the teacher should keep in mind these crucial factors:

1. Each item must be related to a specific objective.

2. Each test item must be mathematically correct.

3. Each test item must be technically correct. It must be correctly stated and have a specific answer.

The items should then be identified according to the specific objective they have been meant to test so that the student's response will indicate a specific level of achievement.

The following sample test items were written to test knowledge of facts, terms, properties, symbols, and concepts about number systems. They are identified according to the objective tested and are arranged in an estimated ascending order of difficulty. They should suggest ways of writing test items which test modern concepts.

1. *Recognition of a definition.*
   What is a number?
   (a) A symbol such as 7.
   (b) A point on the number line.
   (c) A common property of sets.
   (d) A one-to-one correspondence.
   (e) A pattern.

2. *Recall of a fact.*
   Which one of the following systems of numeration uses the greatest number of different digits?
   (a) Roman.
   (b) Binary.
   (c) Base five.
   (d) Decimal.
   (e) Base twelve.

3. *Restatement of an idea in different symbols.*
   In which one of the following pairs of numerals does the numeral 5 represent the same value?
   (a) 453_{twelve} and 543_{twelve}.
   (b) 453_{ten} and 453_{seven}.
   (c) 543_{seven} and 345_{seven}.
   (d) 45_{seven} and 45_{ten}.
   (e) 50_{seven} and 50_{ten}.

4. *Differentiation between properties of a number* (0).
   Which one of the following statements is false for all values of n?
   (a) $n \cdot n = 0$
   (b) $0/n = 0$
   (c) $0 \cdot n = n$
   (d) $0/n = n$
   (e) $0 - n = 0$

5. *Interpretation of an implication of order.*
   If n is an integer between the integers x and y, then which of the following is true?
   (a) n is between $x + 1$ and $y + 1$.
   (b) $n + 1$ is between x and y.
   (c) n is between $x + 1$ and y.
   (d) n is between x and $y + 1$.
   (e) $n + 1$ is between $x + 1$ and $y + 1$.

6. *Integration of an idea into the background of knowledge.*
   Which one of the following sets of whole numbers is closed under both addition and multiplication?
   (a) The set of odd numbers.
   (b) The set of numbers less than 100.
   (c) The set consisting of 0 and 1 only.
   (d) The set consisting of 0, 1, and 2 only.
   (e) The set of even numbers.

7. *Understanding of a computation algorithm.*
   The multiplication of 24 by $3\frac{1}{2}$ is the same as 24 multiplied by 3.5. Why do we not indent the partial product 72 in the second example as is done in the first example?

24	24
3.5	$3\frac{1}{2}$
120	12
72	72
84.0	84

   (a) The multiplier 3 has a different place value in each example.
   (b) The multipliers .5 and $\frac{1}{2}$ are not equivalent.
   (c) The fraction $\frac{1}{2}$ does not have place value.
   (d) The multipliers 3 and $\frac{1}{2}$ have the same place value.
   (e) 3.5 is more precise than $3\frac{1}{2}$.

8. *The relationship of an algorithm to properties of operation.*
   What property of multiplication explains why $34 \times 15 = (34 \times 3) + (34 \times 5)$?
   (a) Closure.
   (b) Commutativity.
   (c) Associativity.
   (d) Distributivity.
   (e) Inverse operation.

9. *Understanding of the logic and precision of an idea.*
   Which of the following is/are correct for both the set of integers and the set of rational numbers?
   I. Between any two numbers of the set there is a third.
   II. There is a least positive number of the set.
   III. There is a greatest number of the set.
   (a) I only. (b) II only. (c) III only. (d) II and III only. (e) None.

10. *Application of an idea in a new situation.*
    Suppose that we write fractions as ordered pairs. Then $\frac{3}{4}$ is written (3, 4) and $\frac{5}{8}$ is written (5, 8). What would be the sum of (2, 5) and (4, 5)?
    (a) (6, 10).
    (b) (7, 9).
    (c) (6, 5).
    (d) (8, 25).
    (e) (7, 9).

11. *The invention of a new operation and investigation of its properties.*
    The "mean" operation (M) computes the average of two numbers. Thus

    $$aMb = \frac{a + b}{2}$$

What are the properties of the *M* operation?

12. *The invention of a new generalization.*
    Invent a numeration system which has four symbols: □ for zero,
    1 for one, ∧ for two and ▽ for three. What pattern of symbols will
    indicate a number that is divisible by 16?

A 1966 SMSG conference on measuring achievement in mathematics
selected the following behaviors, which indicate increasing levels of cognitive behavior.

Knowing: Knowing terminology, facts, properties, reasons, princi-
                     ples, structure.
                 Knowing why algorithms work.

Translating: Changing from one language to another.
                 Expressing ideas in verbal, symbolic, or geometric form.

Manipulating: Carrying out algorithms.
                 Using techniques.

Choosing: Making comparisons.
                 Selecting appropriate facts and techniques.
                 Conjecturing.
                 Estimating.
                 Changing one's approach.
                 Selecting new symbolism.

Analyzing: Analyzing data.
                 Finding differences.
                 Recognizing relevant and irrelevant information.
                 Seeing patterns, isomorphisms, and symmetries.
                 Analyzing proofs.
                 Recognizing need for additional information.
                 Recognizing need for proof or counter-example.

Synthesizing: Specializing and generalizing.
                 Formulating problems.
                 Constructing a proof or a problem.

Evaluating: Validating answers.
                 Judging reasonableness of answers.
                 Validating the solution process.
                 Criticizing proofs.
                 Judging the significance of a problem.

The following outline lists, in ascending order, various activities that
indicate an individual's mastery of the objectives of the cognitive domain:

1. *Knowledge of concepts.*
    1.1 Recognize a statement, definition, formula, symbol.
    1.2 Recall a fact, term, symbol.
    1.3 Restate an idea in new terminology.
    1.4 Differentiate between the properties of the ideas, events, data or
         objects involved.

1.5 Interpret an implication of a principle.
1.6 Integrate an idea into the background of knowledge.
1.7 Understand the logic and precision of an idea.
1.8 Apply an idea in a new problem situation.
1.9 Apply an idea in inventing a new generalization.

2. *Computational skill.*

2.1 Perform the computation correctly.
2.2 Perform the computation efficiently.
2.3 Understand the computation algorithm.
2.4 Relate the algorithm to properties of operations.
2.5 Write a proof of the algorithm.
2.6 Use the operation to establish a mathematical structure.
2.7 Invent a new operation and investigate its properties.

3. *Problem-solving skill.*

3.1 Identify the question to be answered.
3.2 Select the relevant facts.
3.3 Classify the problem according to known types.
3.4 Estimate the answer.
3.5 Set up a model.
3.6 Find the solution of a related problem with simpler conditions.
3.7 Write mathematical sentences expressing relationships.
3.8 Find the solution set.
3.9 Generalize or interpret the solution.
3.10 Determine when a solution is impossible, meaningless, or trivial.
3.11 Analyze the method of solution.

4. *Knowledge of mathematical structures and proof.*

4.1 Recall a proof.
4.2 Complete missing steps of proof.
4.3 Outline a proof. Select related definitions, assumptions, theorems.
4.4 Complete a proof of a statement.
4.5 Prove a theorem by several methods.
4.6 Analyze the steps of a proof by symbolic logic.
4.7 Relate the proof to a mathematical structure.
4.8 Determine the structure of a mathematical topic.
4.9 Invent a new original proof.
4.10 Invent a new mathematical structure.

5. *Skill in communication.*

5.1 Select the correct terms or symbols to complete a statement.
5.2 Restate a generalization in correct language.
5.3 Identify incorrect or irrelevant terms.
5.4 Read and understand a statement of mathematical ideas.
5.5 State generalizations, definitions, ideas in correct languages.
5.6 Present a mathematical idea in terms of a model.
5.7 Write a theme on a mathematical topic.

Benjamin Bloom has classified the objectives of instruction into the cognitive, affective, and psychomotor domains.[1] This classification relates to mathematics in the following categories:

1. *Cognitive Domain: Knowledge, intellectual abilities and skills.*
   a. Knowledge of facts, terms, principles, symbols, concepts.
   b. Computational skill.
   c. Problem-solving skill.
   d. Knowledge of mathematical structures and logical proof.
   e. Skill in communicating mathematical ideas.
2. *Affective Domain: Attitudes, interests, values, habits.*
   a. Appreciation of the role of mathematics in our society.
   b. Interest in learning mathematical ideas.
   c. Independent, well-organized study habits.

Bloom's *Taxonomy* arranges the objectives in ascending order of complexity, each major category building on and including the preceding division. The sample test items below are arranged according to these categories.

1.00 Knowledge.
   1.10 Knowledge of specifics.
      1.11 Knowledge of terminology.
         A meter is a unit of
         (1) Energy.
         (2) Force.
         (3) Distance.
         (4) Area.
         (5) Volume.

      1.12 Knowledge of specific facts.
         The author of the *Elements,* a basic source of geometric information, is _____.

   1.20 Knowledge of ways and means of dealing with specifics.

      1.21 Knowledge of conventions.
         The number of significant digits in 0.0340 is _____.

      1.22 Knowledge of trends and sequences.
         In what sequence are the following area formulas postulated or proved in geometry:
         (1) Triangle $A = \frac{1}{2} bh$.
         (2) Rectangle $A = lw$.
         (3) Parallelogram $A = bh$.
         (4) Trapezoid $A = \frac{1}{2} h (b + b')$.

[1] Benjamin S. Bloom (ed.), *Taxonomy of Educational Objectives* (New York: David McKay Company, 1956).

1.23 Knowledge of classifications and categories.
Which one of the following is *not* a rational number:

(1) π.
(2) $-3\frac{1}{5}$.
(3) 0.
(4) 2.76.
(5) 112_{three}.
(6) .333. . . .

1.24 Knowledge of criteria.
If we set out to prove two polygons similar, which one of
the following is it usual to seek?
(1) Congruent sides.
(2) Congruent sides and angles.
(3) Proportional sides and congruent angles.
(4) Congruent sides and proportional angles.

1.25 Knowledge of methodology.
In indirect proof, alternate conclusions, one of which
must be _____ (true or false), are listed and then all
but one are proved _____ (true or false).

1.30 Knowledge of the universals and abstractions in a field.

1.31 Knowledge of principles and generalizations.
If the product of two natural numbers greater than one
is odd, their sum is:[2]

(1) Odd and less than their product.
(2) Even and less than their product.
(3) Odd and greater than their product.
(4) Even and greater than their product.
(5) Either even or odd.

1.32 Knowledge of theories and structures.
Which of the following is (are) subsystems of the real
number system:
(1) Rational numbers.
(2) Natural numbers.
(3) Complex numbers.
(4) Integers.
(5) Algebraic numbers.

2.00 Comprehension.

2.10 Translation.
Write an equation to represent the graph:

[2] Adapted from Cooperative Mathematics Tests, Form A, Arithmetic, p. 8.

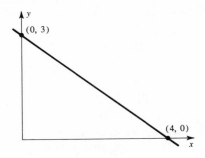

Fig. 23–3

2.20 Interpretation.
    The solution set of the equation $x^2 + px + q = 0$.
    (1) Contains two elements if $p^2/4 - q < 0$.
    (2) Is the empty set if $p^2/4 + q = 0$.
    (3) Is $\{p/2\}$ if $p^2/4 - q = 0$.
    (4) Contains at least one element if $p^2/4 - q \geqslant 0$.
    (5) Is a real number only if $p^2/4 - q > 0$.

2.30 Extrapolation.
    Which of the following numerals represents the largest number?
        (1) 1011_{two}.
        (2) 102_{three}.
        (3) 23_{four}.
        (4) 21_{five}.
        (5) All the numerals above represent the same number.

3.00 Ability to apply knowledge.
    If a and b are two prime numbers each greater than 10, which of the
    following is true?
        (1) $a \times b$ is a prime number.
        (2) $a - b$ is a prime number.
        (3) $a \div b$ is a whole number.
        (4) $a + b$ is an odd number.
        (5) $a \times b$ is an odd number.

4.00 Ability to analyze relationships.

    4.10 Analysis of elements. $\dfrac{(x + 5)}{2}$ is also an integer, then x could
        If x is an integer and
        be

        (1) Any negative integer.
        (2) Any positive integer.
        (3) Any even integer.
        (4) Any odd integer.
        (5) Any multiple of 5.

4.20 Analysis of relationships.

In the problem 54×23, what is the mathematical explanation of the reason we write the 8 under the 6?

$$
\begin{array}{r}
54 \\
23 \\
\hline
162 \\
108 \\
\hline
1242
\end{array}
$$

(1) We write the product under the multiplier.

(2) We write the product in the ten's place because the multiplier is a ten.

(3) We move over one place when multiplying by the second figure.

(4) We are using a shortcut that works.

4.30 Analysis of organizational principles.

Compare the assumptions of euclidean geometry with those of a geometry on a sphere.

5.00 Synthesis.

5.10 Production of a unique communication.

Given the symbols $a, b, c, d, ba, bb, \ldots$ as numerals for $0, 1, 2, 3, 4, 5, \ldots$

Use this new numeration system as answers for these questions.

(1) Write the numeral for forty-five.

(2) What number is represented by the numeral $b\ a\ d$?

(3) Write the numeral for the sum $b\ c + c\ d$.

(4) Write the numeral for the product $(d\ c \times c)$.

(5) What is an equivalent "dot" fraction (decimal) for c/d?

5.20 Production of a plan or proposed set of operations.

Develop a procedure for laying out a baseball diamond by use of plane table and angle mirror.

5.30 Derivation of a set of abstract relations.

Develop a finite mathematical system of four elements with a well-defined operation. Determine the properties and relationships of this system. What mathematical system does it illustrate?

6.00 Evaluation.

6.10 Judgments in terms of internal evidence.

Given H_1, and H_2, is C a valid conclusion?

H_1 All grasps are harpies.

H_2 X is not a grasp.

C X is not a harpie.

6.20 Judgments in terms of external criteria.

Occasionally some people state that euclidean geometry is no longer acceptable, sometimes that it is not correct. Are these statements true? Defend your position. Consider in your answer what you mean by a statement and what you mean when you say a statement is true or false.

The foregoing test items indicate some of the wide variety of areas to be measured. They also indicate to some extent the variety of forms of questioning: completion, multiple choice, true–false, essay, proof, problem solution. Excellent books are available that consider the special values of the various forms of objective and subjective questions.[3]

Question construction is a difficult art. Even national examinations occasionally include errors, for it is difficult to avoid clumsy construction of items or a poor choice of test format. Great care should be taken in test construction, but the teacher must recognize that he will sometimes make errors and have to adjust grades.

The following is an example of the kind of unexpected difficulty that sometimes negates the value of an item:

Considering that $\sqrt{2} = 1.4$, the absolute value of $1 - \sqrt{2}$ is:
   (a) $1 - \sqrt{2}$
   (b) $\sqrt{2} - 1$
   (c) 1.4
   (d) -1.4
   (e) -0.4

Any answer may be justified on the basis that a false hypothesis may lead by correct logic to any conclusion. In this case we cannot "consider that" $\sqrt{2} = 1.4$. Omitting that introductory phrase and appending the word "approximately" after items (c), (d), and (e) would make the item satisfactory.

Careful thought should be given to each test item in order to aim at higher level objectives. This does not mean that factual questions are to be eliminated. They should continue to enjoy a place on examinations. What should be sought, however, is a proper balance between such items and items requiring higher level thinking processes. Consider in this regard the following two items. The first requires only a straightforward application of a basic concept, the second a more thoughtful application of that concept in a broader context:

1. If $N < 0$, which of the following is negative?
   I. N^2 II. N^3 III. N^4

   (a) Only I.
   (b) Only II.
   (c) I and II only.
   (d) I and III only.
   (e) None of these answers.

[3] See William D. Hedges, *Testing and Evaluation for the Sciences* (Belmont, Calif.: Wadsworth Publishing Company, 1966). See also *Evaluation in Mathematics* (Washington, D.C.: National Council of Teachers of Mathematics, 1961).

2. If a, b, and c represent real non-zero numbers, which of the following expressions can equal zero:

  I. $a + b + c$.   III. $a^3 + b^3 + c^3$.
  II. $a^2 + b^2 + c^2$.   IV. $a^4 + b^4 + c^4$.

  (a) Only I.
  (b) Only II.
  (c) II and IV only.
  (d) I and III only.
  (e) None of these answers.

SPECIFIC POINTS TO CONSIDER IN WRITING TEST ITEMS

The writing of good mathematics test items is a complex process. It requires background and skill in mathematics, writing, test construction, learning theory, and curriculum. This section gives only a few specific suggestions or "tricks of the trade" for test construction. For further study, the reader is referred to the test-construction books listed in the bibliography.

1. Plan the test so that major ideas, structures, principles, skills are included. To make the test comprehensive, allocate a balanced number of items to each objective. Exclude insignificant and trivial items.

2. Devise items which test the student's ability to deal with the implementation of facts rather than with the mere recognition of them. Rather than "What is the formula for the area of a circle?" ask "How does the area of a circle with a 3-inch radius compare with the area of a circle with a 6-inch radius?"

3. Write a variety of test items including some in objective form, such as multiple choice, true–false, matching. The type of question used should depend on what is being measured.

4. Write the items in simple, concise, correct language that every student taking the test will understand.

5. Have other mathematics instructors take the test so that they can evaluate it.

6. Write test items on index cards and file them according to topics or objectives for future use.

7. Use some open-ended or interpretive items that measure originality or creativeness. For example: Select a set of four elements, invent a binary operation for combining these elements, and investigate the properties of your system.

8. Write test items which measure aspects of problem solving, such as estimating, selecting a search model, reasoning, and generalizing.

9. Use some essay items which measure communication skill, organization, reflective thinking, and ability to build a mathematical structure. Here is an example: What is wrong with this definition? A triangle is a polynomial with three sides. Write a correct definition of a triangle.

10. Make each item independent of the others. Make sure that no item gives a clue to the answer to another item on the list.

11. Arrange the space for answers in a convenient place. Provide adequate space for writing answers and performing computations.

12. Avoid the use of trick questions. These questions produce hostility and resentment among the students and probably do not measure the objective to which the item is related.

13. Arrange the test items in each section of the test in ascending order of difficulty. Easy items build confidence, reduce tension, and encourage the low achiever to do his best.

14. Discuss test construction, test taking, and test scoring with the students. Describe your method of selecting test items and how you score the test. Discuss time allotment, scoring for guesses, and the problem of cheating. Illustrate how test scores are only approximations of achievement and indicate your concern for giving correct marks.

ACHIEVEMENT EVALUATED BY OBSERVATION

Evaluation by observation of learning activities has decided advantages over paper-and-pencil tests. Some of these advantages are:

1. Observations can be made of the performance of the pupil in a natural, practical situation.

2. Observations permit the pupil to respond without restrictions or tensions that frequently are concomitant with testing.

3. Observations permit the evaluation of certain outcomes that cannot be obtained in any other way.

4. Observations can be continuous and part of the instructional activities.

5. Observations make possible immediate guidance and remedial teaching before undesirable or incorrect habits become established.

If these observations are to be used effectively, the teacher must know what behavior indicates the attainment of the objectives being evaluated. This will involve factors such as:

1. Understanding the scope of problems at hand.

2. Planning the assembling of information or materials.

3. Locating information and materials.

4. Using instruments and materials skillfully.

5. Organizing activities and recording information.

6. Using ingenuity and resourcefulness in attacking the problem.

7. Exhibiting enthusiasm, energy, interest in the activities.

8. Working cooperatively with others.

9. Completing projects promptly and independently.

Since the recording of these observations is time consuming, it is essential that the teacher use a checklist. The validity and reliability of these observations will also be enhanced if the results of observations are recorded on a progress chart or rating scale.

These rating scales may be constructed in the following manner.

MATHEMATICS PROGRESS CHART

Problem, Unit, Activity_____ Grade____ Date____

Performance			
Code: Excellent (+) Average (0) Unsatisfactory (−)	Paul	Mary	Bill
1. Planning activities			
2. Locating information			
3. Using measuring instruments			
4. Organizing information			
5. Recording data			
6. Computing accurately			
7. Cooperating with others			
8. Completing projects promptly			

ASSIGNING MARKS IN MATHEMATICS

After measuring instruments have been used to provide data, how should marks be determined for each student? A first requirement is that all measures be recorded correctly and be labeled completely so that they can be properly identified. Whenever an error in marking has been made, it should be admitted and corrected. Then these records should always be available for examination by the student, parents, counselors, or substitute teachers. Each student should know what items are taken into account in determining his final course mark. He should know how his teacher will go about determining his mark. And he should know his standing in relation to the comparison group involved. When a student inquires about his standing, the teacher should give complete information and use this opportunity to encourage and inspire better achievement.

Students of all ability levels are sensitive about their marks. They need to be assured that they will be given fair treatment and that their marks will be correct.

Teachers use a variety of schemes for combining measures to determine a final mark. As each teacher does this he (as well as his students) should recognize that all measures are approximations. No matter how carefully he goes about his measurement, some students will be assigned marks which are not correct. Some A's should be B's or C's, and some C's should be A's or maybe F's.

Mathematics teachers like to use a quantitative system for combining measures to determine grades. To do this properly, they should use some system of standard scores to control the weights of different measures. There are teachers who keep a folder of material for each student, so that samples of the student's work are available for conferences and for help in rendering subjective evaluations. The more information available, the more confident the teacher can be in his marking. Hopefully, teachers of the future will have the necessary clerical help and computer facilities so that marking can be less tedious and more accurate.

With computer facilities now available for many schools, it would seem appropriate to keep significant information on a mathematics record card. This card should be a cumulative record of standardized test scores, marks in mathematics, and any other pertinent information. It should be kept in the mathematics department file so that the teachers have at hand significant information about each student.

If feasible, it is recommended that marks for achievement in mathematics be recorded on a special mathematics report form for parents and counselors. Only then can achievement be reported in sufficient detail to be meaningful. This report should indicate achievement in terms of specific objectives and it should also report this achievement with reference to specific comparison groups. Additional information such as standardized test scores or comments should be included. These comments should record special talents, certain difficulties, and unusual achievement. A suggested mathematics report card is illustrated below.

STUDENT REPORT FORM FOR MATHEMATICS

Name: _____

Reporting Period: __First, __Second, __Third, __Fourth, Year____

Course: _____

Section: _____

Mathematical objectives based on measurements	Comparison base				Comments
	Potential ability	Other class members	National norm	College entrants	
1. Understanding of concepts.					
2. Skill in computation.					
3. Ability to solve problems.					

General objectives based on subjective rating	Poor Acceptable Excellent	Comments
1. Attitudes such as appreciation.		
2. Values such as respect for others.		
3. Study habits.		

Mark: _____ Based on achievement in this class as compared with _____.

Comments: _____

Instructor: _____

MARKS FOR STUDENTS IN SPECIAL CLASSES

The assignment of marks for slow learners in special classes or for the accelerated student poses certain questions. Should the top student in the general mathematics class get an A? What mark should the bottom student in the accelerated class get? Some schools prescribe that all grades be below B in general mathematics or that all grades be above C in the accelerated class. This prescription is based on two assumptions: (1) that the mark in a mathematics class is an indication of the absolute level of achievement in mathematics and (2) that the mark in a mathematics class should have its proper weight in determining class rank at graduation or for college entrance. Neither of these arguments is completely acceptable.

Every mark is a comparison, for the mark indicates relative status with respect to a group. An A indicates that this student ranks with the top students of the comparison group (the local school, the city system, a state or national norm group, etc.), and an F indicates a very low rank. However, the crucial question here is of *which* comparison group is the student a member? This group may be the specific class involved, it may be all students of the same course, or all students of the same grade. Only when the A or F is related to the comparison group does it convey much meaning.

It would seem reasonable then that grades for every course in which the students of that course are the comparison group should have an entire range of marks. Thus, the general math student should be able to achieve an A; a calculus student should be able to fail. Only then is maximum information given about a student's relative achievement. Just as a typing class gives grades from A to F, so the general mathematics or accelerated class should have a range of marks from A to F. It is not likely that an A in general mathematics will be equated to an A in accelerated mathematics as far as mathematical competence is concerned.

However, this may pose problems with respect to college entrance possibilities for the talented student in the accelerated class. Rank in a high school graduating class is based on the student's grades in all courses, and this rank is a significant factor in college entrance. If students are to accept assignment to an accelerated class they should not have their college entrance opportunities limited by this assignment. Some system such as the use of an "S" mark or a system of weighting marks in the accelerated class is needed for ranks based on absolute achievement. Another possibility is the use of an appropriate standardized test or common examination to determine the absolute level of mathematics achievement. Where there are multiple sections, common examinations will make it possible to use the larger group as a comparison group. In the case of general mathematics, where motivation is already low, it would seem that successful students should be marked accordingly. Ideally, then, the report form should be such that the mark in any course can be properly interpreted in terms of course content and the comparison group.

LEARNING EXERCISES

1. Write a series of objectives for mathematics in behavioral terms. Arrange the behaviors in a sequence according to the level of mastery indicated by each behavior.

2. Write a mathematics test for a unit or topic.
   a. Write a list of objectives for this unit.
   b. Describe the behavior of a student who has attained these objectives.
   c. Write a series of not less than 25 items of situations, problems, statements in which the student can exhibit the attainment of these objectives. Include a variety of test items. Label each item or section with the objective it measures.
   d. Administer and score the test.
   e. Make an item analysis to determine the difficulty level and discriminatory power of each item.
   f. Use the item analysis to revise the test items.

3. Analyse and evaluate a published standard text. This should include purpose of the test, types of questions, grade level, validity, reliability, norms, ease of administration and scoring, source, and cost.

4. Write a report to a parent, describing the achievement of a student as indicated by a series of recorded measures.

5. Design a record card for the mathematics department which will establish a cumulative record of information significant for mathematics teachers.

6. Design a mathematics report card that will report achievement in mathematics according to objectives. Be sure that the report card indicates the comparison group and the relative status indicated by the marks used.

24

classroom management

As human beings we all want to succeed in our endeavors. We want our colleagues, our administrators, our students, and their parents to say "Well done." However, one of the major stumbling blocks in the way of success as a teacher is the failure to deal with the day-to-day problems of student activities. Consequently, this chapter will suggest ways to meet these problems, even though they are not all unique to the mathematics classroom. A major step toward success is taken when the teacher finds the key to efficient classroom management.

How does a teacher prevent discipline problems? How does he meet them when they occur? What can he do to establish (or even regain) his authority in the classroom? We believe that the basic answers to these questions lie not in a "law enforcement" program, but rather in careful organization of classroom activities and in proper motivational activities. There will always be some students who resist all efforts by adults to help them. Sometimes teachers themselves lack the qualities needed to control a class. The majority of discipline problems are, however, a result of poor classroom management and poor instruction on the part of a teacher who would otherwise succeed.

The adage "Teacher and student suffer together" applies best—or perhaps worst—to the poorly managed classroom. Students who do not know or understand what is expected of them become discipline problems. These students irritate the teacher who in turn reacts harshly and unwisely, and the cyclic pattern, the self-serving spiral of difficulty, resentment, and antipathy is initiated.

The best time to control this ever present teaching danger is at the beginning of the school year. At this time classroom routines should be established and students should be made aware of what is expected of them and what they may expect of you. Unfortunately, it is the beginning teacher who most needs to set up careful ground rules for his teacher-student interaction and who at the same time most often fails to do so. Because of this early failure in their teaching assignments, some teachers leave the profession. Others learn this lesson, salvage their first teaching year as best they can, and start off better in subsequent years. The less fortunate never learn; they merely stagger along, usually hating their work and blaming their lack of success on students or school administrators. Meanwhile, those who start out on the right foot, who provide their students with the real *security* of knowing the rules of learning, who establish in a friendly atmosphere reasonable standards of conduct and work before problems arise, reap the benefits of a much more satisfying experience.

Although we focus on classroom rules and routines in this discussion, each teacher should set out to establish class regulations in a friendly, supportive atmosphere. The teacher should explain why these regulations are necessary, indicating his genuine and primary concern for the student and his progress. The teacher must be sincerely interested in students or such statements will sound foolish, for students today are quick to react negatively to insincerity.

BEGINNING OF THE TERM

One or more periods at the beginning of any course should be devoted to giving students a clearer idea of the content they are to study and the techniques of instruction to be utilized. Specifically, you will wish to answer the following five questions:

1. *What content will the course cover?* Course titles like "Plane Geometry," "Trigonometry," or even "Intermediate Algebra" usually mean little to students. A student's ideas of what a specific course involves are often far from the truth. For example, many students enter a geometry course thinking that it will merely continue and extend the informal—even superficial—study of geometry of the upper primary grades: that is, computing areas and perimeters, identifying figures, and perhaps drawing more complicated diagrams. In this regard, there have been too many cases of weak students being counseled into geometry because they like to draw.

Just telling what the course is, is not enough. Examples are needed in this first introduction to the course. They are especially useful when they relate to what is already part of the students' experience. For example, in geometry a careful proof, in the basic form you plan to use for the course, of an algebraic theorem familiar to the students will show the formal nature of what is to follow.

In many courses you will be traversing ground already familiar to the student but doing so in greater depth than was the case in earlier courses. In college or advanced algebra, for example, logarithms are usually re-examined. An example or two comparing the level of attack you plan to employ with the earlier method of intermediate algebra will quickly demonstrate the approach of the new course:

> In intermediate algebra we were mainly concerned with the use of logarithms to compute problems like simplification of

$$\frac{3.24\,(23.7)^2}{.0674}$$

> We will now be more concerned with deeper understanding of the logarithm as a function, the properties of its graph, and such problems as

> Prove: $\log_N b = 1/\log_b N$

2. *How is the course related to the rest of the academic program?* Students should be told how the course will develop and to what future program it may lead. Consider the following statement:

> Advanced algebra may extend the ideas of elementary and intermediate algebra programs to polynomial equations of degree higher than two, introduce concepts of probability, and provide the algebraic and some of the analytic foundations for a more careful study of the calculus.

While this statement has real meaning to a person familiar with mathematics, it is virtually meaningless to the student. Examples, however, tend to clarify the relation:

> You recall that in intermediate algebra we learned to solve equations of the form $ax^2 + bx + c = 0$, to recognize relationships between roots and coefficients such as the sum of the roots is b/a, and to identify properties of the graph of $f(x) = ax^2 + bx + c$. Now we examine higher degree equations, like $ax^5 + bx^4 + cx^3 + dx^2 + ex + f = 0$, to develop similar methods of attack.

In your introductory discussion it would be well to relate the course to science, business, or education—to mention but three areas in which mathematical applications can be found and in which students have some background and interest. For instance, in an introduction to intermediate algebra you might say:

> In junior high school you learned the simple interest formula $i = prt$. In this course we will develop a formula that extends this idea to the calculation of the return, A, at compound interest: $A = p(1 + r)^t$.
> Such formulas, solved by appropriate short cuts, using calculators or logarithms, provide the basis for the solution of many problems in banking.

Be sure to indicate to students how the course they are now taking fits into the pattern of prerequisites for future study:

> Algebra provides basic tools for solving problems in many fields of study from physics to history, from botany to foreign languages and at the same time for further study in mathematics. Thus, it is one of a sequence of courses required for admission to most colleges. It lays the groundwork (with geometry) for the study of the calculus itself, a basic tool of the sciences, and for the study of finite mathematics, probability, and statistics—all important tools for study in the social sciences.

3. *What will be the teaching techniques used?* The serious student is interested in *how* you plan to teach so that he can adjust to your mode of presentation. The less serious student also needs to know what techniques you will use, if only to avoid later confusion. Will work assignments merely be applications of skills developed in class, or will they require the learning of new material to supplement and extend ideas presented in class? Do you expect students to take notes of ideas developed in class discussions? Will your course be formal—concerned with mathematics developed from a postulational approach—or will it be more concerned with problem solving, discovery, applications of principles, or even immediate utility? A teacher taking a middle-of-the-road approach might say:

> In this class we will be interested in basic principles, of course. One of these is the distributive law which says that for all a, b and c:

$$a(b + c) = ab + ac$$

> We will learn how this law applies to many examples like $(x + 3)$ $(x - 5)$ and $3\frac{1}{7} \times 5$, and even 32×2. Once we have noted how and when to apply the law, I will expect you to use any shortcuts in computation available to you. However, whenever you use a shortcut, you should know its basis so that you could defend it as being mathematically correct.

Your teaching may also rely strongly on student participation. Such participation must be the result of good interaction based on mutual trust, liking, and respect between students and teacher. But it is often well to explain when you want students to participate informally and when you don't, how you expect them to answer your questions, and what are your goals in doing this. Without such background some students will fail to understand that a lesson that is fun for them is also developing good mathematics. (Some teachers actually have had complaints from parents or administrators who are upset by hearing students comment that their math class is "a blast.") Students should understand the serious purpose underlying your most informal classroom activities.

Inexperienced teachers would, in fact, do well to use fewer informal techniques early in the year than they would normally wish to utilize. Informality in the classroom is very useful in relaxing students, in giving them an incentive to participate; but the teacher whose reputation is not already established has difficulty in controlling such a class. It is easier to move from much to little control than to move in the reverse direction.

4. *What will be the role of the student?* Students should know from the outset what will be expected of them in class and out. Are they to participate freely in the development of new ideas? Are interruptions, even contradictions, welcomed?

Will homework be collected regularly? Corrected? Returned? Graded? When can students ask questions? When are they expected to get help with difficult homework—before, during, or after class sessions in which the homework is due? Is cooperative effort on homework between students encouraged or discouraged?

Here is one of many possible plans with regard to homework:

> Homework assignments will usually be given daily. These assignments will be written on the board and should be copied in an assignment notebook or in the upper left corner of the paper to be used for the work. The written part of an assignment should be on 8½" by 11" paper with your name, the date the assignment is due, and the class period recorded in the upper right corner of the first page.
>
> Although I expect reasonable standards of neatness and legibility, I will leave style of presentation flexible and will talk to you individually about it only when I am not satisfied with your work.
>
> Answers for some exercises will be provided so that you have a check on your work. If you have difficulties, make a record of them and we will answer them in class. Do not forget them! Mark the number or numbers of problems about which you still have questions in a circle on the top of your paper. I will go over your work on those problems in detail and will try to write suggestions or corrections. If necessary, I will ask you to see me for more extensive assistance.
>
> Papers should be turned in not later than the second school day after the assignment is given. Although I will check some individual papers each day and all papers on some days, I will always carefully check the problems you indicate.
>
> One final word about homework. Homework is important. I do not assign it merely to keep you busy and out of trouble in study halls. It is assigned to help you learn mathematics and to give direction to independent study—study that is a necessary part of learning the mathematics in this course. In fact, it might well be the most important part of the course for you. Don't shortchange yourself by failing to put real effort into this work.

Along with this information, the teacher should indicate where extra help is available and state a policy regarding absence. Many teachers require a student conference after any absence of more than a day or two, both to check on the student's understanding of material studied independently and to provide extra assistance if it is needed.

5. *What methods of evaluation will be applied?* In these days of the increasing pressure of college entrance and academic success, grading is a serious problem for both student and teacher. Next to problems related to misbehavior, the most common teacher-student difficulties are related to this aspect of the teaching assignment. Your grading policies should be made clear to students early in the term. A written statement directed to

parents as well as students is often appropriate. This statement should outline your grading practice in clear and careful terms.

High school students expect and demand equal treatment. They rebel at anything that smacks—no matter how remotely—of favoritism. For that reason a stated grading policy (obviously one that is not in conflict with school policies) to which the teacher closely adheres gives students real confidence. Here is part of one such statement:

> Semester grades will be based on four factors: (1) one-hour unit tests, (2) short announced and unannounced quizzes, (3) assignments, and (4) my classroom evaluation. The test average, (1) and (2), will determine a basic grade, unit tests counting four times as much as the shorter quizzes. The last two factors will then be used to modify this grade. Homework, because it is not completed under supervision, will not raise grades. Failure to complete assignments without any acceptable reason will reduce borderline grades to the lower grade. Finally, my evaluation will reflect my judgment of your ability to achieve and the effort you evidence in participation in classroom activities. Conduct, good or bad, is evaluated on a separate part of the semester report and will *not* affect the academic grade.

This statement is objective—although teachers who wish to record items in terms of points may find it too subjective. The teacher should modify his grading program, using his professional judgment when necessary and appropriate. However, the more subjective the grading system is, the more it is open to question by student and parent. More important, a subjective system which does not provide for adequate recording tends to make the student unsure about receiving an objective grade.

In discussing grading policy with students, the teacher should be frank to admit the inaccuracies of these measures and the bias in favor of good "test takers." He may even wish to discuss with students their own preference for evaluation procedures. Interestingly enough, students—aside from those clearly identifiable as goldbricks or classroom politicians—tend to favor objective over subjective ratings. Many teachers also carry this one step further, arranging individual conferences when or shortly before marks are assigned. At this time the teacher takes the student's self-evaluation into consideration and compares it with his own evaluation. Often misunderstandings can be averted in this way. When the conference is held a few days before the end of the marking period, students are given the opportunity to make up missing work and are often given the (admittedly superficial and extrinsic) motivation to study hard for that last quiz.

Procedures such as these set the tone for a course, give the student an understanding not only of what he is to study and what is expected of him, but also of what he can expect in return from his teacher. They provide him with a good measure of security.

HOW TO COVER REVIEW

"Deadly" is perhaps the best adjective to describe the extensive review built into many mathematics textbooks and unfortunately translated directly into classroom practice by many teachers. After a summer vacation all students need a review, but a long sequence of review lessons, uninterrupted by anything that could be called new material, impairs student morale.

Perhaps the most striking example of such misguided review is illustrated by an experience of one of the authors of this text. Introduced as a speaker by the president of a junior high school PTA, he was stunned by the final sentence of the introduction:

"Perhaps our speaker this evening will be able to tell us why our sons and daughters in the seventh grade are still—in January—studying the same content they studied last year."

While the teacher should recognize the need for review, he should seek to introduce new ideas early in the course to motivate students and to build their enthusiasm. If this is done in the first few weeks, review can be made part of the over-all program. This program of introducing new material at the outset has an additional advantage not readily apparent to many teachers. During the first week or two of a school year students are rusty. Their past studies are not at their fingertips yet, and they often give the unthinking teacher the impression that they have been poorly taught. (This is one basis for an interesting phenomenon often noted: the tendency for grades to improve from September to May or June.) Tests administered early in September show weaknesses that very probably would be less striking a few weeks later. For this reason it is better to start with fresh material before embarking on review activities in order to give students time to reaccustom themselves to school and to accommodate themselves to you.

But review is necessary and, in fact, is central to the idea of the spiral curriculum, the program in which at higher grade levels you study the same topics but in more sophisticated form and in greater depth. For example, in intermediate algebra the solution of quadratic equations is studied, but the treatment there is in greater depth than the corresponding treatment given in elementary algebra. Here the emphasis is on structure and relationships such as those between roots and coefficients. If such a program is to function properly, topics will be restudied. This does not mean that they should be restudied in the same form. New strategies should be utilized that make review more palatable and that make it, in fact, as exciting as studying new content.

Too often teachers do not think about instruction of a review topic in the same way they think about the instructional program for a new topic. They, too, are bored by repetition. This is a truly unfortunate situation because teaching a topic in a different way can be an exciting challenge, which demands real creativity. (Chapter 4 discusses some of these alternate approaches.) The teacher should seek to develop his own approach, and he should continually search the literature to find ways others have used. In any case, he should be sure that his students recognize the role of review.

All this does not mean that there is no room for straightforward review of content only partly learned or retained. Such review is sometimes necessary and should be part of the program of maintenance for one's own course as well as those taught during previous years. For this kind of maintenance a summary examination is useful to identify general difficulties and to pinpoint specific weaknesses. Usually, such a test will indicate which students need special help and which may be exempt from the review program. These latter students may devote their time more profitably to the study of some optional topic while their classmates seek to strengthen their knowledge of fundamentals.

Every mathematics teacher should accept the responsibility for reviewing concepts and skills of previous mathematics courses. Thus, the algebra teacher includes review of arithmetic skills, and the geometry teacher introduces algebraic concepts whenever possible. Similarly, previously taught concepts are reviewed by including problems from previous lessons in current assignments. One teacher includes some exercises of the previous day's lesson in his daily assignment. He also includes some exercises from lessons or units taught weeks or months previously. Another teacher confines his homework assignments to review exercises so that his students have the necessary background for learning new ideas in class.

Another useful device, one that may supplement the test, is the frequent use of a series of short worksheets. The worksheets are constructed in such a way that the problems on them take a total of about five minutes to complete. Students work a single sheet and correct their work by reference to the answers provided. They note the number of errors they made and seek to determine the cause of their errors. When necessary, they seek help from the teacher or another student. In the next review session they retake the same sheet, or, if they made no errors, move on to the next one in the sequence. Since the stress in such a program is on individual independent activity, the teacher can usually work with a small group of students or with an individual having a specific problem.

Teachers have tried a variety of other approaches to review. Some utilize a short arithmetic-oriented warm-up at the beginning of each class: "Start with 5, add 2, subtract 1½, multiply by . . ." Such a procedure not only provides a short review but it alerts the students, readying them for the classwork ahead.

Elliott Pierson of Weston Junior High School, Weston, Connecticut, has used a game called mathematical baseball with great success. In this game the usual activities of baseball—strikes, hits, outs—are replaced by mathematical questions. The class is divided into two teams and the contest begins. In an activity of this sort, students are excited by the contest and are motivated to do well for their team, a form of motivation that forms the thesis of James S. Coleman's book *The Adolescent Society* (New York: The Free Press of Glencoe, 1961).

Review and maintenance activities should be justified to the students, their importance explained and stressed. One way to do this is to frame questions related to a topic in class in such a way that student responses indicate clearly any need to retrace steps. For example, once a factor of a polynomial is located by an application of the factor theorem, the students may be asked to carry out the division to find the other factor, the depressed polynomial. This latter activity may make it apparent that review of this topic is necessary (before introducing such shortcuts as synthetic division).

Review, reinforcement, and maintenance may best be considered cooperative activities involving student and teacher together. Sometimes parents or fellow students may also play a role in helping students. It is always helpful to make clear to a student what his difficulties are and how he stands in comparison to his classmates in regard to background. It is also appropriate to indicate to him the relative importance of his difficulties so that he can attack the most important problems first. Of course, the sequential character of the mathematics program often makes this difficult. For example, a student may have difficulties in addition and multiplication. Multiplication may be a more important tool for the work you are doing but since it depends on addition—in most developments—addition must be stressed at least equally.

SCHOOL ROUTINES

Each teacher must seek a mean between a classroom program that becomes boring because of its predictable sequence and a program that makes students insecure because they don't know *what* to expect. In a reasonable program this kind of imbalance does not usually become a problem, however. Instead, the routines of attendance taking, announcements, assigning and collecting homework, and record keeping are uniform. Students know that the routine activities of yesterday will be the essential pattern for routine activities today and tomorrow. On the other hand, the mode of presentation of new material, the length of time spent on homework, and the entire structure of the teaching program are modified from day to day to suit content, teacher and student preferences, and even such factors as the day of the week, proximity to a holiday, or time of day.

Routine school tasks in the main require no professional training. Consequently, many schools are turning over such duties to nonprofessionals (or, to use the pedagogical term in current favor, paraprofessionals). Whether or not this is the policy in his school, each teacher should seek to minimize or at least to put into balance the amount of time and energy he expends on these tasks. It is easy for a teacher to become so weighted down with these peripheral activities that they keep him from his central task of planning and executing his teaching program. This does not mean that these "housekeeping" duties should be taken lightly. They are necessary to a successful program. What it does mean is that these duties should not intrude on other classroom responsibilities.

Some teachers use an interesting device for reviewing homework. Students who have difficulty with specific exercises on an assignment put the number of the problem on the board before class. Each student checks the board as he arrives and if he sees the number of an exercise he has solved, he writes out the solution on that panel. This is all accomplished during the first few minutes of class and even a moment or two before class while the teacher makes announcements, takes attendance, or confers with individual students. It not only saves class time and frees the teacher from another directive activity but it also fosters self-reliance and cooperation on the part of students. Once the problem solutions are written out, a few extra minutes for general discussion or further questions completes this part of the class activity.

Some teachers appoint class clerks. Such an assignment may be rotated if it appears to be a burden for any one student. The clerk takes over the duties of taking attendance and reading announcements, if the latter are part of class activity. Clerks or aides may also help with the preparation of hectographed or mimeographed materials, or getting films or tapes ready for class use. Occasionally, with adequate supervision and control, a student may collect and record completed homework and correct objective tests. In fairness to students, such sharing of responsibilities should not only free the teacher but should result in greater return to the students in the form of additional individual attention and an improved learning program. Such student cooperation should be voluntary for these students whose principal goal in school is learning.

Some teachers appoint a student as a class host or hostess. Whenever a visitor arrives in the class, this host or hostess goes to the visitor's assistance, finds a seat for him, gives him a textbook or other material, and describes the lesson being taught. Sometimes a seating chart is handed out so that the visitor can identify each student.

Students may also be involved more directly in the teaching program. One student's helping another may be justified on the basis of the contribution this makes to *both*. Any teacher knows he has learned his subject better when he has to teach it than when he has studied it only for his own benefit. In the same way, the student who tutors a fellow student or even teaches a group of students is forced to organize his information. At the same time, some of the bars to free exchange are let down when a student works with his peers, and some students facing difficulty can better explain and resolve their problems in this setting. However, the teacher should not overwork this technique.

Many students enjoy using the classroom equipment. Some teachers give a special assignment in the use of this equipment to one or two students each day. Instead of preparing the entire assignment, the student prepares only one problem, writing it out in detail on either a ditto master or an overhead-projector transparency for presentation in class. Preparing dittoed copies of homework solutions is also a useful technique in helping a teacher save class time.

In today's secondary school classrooms, little grouping is attempted. In most classes the teacher works either with individual students or with the entire group. Secondary school teachers could learn much from elementary school classroom teachers about the values of smaller groups. There are, however, some bars to grouping at the higher level, the principal one being the fact that students and teachers are unprepared to accept the technique. One useful procedure that does work well is utilization of a tape table and prerecorded lessons on tape.

Each student wears earphones that carry to him the voice of the teacher prerecorded on tape. The taped voice tells him what to do on a worksheet, explaining procedures and teaching as the teacher would in a tutorial setting. The student's attention is concentrated on the voice and the worksheet. He is virtually oblivious to his neighbor at the table, to whom he cannot speak anyway. While the tape table has a variety of uses, from introducing new material to reviewing old, one of its main advantages lies in the fact that it "assumes complete responsibility for" a group of students. At the same time, the teacher can work with other students in a more intimate setting.

Similar stations with video-tape presentations are already being used in some schools.

DISCIPLINE

Discipline, as has been noted, is largely determined by carefully planned classroom procedures, well identified to students and carried out consistently. But proper discipline is also determined by the teacher's recognition of each student as an important person and by three fundamental teacher qualities: common sense, a sense of humor, and dignity.

Recognition of the problem student as an important person is often a very difficult and complicated procedure for the teacher. The teacher can go just so far in accepting a rebellious, rude student; but the teacher should constantly attempt to think of such a student as at the most only a temporary combatant. Many teachers have had the pleasant experience of meeting a difficult student outside of the school environment—perhaps as a clerk in a store or a service-station attendant—and finding him to be friendly and courteous in the different setting. Thus, it is often best to deal with a student who has a discipline problem outside of the classroom because he might feel more relaxed in a less formal atmosphere.

Students want attention, and they seek it in many ways. The best way is through effort and resulting achievement. The teacher should support such effort with strong positive reactions. Other students seek attention in less socially acceptable ways. If these ways do not gain the desired attention, they are not achieving their purpose. A busy classroom with continual activity works against such students, as does a soft word that doesn't give the sought-for class attention.

Common sense does many things for a teacher. It identifies student attitudes; it tells him if there is time to relax a little in the face of student high spirits; it spots difficulties before they start; and it helps to put the daily work into proper perspective. A sense of humor is only an offshoot of this. It buoys up the teacher and the class and lightens the burden of hard work. Students appreciate a sense of humor when it does not substitute for teaching. In the same way they enjoy fellowship with a teacher, but they soon recognize it as a façade if they discover it masks the style of a lazy teacher.

But most important is dignity. Dignity is not superficial. It is not familiarity—rather it is an acceptance of the basic role of the teacher as an adult acting *in loco parentis*. He is not and cannot be "one of the boys" even though his teaching methods may often bring him into cooperative activity with students. He enjoys his students but does not seek to join them; he understands their motivations, their talents, their ways; but he does not adopt them as his own. He maintains his adult standards and in this way communicates them to the students. He is the authority in the classroom and must not be over-ruled by his students. If students are allowed to defy authority, classroom control becomes impossible.

One characteristic that a teacher might well add to his profile is willingness to accept an occasional defeat. Sometimes a classroom confrontation will turn out badly. A teacher will occasionally require help from an administrator in resolving a discipline problem. And sometimes a class period or even a school day will seem a shambles. The teacher to whom this does not happen is a rarity. The quality teacher accepts this for just what it is, a failure; but he rebounds and tries harder the next day, using new techniques but without hostility.

UNIT PLANS

Many teachers do not prepare unit plans; instead, they prefer to focus their thinking on the day-to-day activities and let the text structure the course. This is unfortunate because the unit plan helps put the daily lessons into broader perspective and at the same time forces a deeper analysis of the content to be taught. It also encourages the teacher to plan for special materials such as films. Such supplementary aids usually require advance requests or at least prior planning for classroom use. The day-by-day planner often thinks of such things too late.

Any experienced teacher who has not tried unit planning should try one unit in one course as a first attempt. If real justice is done to this initial effort, the results will well warrant further work. Here are some of the things that should be considered in organizing the plans for a substantial segment of classwork:

1. Why is this unit important? What are the objectives of the unit? How can I motivate my students? What concepts and skills are directly applicable? Which are the keys to future progress?

2. What are the central ideas and the unifying concepts of the unit, around which activities may be organized? What should be stressed most? How should the class time be divided? How much time should the entire unit take?

3. What teaching strategies are appropriate? Is this the first time students have met these ideas? How can they be tied to past work? How can students develop the ideas themselves? What materials are available to provide a varied attack on the unit? What alternatives are available?

4. What concepts, skills, and experiences are needed as background for this unit? How can the content be modified for students of varying ability? What extra practice can be provided for weak students? What

special teaching techniques may be used with them? What can other students do when weaker students receive special attention? What enrichment topics should be included for all students? What topics should be assigned to bright students only?

5. What teaching techniques will best suit this class? What are the tough spots that require special attention or a different approach? How did I teach this material previously? Should I change my approach or techniques? What lessons are appropriate as laboratory lessons?

6. What materials will this unit require? What supplementary books or pamphlets would be helpful for students? What models, films, or projectuals are appropriate? What should the bulletin board display? Are any field trips or excursions suitable? Who might be a suitable outside speaker or class participant?

7. What kind of evaluation should I use? What ways are best suited to this content and this class? Should I pretest?

8. What kinds of assignments should the students prepare? Are long-term assignments appropriate? Can the students learn part of the material independently?

These questions help to pin down amorphous thinking about teaching problems and help the teacher escape from the textbook. They provide the basis for developing a careful plan of attack that may be put into operation via the daily lesson plans and classroom procedures.

A unit plan should contain these elements:

1. A pretest to determine the skills and background concepts of the students.

2. A statement of objectives in behavioral terms.

3. An outline of the content included, with basic skills and big ideas selected for mastery.

4. A selection of possible learning activities.

5. The teaching procedures and techniques to be used, including motivation and provision for individual differences.

6. A list of materials to be used.

7. A complete set of assignments, differentiated for several levels of ability.

8. An outline of the tests, examinations, and evaluation procedures.

THE DAILY LESSON PLAN

A well-planned lesson builds the confidence of the teacher and gains the confidence of the class. It adds to the effectiveness of every teacher and gains valuable time. Its format may vary, but in general the lesson plan should answer the same questions as asked by the unit plan. Similarly, the lesson plan has the same elements as the unit plan except that it is focused on the objectives and content for a single period. The lesson plan should answer questions such as the following:

1. What are you going to teach?

2. Why is it important for students to learn these ideas?

3. How are you going to introduce the lesson?

4. How are you going to teach the lesson? What key questions are you going to ask? How are you going to get students to discover the generalizations?

5. What materials are you going to use?

6. What learning activities are going to be assigned for independent study?

7. How are you going to end the lesson?

The lesson plan may have any convenient format and may vary in its thoroughness. Ordinarily it is arranged in the order in which activities are to take place. For the novice, a time schedule is helpful. In any case, the plan should be flexible enough to allow for student response. Also, the teacher should know it well enough so that he need not refer to it throughout the lesson.

Here is a sample lesson plan:

SAMPLE LESSON PLAN

Topic

Introduction to the set of integers.

Objective

To learn the order of the set of integers so that we can learn to compute with them.

Introduction

Today we will find a new set of numbers. This set is called the integers. Integers are numbers frequently used in games, in science, and in industry. They are also called the positive and negative integers. Zero is also an integer.

Investigation

What sets of different numbers have we already studied?
What operations have we performed with these numbers?
What properties have we found for these sets of numbers and these operations?
For which operation are these sets not closed?

Procedure

Use a number line to represent the counting numbers. Relate this number line to the scale on a thermometer. Show the one-to-one correspondence of the counting numbers to positive numbers (temperature readings above zero). Show the one-to-one correspondence of the counting numbers to the negative integers (temperatures below zero).

In what situations have you heard about negative numbers?
How are positive and negative integers related to subtraction problems?
How are positive and negative integers related to direction?
How are positive and negative numbers related to opposite quantities?
What is the order of numbers on a temperature scale?
What is a reasonable way to compare numbers on the number line?
If a is a positive integer and b is a negative integer, which of these statements is correct?

$$a < b \qquad a \neq b \qquad a \not< b \qquad a \not> b \qquad a \leq b \qquad a \geq b$$

Assignment

1. Find several illustrations of the use of positive and negative numbers.
2. Write some problems which need positive or negative numbers to represent the quantities involved.
3. What would be a reasonable sum for these additions? Explain your answer.

$$^+5 + {}^+3 \qquad {}^-5 + {}^-7 \qquad {}^+6 + {}^-4 \qquad {}^-7 + {}^+13$$

Here is another sample lesson plan where the goal is to learn to solve a quadratic trinomial by completing the square. The big events of the class period are sketched as follows:

1. Students recognize that there are equations that are difficult to solve by factoring.
2. (*Review.*) Squaring binomials and factoring perfect trinomial squares.
3. Students discover (or help to develop) the technique for changing an equation of the form $x^2 + 2bx + c = 0$ into the form $x^2 + 2bx + b^2 = b^2 - c$.

Now a few questions (more for the beginner) are written out to support big places in the development and problems are solved to avoid pitfalls:

1 a. Solve by factoring: $x^2 - 5x + 6 = 0$; $x^2 - 5x - 6 = 0$; $x^2 - 2x + 1 = 0$; $x^2 - 2x - 1 = 0$. Does the fact that the last equation doesn't factor easily (or in fact factor at all over the integers) mean that it has no roots?

2 a. Perfect trinomial squares: $x^2 - 6x + 9$; $x^2 + \underline{\quad} + 16$; $x^2 + \underline{\quad} + 4$; $x^2 + 10x + \underline{\quad}$; $x^2 + x + \underline{\quad}$; $x^2 + 3x + \underline{\quad}$.

b. Their roots?

c. $x^2 = y^2$ is equivalent to what two linear equations? ($x = y$ and $x = -y$)

3 a. Return to $x^2 - 2x + 1 = 0$ and then $x^2 - 2x - 1 = 0$.

Now prepare the assignment based on your classwork. Know what new concepts you wish to introduce in the assignment and point these out. For example, instead of just saying, "Read pages 136–138," tell what is your purpose in assigning these pages:

Read pages 136–138 to review the class discussion and to learn the steps for solving, by completing the square, quadratic trinomials of the form $x^2 + bx + c = 0$ and $ax^2 + bx + c = 0$, with a, b, c, integers $\neq 0$.

Include textbook exercises when appropriate but supplement or replace them with your own when necessary. Many teachers include one or more review problems with each assignment and often a problem that relates to future work.

Finally, review your plan to see if:

1. You can improve any part.
2. It is about the right length to allow for completion of classroom routines and, if you wish, to allow time for starting the assignment in class.
3. You can use special materials, and which materials you will need.

4. You should assign special responsibilities to your students. Should assignments be varied?

QUESTIONING TO STIMULATE THINKING

Questions can be a means of arousing curiosity, of directing thinking, of checking understanding, of providing practice. Hence, it is important that questions be well planned and that the teacher use a good technique of questioning.

If questions are to be most effective, they should have the following characteristics:

1. The wording of the question should be brief, clear, and definite. A great deal of the difficulty involving questions is due to the fact that the student does not comprehend the question.

2. The question should be adapted to the purpose for which it is used. Thus, discovery questions are open-ended while drill questions are highly specific.

3. The question should be adapted to the ability and background of the students. The language, difficulty, and content will vary from one class to another. Easy questions are directed to the low-ability student and challenging questions to the more talented. However, the question is normally directed to the entire class before designating the specific student for reply. There is no better way of building hostility to mathematics than asking questions which the student can't answer.

4. The question should be stated loudly enough for all students to hear. It is not repeated for the student who is inattentive. Similarly, the student response should be loud enough for the entire class to hear. Expect the class to hear all questions and answers. Do not repeat answers. Require individual responses rather than class responses.

5. Have students ask questions. They should feel secure to ask, but their questions should also be stated clearly.

6. Allow ample time for the student to think about his answer. This time should vary depending on the nature of the question and the student involved.

7. Questions should be asked in a natural conversational tone that indicates confidence in the student. The question or the tone should not suggest the answer.

8. Ask questions that require thinking and understanding. For example: How do you know that is true? What does this mean? Why doesn't John's method work? How can you prove that? Can you think of another example of this idea? What's wrong with Mary's definition?

MOTIVATION

Motivation is the key to learning as well as to an understanding of the dynamics of behavior. We must develop motives in the students that are psychologically sound and socially acceptable, for, when our students are properly motivated, learning becomes a pleasure and teaching becomes an exciting adventure.

As teachers we usually rationalize our lack of success by saying that our students are uninterested, uncooperative, or unable to learn. Instead we might ask whether the trouble lies with the learner or with the teacher. If we could properly motivate our students, we would eliminate or at least reduce most of our behavior problems and problems of individual differences.

Motives largely determine what students learn. At the basic level motives satisfy biological or physiological needs like hunger and sex. While these needs are not acceptable as motivation instruments, they are frequently factors in the classroom environment. Motives must also satisfy social and psychological needs that are the direct responsibility of the teacher. These include:

The need for emotional security, affection, and acceptance.

The need for intellectual security, recognition, and status.

The need for acceptance by and identification with peers.

The need for philosophical security: understanding of values, ideals, goals, and interests.

These basic needs should result in student and teacher concern with reducing emotional tensions such as anxiety, insecurity, anger, frustration, and doubt. In fact, concern with these problems should often override concern with questions of content and presentation.

Here are some specific ways of motivating students to learn mathematics:

A. *Make the work of the mathematics class worthwhile.*
   1. Help the student state his goals.
   2. Find how the mathematics learning will help attain these goals.
   3. Illustrate how the mathematics learning is applied to daily activities, hobbies, sports, interests.
   4. Emphasize the power, usefulness, uniqueness of mathematics.

B. *Make the goals of instruction attainable.*
   1. Adapt the learning activities to the students' ability so that there is some success possible.
   2. Promote a realistic understanding on the part of the student, one which allows him to accept his strengths and weaknesses.
   3. Emphasize the meaning of the mathematical ideas. Build understanding through concrete representations, invention, discovery.
   4. Establish an emotional climate in which the student has a feeling of security even when he is unsuccessful.
   5. Relate the new mathematical idea to an experience in which the student has had a successful or pleasant experience.
   6. Present the idea at a time when the student has the necessary background and achievement, so that success is likely.

7. Establish security by showing how to check solutions, how to correct errors, how to become more efficient.

C. *Use a variety of stimulating classroom techniques.*
   1. Emphasize the pleasure of learning mathematical ideas. Illustrate this by your own enthusiasm, curiosity, and interests.
   2. Use a variety of materials of instruction such as films, models, projectuals, exhibits.
   3. Have a repertoire of anecdotes, illustrations, background information, historical sidelights, unusual problems, unique solutions.
   4. Have each lesson well prepared, so that the student will grow in his confidence in your ability.
   5. Provide laboratory lessons for discovery activities that stimulate curiosity, independent thinking, reasoning, and problem solving.
   6. Assign open-end problems to challenge the gifted.

D. *Provide for student participation in classroom activities.*
   1. Present lessons by a discovery-discussion method that involves all students.
   2. Select students to be responsible for classroom mechanics such as reporting absences, returning paper, collecting material.
   3. Use students as assistant teachers for activities such as writing material on the chalkboard, giving remedial instruction, supervising games.
   4. Plan student demonstrations and discussions of projects, reports, problems, enrichment topics.
   5. Organize student committees to prepare bulletin board displays, assemblies, contests, games.

E. *Provide enrichment material and extracurricular activities.*
   1. Provide a library of enrichment books and pamphlets.
   2. Arrange projects, exhibits, science-fair demonstrations, or assembly programs.
   3. Organize a mathematics club.
   4. Provide student mathematics journals and related periodicals.
   5. Use recreations such as puzzles, games, paradoxes, and tricks.

F. *Use a fair system of marking and reasonable competition.*
   1. Use a fair, understandable method of grading. Keep students informed of their progress and inform them of the basis of grades.
   2. Organize reasonable competition in the form of classroom games, contests, or fairs.
   3. Reward outstanding achievement but avoid publicizing low achievers.
   4. Praise accomplishments instantly and sincerely.

G. *Know the students as individuals.*
   1. Bring the shy student gradually into group activities.
   2. Help the aggressive student by talking to him outside of class.
   3. Note student achievements in outside activities such as athletics and remark on them in class.

4. Avoid harsh sarcasm directed at students.
5. Do not be patronizing.
6. Be fair in discipline.

LEARNING EXERCISES

1. Observe a master teacher. How are routine activities organized? How are discipline problems handled?
2. Read and review recent articles or books on classroom discipline.
3. Compile a list of specific procedures which teachers have found effective in dealing with students.
4. Make up a statement of the basis on which you will determine the report and grades of your students.
5. Select an enrichment topic appropriate for your class. Write a complete unit for this topic.
6. Select a topic for a day's lesson. Write a complete lesson plan for this topic.
7. Make up a set of short review exercises to be used for your course.
8. Write out the lesson plan for your first lesson of the year.
9. Plan a lesson in which you guide your students in a discussion of your problems of discipline, technique of teaching, or method of evaluation.
10. Write a story about a hypothetical discipline problem. Present it to your class as a basis for determining a solution to the problem.
11. What would you do to motivate the following students?

A. A freshman with IQ 140 is taking general mathematics. He finds mathematics very easy but he is too lazy to do more than the required minimum. Due to carelessness his test scores are usually only average. He irritates the teacher by asking irrelevant questions at inopportune times. He is an excellent chess player and athlete.

B. A freshman with IQ 95 is taking general mathematics. He is having a difficult time. He blames the teacher and sees no reason for taking the course, except that it is required for graduation. He is interested in automobiles and hopes to work in a garage someday or to be a pilot. He comes from a culturally deprived home.

C. A sophomore with IQ 105 is taking geometry and doing D work. He is a transfer student from a school where he did C + work in mathematics. His father is a wealthy and successful executive who expects his son to go to college. The student has been in for much extra help, mostly to no avail. His desire to do college-acceptable work has been reduced to an inner fear that he will fail the course.

D. A junior with IQ 115 is taking eleventh-grade algebra. His parents have selected his course of study, expect him to do well in mathematics and science so that he can enter the University. He is not interested in mathematics and has done near-failing work. He feels that he would like to join the army or get a job when he graduates rather than go to college.

E. A junior with IQ 125 is taking eleventh-grade algebra. He works many hours a week at a supermarket to help his widowed mother. He likes algebra, but is depressed by his situation and the possibility of not going to college. Recently he attended a high school event intoxicated. He has been put on probation by the principal.

F. A junior with IQ 110 is taking first-year algebra. He owns a car and works in a garage. He says that he does not understand algebra, but refuses to complete his homework. He always has an excuse for a late assignment or a poor test score. He has been found to cheat on a test. He brags to his friends about his low grades and cheating on tests. He asks what else can life offer besides a car, a job, money, and "friends."

G. An eighth-grade student with IQ 130 dislikes mathematics intensely because her mark is always D. In most of her classes she gets A's and B's. Her computational skill is very poor ($PR = 5$). She seems to be content just to get by in mathematics. Her file shows that she missed a great deal of school during the second and third grades. A note from the counselor interview states that the girl enjoys English and is considering becoming either an English teacher or an elementary teacher.

25

evaluation of teacher effectiveness

There are so many variables in school situations that it is impossible to identify those which influence student achievement significantly: parents, friends, students, school personnel, and the school setting all contribute to the learning of students. This complexity of situation makes the evaluation of instruction, that is, evaluating the teacher's contribution to learning, extremely difficult.

It has been suggested that the effectiveness of instruction should be evaluated in the same manner as performance in business is evaluated, namely on the basis of results produced. A frequently used method of evaluation has been for the teacher to determine what mathematics achievement has resulted from a year of instruction. If the teacher is effective, the students will have learned a great deal. This method of evaluating instruction is rejected by most educators because the amount of mathematical knowledge achieved depends on many factors beyond the control of the teacher: the ability of the students, their previous educational experience, their home and community environment, the total school program, and so on.

QUALITIES REQUIRED FOR SUCCESSFUL TEACHING

The following qualifications are necessary for someone who wants to be a successful mathematics teacher:

1. *Competent in mathematics.* A major requirement for a mathematics teacher is a broad mastery of the subject so that mathematical structure, elegance, and applications are always apparent. The minimum standards for mathematics teachers at various levels are shown in Table 25–1:

TABLE 25–1.   SUMMARY OF RECOMMENDATIONS.[1]

Level	Description	Degree	High School prerequisites	Minimum number of college courses
I	Elementary school.	B. A.	Two years of college preparatory mathematics.	4
II	Elements of Algebra and Geometry.	B. A., Mathematics Minor.	Preparation for Analytic Geometry and Calculus.	7
III	High school.	B. A., Mathematics Major.	Preparation for Analytic Geometry and Calculus.	11
IV	Elements of Calculus, Linear Algebra, Probability, etc.	M. A. in Mathematics.	Preparation for Analytic Geometry and Calculus.	18 (approx.)

COLLEGE MATHEMATICS COURSES

Level	Numbers	Analysis	Algebra	Geometry*	Probability-Statistics	Elective
I	2		1	1		
II		2	1	2	1†	1§
III		2	2	3	2†	2§
IV‡		4	2	3	2	7

*Including Analytic Geometry.
† An introduction to the language of logic and sets should appear in some one course.
‡ The numbers in this row indicate the approximate number of courses.
§ Preferably from the areas specified.

[1] "Recommendations of the Mathematical Association of America for the Training of Teachers of Mathematics." *The American Mathematical Monthly,* December, 1960.

2. *Skillful in communication.* The successful teacher must make mathematical ideas meaningful and comprehensible to his students. Mathematics is not a "spectator sport": communicating mathematics depends on the active participation of the students.

3. *Inspiring values and personality traits.* The mechanics of teaching and subject-matter competence are not enough for successful teaching. Of even greater importance is the teacher as a person. He must have a dynamic personality which encourages students to have positive reactions and attitudes. The teacher must inspire students to accept his guidance and authority. He must enjoy mathematics so that he can learn and teach it enthusiastically.

4. *Understands and accepts students.* Every teacher should understand the minds and hearts of his students. He must realize that his greatest task is to keep his students' thirst for knowledge alive. He must know how to help his students develop positive behavior in their relations with others. He must understand the culture of his students and accept each of them as a worthy human being. He must listen to them and learn their needs and interests.

5. *Competent in professional knowledge.* Professional judgment must be used in making decisions about the content to be taught, the strategies to use, the materials to be involved, and the evaluations of achievement to be made. Hence, it is important that the teacher have an acceptable teaching philosophy, an understanding of curriculum, a background in theories of learning, information about materials of instruction, a knowledge of educational measurement, and a mastery of many teaching techniques.

EVALUATION OF TEACHER EFFECTIVENESS

The qualities for successful teaching enumerated above should be the basis for evaluating a teacher's effectiveness.

1. Competence in mathematics is usually measured in terms of courses completed successfully in college. However, a test of mathematical achievement might be a more accurate measure of a teacher's mathematical competence. Sometimes applicants for teaching positions are asked to solve several mathematical problems prior to their interview. From their approach to these problems some insight can be gained into their attitude as well as their mathematical competence.

2. Skill in communication is more difficult to measure. A test of writing skill or a speech test would be of some significance. Several instruments have been devised to measure the effectiveness of communication by measuring the interaction between students and teachers.

An interaction analysis designed by Muriel Wright records the kind of communication which takes place in the mathematics classroom. A checklist is used to record the type of conversation going on at three-second intervals. The teacher communication is classified into these six categories:

a. Clarifying, encouraging, recognizing, summarizing student participation.

b. Questioning which checks student understanding.

c. Questioning which invites extensive student participation.

d. Questioning which is challenging, comprehensive, or open-ended.

e. Lecturing or giving information.

f. Directing student activities by giving assignments or specific directions.

The students' response to the teachers' communication is also recorded
and classified as follows:

a. Passive reception or responses limited to one-step answers.

b. Active, independent response that indicates interest and thought on
the part of the student.

c. Curious, creative remarks which indicate high level of thought,
application, and originality.

Of course, a final category must be available to record the silence,
confusion, or activity that occurs in the classroom which cannot be classified in the teacher-student interaction categories listed above.

This survey of teacher-student relations does not evaluate the appropri-
ateness of the lesson, of the mathematical ideas involved, or the materials
used. It does not indicate the clarity of the communication, the adaptation
to student needs, or the amount of progress made. It is an instrument to
measure only one aspect of the classroom—teacher-student interaction.

3. Measures of personality and values are even more difficult to obtain.
Checklists, rating sheets, and questionnaires are of some help. The Minnesota Teacher Attitude Inventory is a typical example of one of these
measures. Items on this inventory reflect the teacher's hostilities, feeling of
security, self-righteousness, and rigid standards. Scores on this test are
associated with the ratings of teacher success. In a Teacher Characteristics
Study in 1960, David Ryan reported three personality patterns of teacher
behavior which accounted for significant differences in rating success.

> *Pattern x*—warm, understanding, friendly versus aloof, egocentric,
> restricted teacher behavior.
> *Pattern y*—responsible, businesslike, systematic versus evasive, un-
> planned, slipshod teacher behavior.
> *Pattern z*—stimulating, imaginative, urgent versus dull, routine
> teacher behavior.

The values of the successful mathematics teacher are those beliefs,
ideals, and goals which determine his decisions and actions. Hence, values
such as respect for others, respect for excellence, responsibility, honesty,
and humility can only be measured through personal observation. The
statements, the action, the assignments, the responses of the teacher indicate a teacher's values.

4. A test can measure a teacher's understanding of students but of

equal importance is observing the teacher in the classroom and noting how he responds to the student. The interaction analysis and the teacher attitude inventory noted above both probe this area.

5. The teacher's competence in professional knowledge should be measured by determining how this knowledge functions in the classroom. The rating scale below enumerates some of the many factors the teacher should be rated on when he is observed in the classroom.

TABLE 25–2. PROFESSIONAL COMPETENCE RATING SCALE.

Directions: Rate each item according to the teacher's performance. A zero indicates very unsatisfactory performance and a 10 indicates very superior work. Comments can be used to identify the major basis for the rating.

	0	1	2	3	4	5	6	7	8	9	10	Score
1. Preparation, planning, purpose Comments												
2. Selection of appropriate content Comments												
3. Methods of presentation Comments												
4. Materials of instruction used Comments												
5. Strategies for processes Comments												
6. Questioning and student response Comments												
7. Class control and direction Comments												
8. Expression, speech, communication Comments												
9. Appearance, grooming Comments												
10. Poise, posture, manner Comments												
11. Managing classroom routine Comments												
12. Measurement and evaluation Comments												
13. Provision for individual differences Comments												
14. Assignment of appropriate tasks Comments												
15. Provision for a healthful, attractive, comfortable classroom Comments												

The one danger in using such a scale to evaluate a teacher is that the rater is tempted to total all the scores. Such a procedure would fail to give credit to many highly creative teachers who are not as good in some of the housekeeping aspects of teaching as they are in inspiring students.

SELF-EVALUATION

An effective way of improving teacher effectiveness is to provide the teacher with the assistance of a well qualified supervisor who can advise the teacher on classroom methods. However, most schools do not provide mathematics teachers with such help. One way in which the teacher can make a self-evaluation is to tape-record a lesson or make a video tape recording. Another way for a teacher to provide for evaluation is for him to reflect on what is happening in the classroom and think about ways to improve his teaching. To do this, it is helpful to ask the following questions:

1. Do my students know the purpose of each lesson?
2. Do I do something each day to stimulate student interest in mathematics?
3. Do I ask questions that require reflective thinking?
4. Do I ask students to give reasons for their answers?
5. Do my students feel secure enough to ask questions?
6. Is my classroom attractive and conducive to learning?
7. Are my assignments reasonable and purposeful?
8. Do I vary the requirements and assignments for different individuals?
9. Do I use materials outside of the text as frequently as possible?
10. Do my students know the basis for their grades?
11. Do I give instruction in how to learn mathematics?
12. Are my tests based on my objectives?
13. Do I provide ample time and instruction for the mastery of key concepts and skills?
14. Do I listen to students so that I know their problems and needs?
15. Have I used library or department facilities adequately?
16. Do I relate new ideas to past experiences?
17. How well do I know each of my students?
18. Why do I teach the way I do?
19. Do my students know why I do the things I do in the classroom?
20. Do I point out applications of and ways to transfer mathematical knowledge?
21. Do I encourage students to pursue original ideas, solutions, or proofs?
22. Do I use illustrations, examples, devices that add meaning to concepts?
23. Do I present a personality and appearance that my students accept as desirable?

24. Do I use a variety of tests to improve my instruction and measure the learning of my students?
25. Are routine activities administered efficiently?
26. Do I exercise care to present mathematical ideas correctly?
27. Have I done anything new or different during the past month?
28. Have I learned any new ideas recently?
29. Have I helped a new teacher or another mathematics teacher improve his instruction?
30. Do my students appreciate mathematics more now than they did before they began my course?
31. Do I show my students the same courtesy I expect of them?

PROFESSIONAL ACTIVITIES

As mathematics teachers, we may often feel that we are not able to participate in improving mathematics education outside our own school. Such should not be the case. It is not necessary to be an officer or a committee member of a professional organization or an editor of a professional journal to bring about desirable changes. Every mathematics teacher has the opportunity and the responsibility to work for a better profession. The following are suggested areas for effective professional activities.

1. Become a member of local, state, and national organizations of mathematics teachers and of local, state, and national associations of teachers.
2. Read professional journals, yearbooks, pamphlets, and other professional material so that you are well informed about mathematics education.
3. Attend conferences of mathematics teachers sponsored by the local, state, or national organizations of mathematics teachers and other professional organizations.
4. Incorporate into your mathematics instruction the ideas, materials, and techniques recommended at conferences and in the relevant literature you read.
5. Inform your colleagues, administrators, and community about significant changes and accomplishments in mathematics. Speak to lay groups, PTA, faculty meetings, write for the local paper, and organize parent courses.
6. Support legislation and State Department of Education projects for improved mathematics programs.
7. Plan imaginative projects for the use of government funds. Use federal funds for the purchase of instructional materials.
8. Promote institutes, workshops, conferences, department meetings for local development of improved programs.
9. Contribute ideas that you have found successful by writing articles

for professional journals or local publications or by speaking at conferences.

10. Create new materials, new methods, and even new mathematics for the improvement of mathematics teaching.

If each mathematics teacher participated in these activities to the best of his ability, the quality of mathematics education would increase by leaps and bounds. It would also pay big dividends to the teacher in satisfaction, success, and recognition.

PORTRAIT OF AN "IDEAL" MATHEMATICS TEACHER

In order to evaluate a teacher it is well to have a standard for comparison. Such a standard may be provided by constructing a model for the "ideal" teacher.

The ideal secondary mathematics teacher has a mathematics major that includes courses in modern mathematics beyond that required for a bachelor's degree. In addition, he continues to learn mathematics because he enjoys learning mathematics. He does this through independent reading, through graduate courses, through correspondence courses, or at summer institutes. He has a personal library of books, pamphlets, and journals for study and reference. He belongs to local, state, and national organizations of mathematics teachers, reads their journals, and attends conferences.

The ideal mathematics teacher has high academic ability, broad cultural interests, and a storehouse of information. He is dynamic, friendly, sincere, and enthusiastic. He understands young people and accepts the responsibility of educating them to their maximum potential. He has humility and is honest. He has respect for excellence, and respect for others. He can direct and control student activity in his classroom through his strength of character and his leadership ability.

The ideal teacher communicates clearly, concisely, and correctly. His grammar, enunciation, and voice volume are appropriate for the classroom. His questions are thought-provoking and obtain maximum student participation. He is poised, and meets emergencies with a ready response and a sense of proportion. He does not take himself too seriously, is flexible, and is sensitive to student responses. His grooming, posture, and manner gain the respect and confidence of his students.

His teaching technique is inspiring and efficient. He begins each lesson by motivating the students through his explanation of the purpose of the lesson, by offering a dramatic introduction, or by planning unusual activities. He encourages student participation through questioning, through discovery lessons, or through individual assignments. He uses a variety of types of lessons, activities, and materials, including audio-visual aids, models, applications, anecdotes to add meaning to his instructions. He uses text material other than the class text and gives assignments outside of the text. His assignments vary from day to day and are related to student abilities. He uses enrichment materials regularly and gives remedial instruction.

The ideal teacher has clearly defined goals for his instruction. He knows what material is important, what should be mastered, and where basic ideas are leading. He knows what student behavior indicates mastery and measures achievement in terms of these behaviors. He knows how to write good test items and how to interpret test results. He uses these results to improve his instruction, to help individual students, and to report achievement accurately. His judgment is sometimes based on the results of standardized tests.

The ideal teacher demonstrates good sense in the use of his limited time. He prepares his lessons carefully, and does not waste class time answering individual difficulties, nor does he waste time correcting all homework exercises. He does not use lots of class time for lecturing or for routine activities. He does not use class time for disciplining students. He does provide time for student conferences.

The ideal teacher knows his students' ability, difficulties, special interests, and needs. He helps them learn how to learn, how to use their textbook, how to approach problems. He shares with his students his goals, his problems, and the reasons for his decisions. In other words, the ideal teacher and his students work together as a team striving toward common goals.

Of course, it is always impossible to attain the goal of being an ideal mathematics teacher. If teaching is an art, we must assume that just as the perfect painting has never been achieved the perfect mathematics lesson has never been taught. However, as we strive to improve our instruction, we need to have clearly in mind a standard of performance whereby we evaluate our success as mathematics teachers.

LEARNING EXERCISES

1. To which professional organizations should mathematics teachers of your region belong?
2. Which professional journals should every mathematics teacher read regularly?
3. What significant professional books published within the past two years should every mathematics teacher read?
4. What are some commercial tests for evaluating instruction?
5. Observe a mathematics teacher teach a lesson. What were the strengths and weaknesses of the lesson? What should this teacher do to improve his lesson?
6. Make a job analysis of a mathematics teacher's job. For what tasks are teachers least prepared?
7. What usual teacher tasks should be performed by clerks or paraprofessional workers?
8. What are the most frequent causes for lack of success as a teacher?
9. What help should be given a beginning teacher to help him be successful?
10. Observe a teacher and use a rating scale or interaction analysis for the lesson. What important aspects of the lesson are not covered by your observation instrument?

26

a look into
the future

Our society is a dynamic, continually changing one in which knowledge and resources increase rapidly and unpredictably. Recent technological advances have created numerous devices for communicating mathematics and therefore have wide application for new types of mathematics classroom instruction. Federal support for education provides funds for developing new programs for learners of varied ability. Furthermore, experimental projects such as SMSG and UICSM continue to prepare revised curriculum. And professional organizations are offering journals, supplementary publications, and conferences to keep teachers informed of innovations.

In order to predict the future we need some information for extrapolation. We can provide one location by considering the situation in the mathematics classroom a generation or more ago. Next, we can fix a second point by describing the present situation. These two points will give us a trend line from which to predict what the classroom a generation from now will be like.

1. OBJECTIVES

Past. In the past, teaching objectives were largely limited to having students memorize facts and learn to compute. Rote memorization of rules, shortcuts, and mechanical manipulation were considered satisfactory achievements.

Present. Present objectives for students include computational skill and mastery of ideas, but the emphasis is on computation with understanding. Also, present objectives include broad concepts, understanding of structures, and the ability to solve problems. We pay lip service to developing positive attitudes toward mathematics and appreciation for mathematical ideas as objectives but rarely devote classroom time or provide material for them.

Future. In the future it is likely that objectives will broaden and include those difficult to attain: creativity, positive attitudes, learning how to learn, and values. Our scientific society is dependent upon creating new knowledge and new products. Hence, preparation for becoming creative will be an objective in all fields. Since knowledge will continue to expand we will need to become proficient in learning how to learn—the technique basic to continued adult learning. This will involve learning to use computers as auxiliary memories and for information retrieval. Even so, the traditional goals of computational skill and mastery of concepts will remain important.

In our technological society the educated person has so much power that it is necessary for educators to try to develop values in the student which will enable this power to be directed toward worthy ends. By virtue of his instilling these human values and concerns in a machine-oriented age, the teacher is of increasing importance.

2. CONTENT

Past. The mathematics sequence of the past was organized into narrow, unsophisticated courses: arithmetic in the elementary school; algebra in ninth grade; plane geometry in tenth; and so on.

Present. School mathematics today is a precise, integrated mathematics sequence which emphasizes the structure of the number system, logic, functions, and new topics. In general, topics are treated at an earlier grade than in the past but geometry remains a traditional treatment of deduction at the tenth-grade level.

Future. New topics will be introduced and classical topics will be taught at a lower level. Topics from analytical geometry, linear algebra, and calculus will be integrated into the secondary school sequence. Space concepts normally taught in tenth-grade geometry will be relegated to lower grades and new topics such as transformations, vectors, convex sets, combinatorial topology, and projective geometry may be examined in the geometry of tomorrow.

The trend in content has been to lower the grade level at which topics are introduced, keeping most of the traditional topics but presenting the content in more precise, sophisticated language and adding new topics. The future will see a counteracting trend when the proponents of depth of treatment, problem-solving approaches, and independent study call for a slower pace to allow concentration on these non-content goals.

The current trend has also been away from local development of the curriculum to the adoption of curriculum prepared by national groups such as SMSG. The future will face the issue of greater centralization and standardization through a national curriculum.

3. MATERIAL

Past. The teacher's tools of the past consisted of chalk, red pencil, and textbook.

Present. Today, the materials of the modern secondary school include demonstration models, slide rules, overhead projectors, drawing instruments, graph stencils, measuring instruments, and some enrichment pamphlets and books.

Future. The trend toward increased availability and use of equipment and supplies is strong and clear. The variety of instructional aids being invented and produced is accelerating at an exponential rate. Films, commercial projectuals, computer trainers and computer terminals, manipulative materials, kits, teaching machines, demonstration equipment, laboratory devices, and supplementary books may require the mathematics department of the future to have extensive storage space in every classroom. There will be equipment and supplies for the duplication of material, the production of audio-visual material, and the construction of manipulative material within the classroom or in the department office.

The audio-visual equipment will include three-dimensional motion picture films, film and video tapes, and film loops.

4. EVALUATION

Past. In the past, achievement was measured largely by tests constructed by the teacher. These paper and pencil tests were concerned with evaluating the students' computational skills and their recall of memorized facts.

Present. Today, the additional use of published tests with established norms is common in most schools. In addition, many textbooks include chapter tests and course tests. Some teachers are even giving open-book tests in order to emphasize understanding, but most current tests measure only content goals.

Future. As the objectives of school mathematics change, new tests will be needed to measure creativity, attitudes, and values. New tests such as performance tests, reading tests, and problem-solving tests will be devised. It is likely that in the future these tests will be administered by a computer. The computer will score the test, give an immediate analysis of the performance, and prescribe remedial instruction. The computer will also store information about each student and provide the teacher with a cumulative record at the time grade reports are to be completed. The computer will also give the teacher an item analysis to be used as a basis for improving his instruction as well as revising the test.

One of the issues to be faced in the near future relates to a national assessment program. There are advantages in having national norms available for comparisons. But there are great dangers, of conformity, for one instance, in the misuse of this powerful program.

5. INDIVIDUAL DIFFERENCES

Past. In the past, little attention was given to the needs of individual students. The mathematics courses of grades 9 through 12 were largely elective and so a selection process resulted in large numbers of dropouts. There was usually a single-track college preparatory curriculum.

Present. Today, the variation in ability and interests at each grade level is great and is usually allowed for by a multiple-track curriculum. As a result, our able students are far superior in achievement to those of the previous generation. The poor student or reluctant learner, however, may be further behind and a greater discipline problem than his predecessor. Cultural differences as well as the increasing amount of course content have accentuated the problems of students' varying ability to the point where present curriculum planning procedures are extremely inadequate.

Future. In the future, we will have more information about each student and hence will be better able to provide for his needs, interests, and ability. Some of this information will be more readily at hand because of greater and more effective use of the computer. Special courses and multiple-track curricula will be available. Student advancement from one level to another or from one track to another will be determined on an individual basis and arranged for by flexible scheduling. The idea that every learner should spend the same number of days in a given grade, or the same number of minutes in a mathematics class every day, or that he should study the same textbooks with the same class will be abandoned. Individualized instruction will also be presented by specialists—teachers specifically trained for remedial or clinical work or advanced courses. For the talented there will be greater opportunities for enrichment, for independent study, and for advanced placement.

6. METHOD

Past. The method of the past was largely the stereotype lesson: (1) discussion of questions on homework, (2) discussion of the new process or new theorem, (3) assignment.

Present. The method most commonly used in today's classroom is the same as that of a generation ago. There are only a few teachers who give thoughtful presentations utilizing a variety of materials and who guide the student to discover new ideas.

Future. The methods of the future should be varied. With added resources, more time, and a better professional background, mathematics teachers should be able to present lessons based on a systems development approach; the best technique and material should be selected for each presentation. Increased resources and increased pooling of information and techniques means that many more lessons will encourage and exploit student interests and provide students with exciting participation opportunities. Discovery and laboratory learning techniques will be central to this new approach.

The ideal instruction has always been a one-to-one relationship between student and teacher. But it has been impossible to attain this individualized instruction in our classrooms. We lack the time, the material, and the information about each student needed to make this method effective. However, in the not too distant future, an inexpensive terminal, similar in appearance to an electric typewriter, and connected by telephone to a computer or a two-way television set, will provide each pupil with an individual electronic tutor. This teaching device will present a problem, an idea, or a proof, verbally, orally, and visually. The course will be programmed in the memory of a computer. This computer will act like a teacher as it responds to the learner and presents the ideas, the problems, or the tests which are appropriate for the individual learner. It will even answer the questions of the students. As each learner responds to each question, the computer records the response, the errors, and the time used. The computer then gives the teacher information on student performance and selects the appropriate tutorial material for the next lesson for each student. This is essentially what is now being done by Professor Patrick Suppes in his experimental project in the elementary schools of Palo Alto, California.

Although the computer does a great deal of the work of the teacher—asks questions, answers questions, works exercises, assigns problems, administers tests—it will never replace the teacher. It is more likely to result in the teacher becoming more important than ever, for it is the teacher who will furnish the human element—the values, the affection, the interest which are so essential in the classroom. The computer will release the teacher from clerical, routine tasks so that he will have more time to plan lessons, prepare materials, work with individual students, and develop creative ideas.

7. CLASSROOM

Past. The typical mathematics classroom was a rectangular space whose four walls were covered by chalkboards. The furniture consisted of a teacher's desk and students' desks in fixed position.

Present. The mathematics classroom of today is not different from that of the past. Bulletin boards, projection screens, and a bookcase may be recent additions. In some classrooms the students' desks are now moveable and a filing case has been added to the room.

Future. The classrooms of tomorrow will vary greatly in size and appointments according to their use. Some classrooms will include student stations or carrels much like those of the current language laboratories. Each carrel may have a computer terminal which may be used as a teaching machine. Other classrooms will be learning laboratories for the exploration and discovery of new ideas.

In addition to learning laboratories, the mathematics department will have seminar rooms, a department library, tape, television and computer center, storerooms, and a department office. These rooms will be air-conditioned, with wall-to-wall carpeting, adequately lighted and comfortably furnished so that the physical conditions will be optimal for learning.

8. STAFF

Past. The mathematics teacher of the past had a weak background in mathematics and often taught courses in several other fields. He generally taught all day and was expected to shoulder extra janitorial and community responsibilities.

Present. Today's mathematics teacher has a bachelor's degree with a major in mathematics and, usually, some summer institute experience. A major of 32 semester hours in mathematics is commonly required for certification to teach mathematics in senior high schools. Too often these credits include courses now taught in high school, and the demand for teachers forces schools to hire teachers who do not fulfill even these minimal requirements. A slight reduction in teaching load has resulted in teachers having about one preparation period per day.

Future. The increased sophistication of mathematics courses will require at least five years of college preparation and a strong major that includes courses not presently in the college curriculum. At the same time, teachers will be required to continue learning and to attend professional conferences. Weekly seminars, inservice courses, and summer study will be required. Specialization will increase to the point where there will be special teachers for remedial teaching and special teachers of the gifted. Specialization may even extend to various fields so that one teacher will be a specialist in geometry, another in computer science, and so on. The numbers of auxiliary help, clerical staff, laboratory assistance, and maintenance workers will increase greatly.

As objectives broaden, content varies, and materials increase, the teacher will become increasingly influential. He will need to render professional judgment in his daily decisions, provide the human touch in the classroom, and establish orderly procedures in truly complex situations. To remain up-to-date he will constantly call on the computer to retrieve information which will suggest consequences for given decisions.

Also, staff organization will certainly change. Programs will be much more fluid and students will not expect to see the same teacher at the same hour of each school day. Cooperative teaching arrangements will allow teachers of the same course to develop specific topics for presentation to multiple groups, thus providing each teacher with more preparation time. Teachers will work with groups more varied in size and studying under conditions strikingly different from those of today.

In all of this, the teacher's amount of available time and energy will be acknowledged as a central problem. No longer will a teacher's time for classroom preparation be less than 10 percent of the time he spends in class. Preparation time will rapidly increase to 50 percent or more, because of the additional demands placed on the teacher's instruction time. That means that teachers will be responsible each day for two or three hours of classroom instruction.

UNRESOLVED ISSUES

The spirit of innovation is an outstanding characteristic of mathematics education today. Revolutionary changes in school mathematics are altering traditional content, practices, classroom organization, and basic views of learning. This rapid change brings with it the danger that innovations may become established as new orthodoxies without anyone asking where these innovations are leading or how they should be instituted. Here are some of the unresolved issues, implicit in the previous discussions in this book, facing mathematics educators today.

1. *What are the goals of teaching mathematics?* Are we teaching mathematics for vocational needs, for improved citizenship, or for success in advanced courses? Are we teaching mathematics to change our society or to establish values which will maintain our social order? What is the role of mathematics in the life of all pupils of different abilities and cultures? What is the ideal product of our instruction?

2. *How and by whom shall the content be determined?* What mathematical ideas, skills, attitudes, and habits can be most effectively developed at a given grade level? The new programs have found that we *can* teach complex ideas to very young children. Now the question is what ideas *should* be taught to our pupils? What new topics should be introduced? What traditional topics should be dropped?

3. *How shall programs be varied to provide for different levels of ability?* What enrichment should be provided? How do we accelerate the learning of the talented at all levels? Should calculus be taught in the high school?

4. *How do we teach for transfer so that mathematical principles will be used when needed?* What specific applications need to be included? Are the social applications, such as installment buying, to be taught by some other department?

5. *What degree of rigor of mathematical precision in definitions and proofs is appropriate at various grade levels?* Should mathematical ideas be presented in simple language which, by virtue of its simplicity, is somewhat lacking in precision? What vocabulary and symbolism should be used?

6. *What emphasis should be placed on the structure of mathematics?* How important is it to stress the basic axioms of our number system such as commutivity, associativity, or distributivity? And if these basic ideas are to be taught, what is the best time to teach them?

One of the greatest dangers of the new programs is that the reorganization may go too far and confront students with concepts whose degree of abstraction exceeds the youngsters' mathematical maturity. Excessive abstraction might result in students' bewilderment and revulsion against mathematics rather than their increased knowledge.

7. *What is the role of intuition and concrete representation of mathematical ideas?* How can we transfer from the physical representation to the symbolic?

8. *What emphasis should be given to computational skill?* Can this skill be attained by means other than drill? What level of competence is considered satisfactory at a given level?

9. *What is the role of the computer in the mathematics program?* Should mathematics courses teach computer programming? Should the computer be used to solve problems? Are computers and calculators appropriate tools for the low ability student?

10. *How do we prepare teachers for the new programs?* How is the effectiveness of a teacher measured? What are appropriate mathematics courses for the teacher?

11. *How do we evaluate the effectiveness of a new mathematics program?* What behaviors demonstrate the attainment of objectives? What tests can be used to compare two programs each based on different content?

12. *What criteria should be used in selecting instructional aids?* What sequence of textbooks is most appropriate? Should each mathematics class have several texts and supplementary books or pamphlets? What is the role of programmed texts?

13. *How shall the achievement of students of different ability be graded?* Should the general mathematics class as well as the accelerated class receive the entire range of marks from A to F?

14. *How are students selected for different curriculum tracks?* How can provision be made to transfer from one track to another?

The mathematics program of today is largely the textbook treatment of a generation ago. The activities of the mathematics teacher often consist only in answering questions, working sample exercises, reading definitions, giving assignments, and giving tests. This is not enough. The mathematics teacher must use every possible means to help children to be successful in learning and to enjoy learning mathematics. We can no longer afford to ignore the resources now available for improving mathematics teaching. To prepare for anticipated changes in future school mathematics, we must use every possible means for continued improvement in learning how to teach mathematics. It has been the goal of this text to supply ideas and inspiration to meet this challenge. The Appendices which follow suggest resources which will be helpful at all levels of secondary school mathematics.

suggestions for
further reading

Chapter 1. Introduction to the Teaching of Mathematics

Westcott, Alvin M., and James A. Smith. *Creative Teaching of Mathematics in the Elementary School*. Boston: Allyn and Bacon, 1967.

Willoughby, Stephen S. *Contemporary Teaching of Secondary School Mathematics*. New York: John Wiley & Sons, Inc., 1967.

(See also Appendix C: Books, Pamphlets, Monographs, and Tests.)

Chapter 2. The Goals and Objectives of Mathematics Education

Bloom, B. S., *et al. Taxonomy of Educational Objectives*. New York: David Mckay Co., Inc., 1956.

National Association of Secondary School Principals. *Mathematics in Secondary Schools Today*. Bulletin of the National Association of Secondary School Principals, May 1954.

National Committee on Mathematical Requirements. *The Reorganization of Mathematics in Secondary Education*. Boston: Houghton Mifflin Co., 1923.

National Council of Teachers of Mathematics. *The Place of Mathematics in Secondary Education*, 15th Yearbook. Washington: National Council of Teachers of Mathematics, 1940.

———. *The Growth of Mathematical Ideas*, 24th Yearbook. Ibid., 1959.

———. *Evaluation in Mathematics*, 26th Yearbook. Ibid., 1961.

Peddiwell, J. Abner. *Saber-Tooth Curriculum*. New York: McGraw-Hill Book Co., Inc., 1939.

Rosenberg, Herman. "Values of Mathematics for the Modern World." *Mathematics Teacher*, LIII, 5 (May 1960), 353–358.

Chapter 3. The New School Mathematics

Adler, Irving. "The Cambridge Report: Blueprint or Fantasy." *Mathematics Teacher*, LIX, 3 (March 1966), 210–217.

————. "The Changes Taking Place in Mathematics." *Mathematics Teacher,* LV, 6 (October 1962), 441–451.

Allen, Frank B., *et al. The Revolution in School Mathematics.* Washington, D.C.: National Council of Teachers of Mathematics, 1961.

Allendoerfer, Carl B. "The Second Revolution in Mathematics." *Mathematics Teacher,* LVIII, 8 (December 1965), 690–695.

Brown, Kenneth E., Edwina Deans, and Veryl Schult. "The Lively Third R." *American Education,* June 1966.

Brumfiel, Charles, *et al.* "The Ball State Experimental Program." *Mathematics Teacher,* LIII, 1 (January 1960), 75–84.

Commission on Mathematics. *Program for College Preparatory Mathematics. Report and Appendices.* New York: College Entrance Examination Board, 1959.

Fawcett, Harold P. "Guidelines in Mathematics Education." *Mathematics Teacher,* LIII, 6 (October 1960), 418–423.

Fehr, Howard F. "New Thinking in Mathematical Education." *Mathematics Teacher,* LIII, 6 (October 1960), 424–429.

————. "Reform of Mathematics Education Around the World." *Mathematics Teacher,* LVIII, 1 (January 1965), 37–44.

Ferguson, W. Eugene. "Current Reforms in the Mathematics Curricula—A Passing Phase or Progress?" *Mathematics Teacher,* LVII, 3 (March 1964), 143–148.

Hale, William T. "UICSM's Decade of Experimentation." *Mathematics Teacher,* LIV, 8 (December 1961), 613–618.

Johnson, Donovan A., and Robert Rahtz. *The New Mathematics in Our Schools.* New York: The Macmillan Company, 1966.

Keedy, M. L. "The University of Maryland Project." *Mathematics Teacher,* LII, 4 (April 1959), 281–282.

Kemeny, John G. "Report to the International Congress of Mathematicians." *Mathematics Teacher,* LVI, 2 (February 1963), 66–78.

Kinsella, John. *Secondary School Mathematics.* New York: Center for Applied Research in Education, 1965.

Kline, Morris. "The Ancients vs. the Moderns: A New Battle of the Books." See also, A. E. Meder. "The Ancient vs. the Moderns: A Reply." *Mathematics Teacher,* LI, 6 (October 1958), 418–433.

McCamman, Carol V., and Jane M. Hill. "A Bibliography on the Changing Curriculum in Secondary School Mathematics." *Mathematics Teacher,* LVII, 3 (March 1964), 154–159.

May, Frank P. "Innovations in Senior High School Mathematics." *School Science and Mathematics,* LXV, 4 (April 1965), 336–344.

Meder, A. E. "Sets, Sinners, and Salvation." *Mathematics Teacher,* LII, 6 (October 1959), 434–438.

Mueller, Francis, J. "The Public Image of 'New Mathematics.'" *Mathematics Teacher,* LIX, 6 (October 1966), 618–623 B.

National Association of Secondary School Principals. "New Developments in Secondary School Mathematics." *Bulletin of the National Association of Secondary School Principals,* XLIII, 2 (May 1959), 3–189.

"On the Mathematics Curriculum of High School" (and replies by Edward Begle and Phillip Jones). *Mathematics Teacher,* LV (March 1962), 191–198.

Organization for European Economic Cooperation (OEEC). *New Thinking in School Mathematics.* Washington, D.C.: Organization for European Economic Cooperation (OEEC), 1961.

————. *Mathematics Today, A Guide for Teachers.* Washington, D.C.: Organization for European Economic Cooperation (OEEC), 1963.

Payne, Holland. "What about Modern Programs in Mathematics?." *Mathematics Teacher,* LVIII, 5 (May 1965), 422–424.

Pieters, Richard S., and E. P. Vance. "The Advanced Placement Program." *Mathematics Teacher,* LIV, 4 (April 1961), 201–211.

Rindung, Ole. "The New Mathematics Program in the Danish Gymnasium." *Mathematics Teacher,* LVIII, 2 (February 1965), 150–155.

Secondary School Curriculum Committee of NCTM. "The Secondary Mathematics Curriculum." *Mathematics Teacher,* LII, 5 (May 1959), 389–417.

Stone, Marshall H. "Review of Goals for School Mathematics." *Mathematics Teacher,* LVIII, 4 (April 1965), 353–360.

Taylor, Ross. "First Course in Algebra—UICSM and SMSG: A Comparison." *Mathematics Teacher,* LV, 6 (October 1962), 478–481.

Chapter 4. Strategies for Teaching Mathematical Concepts

Arers, Paul W. "A Unit in High School Geometry Without the Textbook." *Mathematics Teacher,* LVII, 3 (March 1964), 139–142.

Baucom, Thomas V. "Division of Fractions for Understanding." *School Science and Mathematics,* LXV, 5 (May 1965), 432–435.

Bidwell, James King. "From Ratio to Rational Number." *School Science and Mathematics,* LXVI, 7 (October 1966), 661–669.

Fukuda, Donald, *et al.* "A Straight Line Model for Multiplication." *Mathematics Teacher,* LIX, 4 (April 1966), 342–347.

Glicksman, A. M. "Vectors in Algebra and Geometry." *Mathematics Teacher,* LVIII, 4 (April 1965), 327–332.

Hall, H. Eugene. "Another Look at Quadratic Functions." *School Science and Mathematics,* LXV, 7 (October 1965), 610–613.

Hoy, Dorothy H. "Reflexive, Symmetric, and Transitive Properties of Relations." *Mathematics Teacher,* LVIII, 3 (March 1965), 205–210.

Leake, L. "An Iterative Application for Elementary Algebra." *Mathematics Teacher,* LVII, 1 (January 1964), 12–15.

Loeb, A. L. "Remarks on Some Elementary Volume Relations Between Familiar Solids." *Mathematics Teacher,* LVIII, 5 (May 1965), 417–419.

Paige, Donald D. "A Symmetric Numeration System." *School Science and Mathematics,* LXV, 5 (May 1965), 401–404.

Papy, G. "Methods and Techniques of Explaining New Mathematical Concepts in Lower Forms of Secondary Schools, Part I." *Mathematics Teacher,* LVIII, 4 (April 1965), 345–352; "Part II." *Mathematics Teacher,* LVIII, 5 (May 1965), 448–453.

Perisho, Clarence R. "The Use of Transformations in Deriving Equations of Common Geometric Figures." *Mathematics Teacher,* LVIII, 5 (May 1965), 386–392.

Steiner, Hans-Georg. "Relations and Functions." *Mathematics Teacher,* LVIII, 3 (March 1965), 251–257.

Stiel, Edsel F. "Relations and Functions." *Mathematics Teacher,* LVIII, 7 (November 1965), 623–628.

Szabo, Steven. "An Approach to Euclidean Geometry through Vectors." *Mathematics Teacher,* LIX, 3 (March 1966), 218–235.

Vaughan, Herbert E. "An Illustration of the Use of Vector Methods in Geometry." *Mathematics Teacher,* LVIII, 8 (November 1965), 696–701.

Walton, Howard L. "An Examination of the Differences Resulting from Iteration." *Mathematics Teacher,* LVIII, 4 (April 1965), 316–317.

Wernick, William. "Variations on a Theme: $y = 2x - 3$." *Mathematics Teachers,* LIX, 3 (March 1966), 215–256.

Chapter 5. Learning Mathematical Concepts through Discovery

Alfred, Brother U. "A Mathematician's Progress." *Mathematics Teacher,* LIX, 8 (December 1966), 722–727.

Ausubel, D. P. "Some Psychological and Educational Limitations of Learning by Discovery." *The Arithmetic Teacher,* XI, 5 (May 1964), 290–302.

Bolding, James. "A Look at Discovery." *Mathematics Teacher,* LVII, 2 (February 1964), 105–106.

Bruner, J. S. "On Learning Mathematics." *Mathematics Teacher,* LIII, 8 (December 1960), 610–619.

———. *The Process of Education,* Cambridge, Mass.: Harvard University Press, 1960.

Cummins, Kenneth. "A Student Experience—Discovery Approach to Teaching Calculus." *Mathematics Teacher,* LIII, 3 (March 1960), 162–170.

Dienes, Z. P. *Concept Formation and Personality.* Leicester, England: University of Leicester Press, 1959.

———. *An Experimental Study of Mathematics Learning.* London: Hutchinson, 1963.

———. "On the Learning of Mathematics." *Arithmetic Teacher,* X, 3 (March 1963), 115–126.

———. *The Power of Mathematics.* London: Hutchinson, 1964.

Hadamard, Jacques. *The Psychology of Invention in the Mathematical Field.* Princeton, N.J.: Princeton University Press, 1945.

Henderson, Kenneth B. "Anent the Discovery Method." *Mathematics Teacher,* L, 4 (April 1957), 287–291.

———. "Abstractions: Generalizing and Explaining Processes or Relations?" *Mathematics Teacher,* LIV, 8 (December 1961), 600–605.

———. "Strategies for Teaching by the Discovery Method." *Updating Mathematics,* I, 3 (November 1958) and I, 8 (April 1959).

Hendrix, Gertrude, "Learning by Discovery." *Mathematics Teacher,* LIV, 5 (May 1961), 290–299.

Jackson, Robert L., "The Development of a Concept: A Demonstration Lesson." *Mathematics Teacher,* LIV, 2 (February 1961), 82–84.

Lovell, Kenneth. *The Growth of Basic Mathematical and Scientific Concepts in Children.* New York: Philosophical Library, Inc., 1962.

Mathematical Learning. A report edited by Lloyd N. Morrisett and John Visonhaler, Society for Research. Chicago: University of Chicago Press, 1965.

Piaget, Jean. *Child's Conception of Number.* New York: W. W. Norton & Co., Inc., 1961.

Repple, R. E., and V. N. Rockcastle. *Piaget Rediscovered.* New York: Cornell University School of Education, 1964.

Van Engen, Henry. "The Formation of Concepts." *The Learning of Mathematics, Its Theory and Practice,* 21st Yearbook. Washington, D.C.: National Council of Teachers of Mathematics, 1953, 69–98.

Polya, George. *Mathematical Discovery.* Vols. I and II. New York: John Wiley & Sons, Inc., 1965.

Ranucci, Ernest R. "Discovery in Mathematics." *Arithmetic Teacher,* XII, 1 (January 1965), 14–18.

Sharpe, Benjamin. "A Reachable Research Area." *Mathematics Teacher,* LVIII, 5 (May 1965), 420–421.

Smith, Joe K. "Discovery of Patterns in the Difference of Two Squares." *Mathematics Teacher,* LVII, 5 (May 1964), 351–355.

Snyder, Henry D. "An Impromptu Discovery Lesson in Algebra." *Mathematics Teacher,* LVII, 6 (October 1964), 415–416.

Willoughby, Stephen S. "Discovery." *Mathematics Teacher,* LVI, 1 (January 1963), 22–25.

Chapter 6. The Structure and Logic of Mathematics

Allen, Layman E. "Toward Autotelic Learning of Mathematical Logic." *Mathematics Teachers,* LVI, 1 (January 1963), 8–21.

Brant, Vincent, and Merwin L. Keedy. *Elementary Logic for Secondary Schools.* New York: Holt, Rinehart and Winston, Inc., 1962.

Byrkit, Donald R. "On the Inverse of a Function." *School Science and Mathematics,* LXV, 9 (December 1965), 799–800.

Carroll, Lewis. *Symbolic Logic and the Game of Logic.* New York: Dover Publications, Inc., 1958.

Chachere, Marvin L. "The Logic of Absolute Value Inequalities." *Mathematics Teacher,* LVII, 2 (February 1964), 73–74.

Conference Board of the Mathematical Sciences. *The Role of Axiomatics and Problem Solving in Mathematics.* New York: Ginn and Co., 1966.

Exner, Robert M., and Myron F. Rosskopf. *Logic in Elementary Mathematics.* New York: McGraw-Hill Book Company, Inc., 1959.

Falbo, C. E. "Some Axioms for Teaching Real Exponents." *Mathematics Teacher,* LVII, 4 (April 1965), 212–214.

Gardner, Martin. *Logic Machines and Diagrams.* New York: McGraw-Hill Book Company, Inc., 1958.

Ginther, John L. "Strategies for Teaching Concepts by Using Definitions." *Mathematics Teacher,* LIX, 5 (May 1966), 455–457.

Heidlage, Martha. "A Coordinate Approach to the 25-Point Miniature Geometry." *Mathematics Teacher,* LVIII, 2 (February 1965), 109–113.

Heinke, Clarence H. "Sufficient and Necessary Condition." *School Science and Mathematics,* LXV, 7 (October 1965), 601–609.

Henkin, Leon W., *et al. Retracing Elementary Mathematics.* New York: The Macmillan Company, 1962.

Hesser, Sister Francis Mary. "The Land of the Gonks, An Original Postulational System for High School Students." *School Science and Mathematics,* LXVI, 6 (June 1966), 527–531.

Johnson, Donovan A. *Logic and Reasoning in Mathematics.* New York: McGraw-Hill Book Company, Inc., 1963.

Kemeny, John G. "Rigor vs. Intuition in Mathematics." *Mathematics Teacher,* LIV, 1 (January 1961), 66–74.

Klingler, Donn L. "Structuring a Proof." *Mathematics Teacher,* LVII, 4 (April 1965), 200–202.

Leake, Lowell Jr. "Axiom or Theorem?" *Mathematics Teacher,* LIX, 2 (February 1966), 107–109.

Lieber, Lillian R. *Mits, Wits and Logic.* New York: W. W. Norton & Co., Inc., 1947.

MacDonald, I. D. "Abstract Algebra from Axiomatic Geometry." *Mathematics Teacher,* LIX, 2 (February 1966), 98–106.

Norton, M. Scott. *Finite Mathematical Systems.* New York: McGraw-Hill Book Company, Inc., 1963.

Plunkett, Betty. "Aba Daba Daba." *Mathematics Teacher,* LIX, 3 (March 1966), 236–239.

Robinson, Edith. "Strategies on Proof." *Mathematics Teacher,* LVI, 7 (November 1963), 531–534.

Tenney, Arthur E. "Another Format for Proofs in High School Geometry." *Mathematics Teacher,* LVI, 3 (December 1963), 606–607.

Thorsen, Carolyn C. "Structure Diagrams for Geometry Proofs." *Mathematics Teacher,* LVI, 8 (December 1963), 608–609.

Wiseman, John D., Jr. "Complex Contrapositives." *Mathematics Teacher,* LVIII, 4 (April 1965), 323–326.

———. "Scrambled Theorems." *School Science and Mathematics,* LXIV, 5 (May 1964), 423–427.

Yarnelle, John E. *Finite Mathematical Structures.* Boston: D. C. Heath and Co., 1964.

Chapter 7. Developing Computational Skills

Begg, J. B. "The Psychopathology of Arithmetic." *New Approaches to Mathematics Teaching,* F. W. Land, ed. New York: St. Martin's Press, Inc., 1965.

Bilodean, E. *The Acquisition of Skill.* New York: Academic Press, Inc., 1966.

Forsythe, Alexandra. "Mathematics and Computing in High School: A Betrothal." *Mathematics Teacher,* LVII, 1 (January 1964), 2–7.

Grossnickle, Foster E. "Teaching Arithmetic in the Junior High School." *Mathematics Teacher,* XLVII, 8 (December 1954), 520–527.

Hannon, Herbert. "The Role of Meaning in Teaching the Fundamental Processes." *School Science and Mathematics,* LVIII, 2 (February 1958), 83–89.

Johnson, Donovan A. *Games for Learning Mathematics.* Portland, Maine: Walch Publishing Co., 1960.

Sawyer, W. W. *Vision in Elementary Mathematics.* Baltimore: Penguin Books, Inc., 1964.

Sueltz, Ben A. "Drill—Practice—Recurring Experience." *The Learning of Mathematics, Its Theory and Practice,* Washington, D.C.: 21st Yearbook of NCTM, 1953: pp. 192–204.

Van Engen, Henry. "Rate Pairs, Fractions, and Rational Numbers." *Arithmetic Teacher,* VII, 8 (December 1960), 389–399.

Wendt, Arnold. "Per Cent without Cases." *Arithmetic Teacher,* VI, 4 (October 1959), 209–214.

Chapter 8. Learning to Solve Mathematical Problems

Botts, Truman. "Problem Solving in Mathematics, 1." *Mathematics Teacher,* LVIII, 6 (October 1965), 496–500; 2. *Mathematics Teacher,* LVIII, 7 (November 1966), 596–600.

Brown, G. W. "Improving Instruction in Problem Solving in Ninth Grade General Mathematics." *School Science and Mathematics,* LXIV, 5 (May 1964), 341–346.

Charosh, Mannis. *Mathematical Challenges.* Washington, D.C.: National Council of Teachers of Mathematics, 1965.

Conference Board of the Mathematical Sciences. *The Role of Axiomatics and Problem Solving in Mathematics.* New York: Ginn and Co., 1966.

Georges, J. S. "Learning to Solve Problems Intelligently." *School Science and Mathematics,* LVI, 9 (December 1956), 701–707.

Getzels, J. W. "Creative Thinking, Problem Solving and Instruction." 63rd Yearbook of The National Society for the Study of Education, 1964.

Henderson, Kenneth B., and Robert E. Pingry. "Problem Solving in Mathematics." *The Learning of Mathematics, Its Theory and Practice,* 21st Yearbook, Washington, D.C.: National Council of Teachers of Mathematics, 1953. Pp. 228–270.

Polya, George. *Mathematical Discovery,* Vols. I and II, New York: John Wiley & Sons, Inc., 1965.

————. *Mathematics and Plausible Inferences,* Vols. 1 and 2. Princeton, N.J.: Princeton University Press, 1954.

————. "On Learning, Teaching, and Learning Teaching." *American Mathematical Monthly,* LXX, 6 (June–July, 1963), 605–619.

Rosskopf, Myron F. "Transfer of Training." *The Learning of Mathematics, Its Theory and Practice,* 21st Yearbook. Washington, D.C.: National Council of Teachers of Mathematics, 1953. Pp. 205–227.

Snyder, Henry D. "Problem Solutions that Ask Questions." *School Science and Mathematics,* LXVI, 4 (April 1966), 373–376.

Trimble, Harold C. "Problems as Means." *Mathematics Teacher,* LIX, 1 (January 1966), 6–8.

Van Engen, Henry. "The Reform Movement in Arithmetic and the Verbal Problem." *Arithmetic Teacher,* X, 1 (January 1963), 3–6.

Wertheimer, M. *Productive Thinking.* New York: Harper & Row, Publishers, Inc., 1945.

Westcott, Alvin M., and James A. Smith. *Creative Teaching of Mathematics in the Elementary School.* Boston: Allyn and Bacon, 1967.

Chapter 9. Developing Attitudes and Creativity through Enrichment

Bernstein, Allen L. "Motivations in Mathematics." *School Science and Mathematics,* LXIV, 9 (December 1964), 749–754.

Careers in Mathematics. Washington, D.C.: National Council of Teachers of Mathematics, 1961.

Gardiner, Martin. *Mathematical Puzzles and Diversions.* New York: Simon and Schuster, Inc., 1959.

Getzels, Jacob, and Philip Jackson. *Creativity and Intelligence.* New York: John Wiley & Sons, Inc., 1962.

Goldner, Bernard B. *The Strategy of Creative Thinking.* Englewood Cliffs, N.J.: Prentice-Hall, Inc., 1962.

Hartung, Maurice L. "Motivation for Learning Mathematics." *The Learning of Mathematics,* Washington, D.C.: National Council of Teachers of Mathematics, 1953.

Hirschi, L. Edwin. "Encouraging Creativity in the Mathematics Classroom." *Mathematics Teacher,* LVI, 2 (February 1963), 79–83.

Johnson, Donovan A. "Attitudes in the Mathematics Classroom." *School Science and Mathematics,* LVII, 2 (February 1957), 113–120.

————. *"Enriching Mathematics Instruction with Creative Activities."* *Mathematics Teacher,* LV, 4 (April 1962), 238–242.

————. "A Fair for Mathematics with Marathons and a Midway." *School Science and Mathematics,* LXV, 9 (December 1965), 821–824.

————. *Games for Learning Mathematics.* Portland, Maine: Walch Publishing Company.

————. *Invitation to Mathematics.* New York: Doubleday & Co., Inc., 1962.

Malerich, Sister Antone. "A New Look at Enrichment." *Mathematics Teacher,* LVII, 5 (May 1964), 349–351.

Minrath, William R., and Barry R. Nathan. *Challenging Puzzles and Questions in Mathematics.* Princeton, N.J.: D. Van Nostrand Company, Inc., 1962.

Nemecek, Paul M. "Stimulating Pupil Interest." *School Science and Mathematics,* LXV, 1 (January 1965), 47–48.

Peden, Irene C. "The Missing Half of Our Technical Potential: Can We Motivate the Girls?" *Mathematics Teacher,* LVIII, 1 (January 1965), 2–13.

Read, Cecil B. "The Use of the History of Mathematics as a Teaching Tool." *School Science and Mathematics,* LXV, 3 (March 1965), 211–218.

Rogler, Paul V. "The Mathematics League—for Motivation and Inspiration in Mathematics." *Mathematics Teacher,* LVI, 4 (April 1963), 223, 267, 274.

Salkind, C. T. "Annual High School Mathematics Contest." *Mathematics Teacher,* LVII, 2 (February 1964), 75–78.

Schaaf, William L. *Recreational Mathematics.* Washington, D.C.: National Council of Teachers of Mathematics, 1955.

Stein, Sherman K. *Mathematics: The Man-Made Universe.* San Francisco: W. H. Freeman and Co., 1963.

Chapter 10. Teaching the Methods of Learning Mathematics

Brannon, M. J. "Individual Mathematics Study Plan." *Mathematics Teacher,* LV, 1 (January 1962), 52–56.

Dadowian, D. A. *How to Study–How to Solve.* Reading, Mass.: Addison-Wesley Publishing Co., Inc., 1949.

Guff, Ernest R. "The Comparative Effectiveness of One-Level and Three-Level Assignments in Plane Geometry." *Mathematics Teacher,* L, 4 (March 1957), 214–216.

Johnson, Donovan A. "The Readability of Mathematics Books." *Mathematics Teacher,* L, 2 (February 1957), 105–110.

Randall, Karl. "Improving Study Habits in Mathematics." *Mathematics Teacher,* LV, 7 (November 1962), 553–555.

Swain, Henry. *How to Study Mathematics.* Washington, D.C.: National Council of Teachers of Mathematics, 1955.

Chapter 11. Special Instructional Techniques

Akin, C. L. "Do You See the Fallacy?" *Mathematics Teacher,* LVIII, 4 (April 1965), 297.

Allendoerfer, Carl B. "Angles, Arcs, and Archimedes." *Mathematics Teacher,* LVIII, 2 (February 1965), 82–88.

Brendau, Brother T. "How Ptolemy Constructed Trigonometry Tables." *Mathematics Teacher,* LVIII, 2 (February 1965), 141–149.

Comfort, Joseph J. "Permutations from a Different Point of View." *Mathematics Teacher,* LVII, 3 (March 1964), 152–153.

Duncan, Dewey C. "Ten Mathematical Refreshments." *Mathematics Teacher,* LVIII, 2 (February 1965), 102–108.

Harris, Edward M. "Geometric Intuition and $\sqrt{ab} = (a + b)/2$." *Mathematics Teacher,* LVII, 2 (February 1964), 84–85.

Kaner, Samuel. "A Compass-Ruler Method for Constructing Ellipses on Graph Paper." *Mathematics Teacher,* LVIII, 3 (March 1965), 260–261. See also, Henry D. Snyder. "Deductive Proof of Compass-Ruler Method for Constructing Ellipses." *Mathematics Teacher,* LVIII, 3 (March 1965), 261.

Maccia, Alex. "Factoring Using a Square Array." *Mathematics Teacher,* LVIII, 5 (May 1965), 458–460.

Merchant, Charles J. "An Extension of the Averaging Method of Computing Square Roots to the Computation of Roots of any Order." *School Science and Mathematics,* LXV, 2 (February 1965), 143–144.

Morton, Robert L. "Pascal's Triangle and Powers of 11." *Mathematics Teacher* LVII, 6 (October 1964), 392–394.

Myers, Donald E. "Irrationals, Area and Probability." *Mathematics Teacher* LVII, 4 (April 1965), 203–207.

Nannini, Amos. "Geometric Solution of a Quadratic Equation." *Mathematics Teacher,* LIX, 7 (November 1966), 647–649.

Pedley, Arthur H. "A Radical Approach to $\sqrt{ab} = \sqrt{a} \ \sqrt{b}$." *Mathematics Teacher* LVIII, 6 (October 1965), 512–513.

Rotando, Louis M. "Continued Square Roots." *Mathematics Teacher,* LVIII, 6 (October 1965), 507–508.

Schor, Harry. "Altitudes, Medians, Angle Bisectors, and Perpendicular Bisectors of the Sides of Triangles." *Mathematics Teacher,* LVI, 2 (February 1963), 105–106.

———. "An Introduction to the Angle Measurement Theorems in Plane Geometry." *Mathematics Teacher,* LVI, 2 (February 1963), 107–108.

Simpson, Ray H. "Mathematics Teachers and Self-Evaluation Procedures." *Mathematics Teacher,* LVI, 4 (April 1963), 238–244.

Smith, Leander W. "Conditions Governing Numerical Equality of Perimeter, Area, and Volume." *Mathematics Teacher,* LVIII, 4 (April 1965), 303–307.

———. "A Dialogue on Two Triangles." *Mathematics Teacher,* LVII, 4 (April 1964), 233–234.

Twaddle, Richard D. "A Look at Base Negative Ten." *Mathematics Teacher,* LVI, 2 (February 1963), 88–90.

Viertel, William K. "Determining the Central Angles of Zone Boundaries of a Sphere for Zones of Equal Area." *School Science and Mathematics,* LXV, 9 (December 1965), 797–798.

Chapter 12. Teaching the Applications of Mathematics

Ahrendt, Myrl H. *The Mathematics of Space Exploration.* New York: Holt, Rinehart and Winston, Inc., 1965.

Alm, Carol. "The Hardy-Weinberg Law and Genetic Drift." *School Science and Mathematics,* LXV, 9 (December 1965), 801–810.

Bittner, Francis. *Mathematical Aspects of Science.* Garden City, N.Y.: Doubleday & Co., Inc., 1963.

Bowen, John J. "Mathematics and the Teaching of Science." *Mathematics Teacher* LIX, 6 (October 1966), 536–542.

Bryan, William W. "Some Modern Uses of Mathematics." *School Science and Mathematics,* LXIII, 2 (February 1963), 133–139.

Chi-Ming, Chow. "The Relation Between Distance and Sight Area." *Mathematics Teacher,* LVIII, 4 (April 1965), 298–302.

Educational Relations Section. *Mathematics at Work.* Resource units. Detroit: Public Relations Staff, General Motors Corporation.

Fehr, Howard. "The Role of Physics in the Teaching of Mathematics." *Mathematics Teacher,* LVI, 6 (October 1963), 394–399.

Fischer, Irene. "How Far Is It from Here to There?" *Mathematics Teacher,* LVIII, 2 (February 1965), 123–130.

Gramann, Richard H. "A Queing Simulation." *Mathematics Teacher,* LVII, 2 (February 1964), 66–72.

Hooke, Robert, and Douglas Shaffer. *Math and After Math.* New York: Walker & Company, 1965.

Kline, Morris. *Mathematics: A Cultural Approach.* Reading, Mass.: Addison-Wesley Publishing Co., Inc., 1962.

————. *Mathematics in Western Culture.* New York: Oxford University Press, Inc., 1953.

Kruglak, Haym, and John T. Moore. *Basic Mathematics for the Physical Sciences.* New York: McGraw-Hill Book Company, Inc., 1963.

Kullman, David E. "Correlation of Mathematics and Science Teaching." *School Science and Mathematics,* LXVI, 7 (October 1966), 645–649.

Polya, George. *Mathematical Methods in Science, Mathematics Through Science.* Stanford, Calif.: School Mathematics Study Group, 1963.

Ruchlis, Hy. "A Basic Concept—The Impossibility of Continuous Growth," *School Science and Mathematics,* LXV, 5 (May 1965), 416–424.

Schaaf, William L. "Scientific Concepts in the Junior High School Mathematics Curriculum." *School Science and Mathematics,* LXV, 7 (October 1965), 614–625.

Schiffer, Max M. *Applied Mathematics in High School; Mathematics and Living Things.* Stanford, Calif.: School Mathematics Study Group, 1963.

Schippert, Frederick. "The Use of Matrix Algebra in the Analysis of Sociometric Data." *School Science and Mathematics,* LXVI, 8 (December 1966), 783–792.

Siemens, David F., Jr. "The Mathematics of the Honeycomb." *Mathematics Teacher* LVIII, 4 (April 1965), 334–337.

Souers, Charles V. "An Integrated Math-Science Activity for Process Teaching at the Junior High School Level." *School Science and Mathematics,* LXVI, 1 (January 1966), 3–5.

Stratton, William C. "The Velocity of Escape." *Mathematics Teacher,* LVI, 6 (October 1963), 400–402.

Thompson, Robert A. "Using High School Algebra and Geometry in Doppler Satellite Tracking." *Mathematics Teacher,* LVIII, 4 (April 1965), 290–294.

Wick, John W. "Physical Mathematics." *School Science and Mathematics,* LXIII, 8 (November 1963), 619–622.

Wilson, Raymond H., Jr. "The Importance of Mathematics in the Space Age." *Mathematics Teacher,* LVII, 5 (May 1964), 290–297.

Chapter 13. Individual Differences in the Mathematics Classroom

Adler, Irving. "Mental Growth and the Art of Teaching." *Mathematics Teacher,* LIX, 8 (December 1966), 706–715.

Carnahan, Walter W., ed. *Mathematics Clubs in High School.* Washington, D.C.: National Council of Teachers of Mathematics, 1958.

Charosh, Mannis, ed. *Mathematical Challenges.* Washington, D.C.: National Council of Teachers of Mathematics, 1965.

Haas, Victor E. "Addition and Subtraction on the Soroban." *Mathematics Teacher,* LVIII, 7 (November 1965), 608–621.

Harwood. E. Hallie. "Enrichment for All!" *School Science and Mathematics,* LXIII, 5 (May 1963), 415–422 B.

Read, Cecil B. "The History of Mathematics—A Bibliography of Articles in English Appearing in Seven Periodicals." *School Science and Mathematics,* LXVI, 2 (February 1966), 147–179.

Salkind, Charles T. *The Contest Problem Book I, II.* New York: Random House, Inc., 1961.

Schmidt, Roland L. "Using the Library in Junior High School Mathematics Classes." *Mathematics Teacher,* LVI, 1 (January 1963), 40–42.

Smith, Rolland R. "Provisions for Individual Differences." *The Learning of Mathematics, Its Theory and Practice,* 21st Yearbook. Washington, D.C.: National Council of Teachers of Mathematics, 1953. Pp. 271–302.

Sott, Joseph J. "Mathematics Enrichment through Projects." *School Science and Mathematics,* LXVI, 8 (November 1966), 737–738.

Steveson, Peter A. "A Geometrical Approximation of π." *School Science and Mathematics,* LXVI, 5 (May 1966), 426–428.

Walton, Howard L. "Linear Transformations and Their Graphs." *School Science and Mathematics,* LXVI, 4 (April 1966), 331–334.

Chapter 14. A Program for the Low Achiever

Easterday, Kenneth E. "A Technique for Low Achievers." *Mathematics Teacher,* LVIII, 6 (October 1965), 519–521.

"Experiences in Mathematical Discovery Series." Washington, D.C.: National Council of Teachers of Mathematics, 1966.

Fremont, Herbert, and Neal Ehrenberg. "The Hidden Potential of Low Achievers." *Mathematics Teacher,* LIX, 6 (October 1966), 551–557.

Greenholz, Sara. "What's New in Teaching Slow Learners in Junior High School?" *Mathematics Teacher,* LVII, 8 (December 1964), 522–528.

Holt, John. *How Children Fail.* New York: Pitman Publishing Corp., 1964.

Kidd, Kenneth P. "Measuring the Speed of a Baseball." *School Science and Mathematics,* LXVI, 4 (April 1966), 360–364.

Proctor, Amelia D. "A World of Hope—Helping Slow Learners Enjoy Mathematics." *Mathematics Teacher,* LVIII, 2 (February 1965), 118–122.

Sassé, Katherine J. S. "Mathematics for the Noncollege-bound in Junior High School." *Mathematics Teacher,* LVIII, 3 (March 1965), 232–240.

Sobel, Max. "Providing for the Slow Learner in the Junior High School." *Mathematics Teacher,* LII, 5 (May 1959), 347–353.

Wirtz, Robert W. "Nonverbal Instruction." *Arithmetic Teacher,* X, 2 (February 1963), 72–77.

Woodby, Lauren G., ed. *The Low Achiever in Mathematics.* Washington, D.C.: U.S. Government Printing Office, 1965.

Chapter 15. A Program for the Talented

Andree, Josephine P. *Chips from the Mathematical Log.* Stillwater, Okla.: Mu Alpha Theta, University of Oklahoma, 1965.

Bleicher, Michael N. "Searching for Mathematical Talent in Wisconsin." *American Mathematical Monthly,* LXXXII, 4 (April 1965), 412–416.

Braunwart, Robert, III. "Negative and Imaginary Radices." *School Science and Mathematics,* LXV, 4 (April 1965), 292–295.

Brown, K. E. *Education for the Talented in Mathematics and Science.* Washington, D.C.: U.S. Office of Education, 1952.

Cannahan, Walter H. "Iteration." *School Science and Mathematics,* LXVI, 6 (June 1966), 551–555.

Cohen, Donald. "On Organizing a Mathematic League—A Report." *School Science and Mathematics,* LXIII, 2 (February 1963), 145–146.

Duncan, Hilda F. "Fermat's Last Theorem." *Mathematics Teacher,* LVIII, 4 (April 1965), 321–322.

Elkin, Jack M. "A Deceptively Easy Problem." *Mathematics Teacher,* LVIII, 3 (March 1965), 194–199.

Fehr, Howard. "General Ways to Identify Students with Scientific and Mathematical Potential." *Mathematics Teacher,* XLVI, 4 (April 1953), 230–234.

Grossman, George. "Advanced Placement Mathematics—For Whom." *Mathematics Teacher,* LV, 7 (November 1962), 560–566.

Hildreth, Gertrude. *Educating Gifted Children.* New York: Harper & Row Publishers, Inc., 1952.

Hlavaty, Julius H., *et al. Mathematics for the Academically Talented Student in the Secondary School.* Washington, D.C.: National Council of Teachers of Mathematics, 1959.

Johnson, Larry K. "Organizing and Sponsoring a Mathematics Club." *School Science and Mathematics,* LXIII, 5 (May 1963), 424–432.

King, Bruce W. "Snowflake Curves." *Mathematics Teacher,* LVII, 4 (April 1964), 219–222.

Kneale, Brendau. "A Mathematics Competition in California." *American Mathematical Monthly,* LXXIII, 9 (November 1966), 1006–1010.

Lloyd, Daniel B. "Ultra-Curricular Stimulation for the Superior Student." *Mathematics Teacher,* XLVI, 7 (November 1953), 487–489.

Manchester, C., and O. Runquist. "Experimental Programs for Talented High School Students in Mathematics and Science." *Bulletin of National Association of Secondary School Principals,* March 1963.

Metzner, Jerome, and William B. Reiner. "Provisions for the Academically Talented Student in Science and Mathematics." *Review of Educational Research,* XXXI, 3 (June 1961), 323–330.

National Council of Teachers of Mathematics. *Enrichment Mathematics for the Grades,* 27th Yearbook. Washington, D.C.: The Council, 1963.

――――. *Enrichment Mathematics for High School,* 28th Yearbook. Washington, D.C.: The Council, 1963.

Rao, D. Rameswar. "Pythagoras's Theorem? Or the Converse? Which Precedes the Other?" *School Science and Mathematics,* LXVI, 4 (April 1966), 342–344.

Rollins, Wilma E., *et al.* "Concepts of Mathematics—A Unique Program of High School Mathematics for the Gifted Student." *Mathematics Teacher,* LVI, 1 (January 1963), 26–30.

Rosenthal, Evelyn B. "A Scale for Scaleness." *Mathematics Teacher,* LVIII, 4 (April 1965), 318–320.

Rappaport, Elvira. *Hungarian Problem Books,* Vols. 1 and 2. New York: Random House, Inc., 1961.

Salkind, C. T. *The Contest Problem Book.* New York: Random House, Inc., 1961.

Smart, J. R. "Searching for Mathematical Talent in Wisconsin, II." *American Mathematical Monthly,* LXXIII, 4 (April 1966), 401–406.

Thumm, Walter. "Buffon's Needle: Stochastic Determination of π." *Mathematics Teacher,* LVIII, 7 (November 1965), 601–607.

Vance, E. P. *Program Provisions for the Mathematically Gifted Student.* Washington, D.C.: National Council of Teachers of Mathematics, 1957.

Wirszup, Izaak. "The Fourth International Mathematical Olympiad for Students of European Communist Countries." *American Mathematical Monthly,* LXXI, 3 (March 1964), 308–316.

――――. "The School Mathematics Circle and Olympiads at Moscow State University." *Mathematics Teacher,* LVI, 4 (April 1963), 194–210.

Chapter 16. The Role of Models

Bruyr, D. L. *Geometrical Models*. Portland, Maine: Walch Publishing Company, 1963.

Cameron, A. J. *Mathematical Enterprises for Schools*. Long Island City, N.Y.: Pergamon Press, 1966.

Courant, Richard, and Herbert Robbins. *What Is Mathematics?* New York: Oxford University Press, Inc., 1941.

Cundy, H. M., and A. P. Rollett. *Mathematical Models*. New York: Oxford University Press, 1961.

Hess, Adrien L. *Mathematics Project Handbook*. Boston: D. C. Heath and Co., 1962.

Johnson, Donovan A. *Paper Folding for the Mathematics Class*. Washington, D.C.: National Council of Teachers of Mathematics, 1957.

Kenna, L. C., *Understanding Mathematics with Visual Aids*. Paterson, N.J.: Littlefield, Adams & Co., 1962.

National Council of Teachers of Mathematics. *Multisensory Aids in the Teaching of Mathematics,* 18th Yearbook. New York: Teachers College, Columbia University, 1945.

Sawyer, W. W., and L. G. Srawley. *Designing and Making*. Oxford: Basil Blackwell, 1952.

Steinhaus, H. *Mathematical Snapshots*. New York: Oxford University Press, Inc., 1950.

Stover, Donald W. "Projectiles." *Mathematics Teacher,* LVII, 5 (May 1964), 317–322.

Syer, H. W. "Sensory Learning Applied to Mathematics." *The Learning of Mathematics, Its Theory and Practice,* 21st Yearbook. Washington, D.C.: National Council of Teachers of Mathematics, 1953. Pp. 99–155.

Turner, Billy L. *Geometry Teaching Aids You Can Make*. Portland, Maine: Walch Publishing Co., 1958.

Wenninger, Magnus J. "Stellated Rhombic Dodecahedron Puzzle." *Mathematics Teacher,* LVI, 3 (March 1963), 148–150.

————. *Polyhedron Models for the Classroom*. Washington, D.C.: National Council of Teachers of Mathematics, 1966.

Chapter 17. The Role of Audio-Visual Aids

Caroline, Sister Mary. *Bulletin Boards for the New Math*. Dansville, New York: F. A. Owen Publishing Co., 1965.

Educational Media Council. *Educational Media Index, Vol. X. Mathematics*. New York: McGraw-Hill Book Company, Inc., 1964.

Hansen, Viggo P. "New Uses for the Overhead Projector." *Mathematics Teacher,* LIII, 6 (October 1960), 467–469.

Hoisington, Robert. "Semi-Permanent Chalk for Teaching." *Mathematics Teacher,* XLVII, 6 (October 1954), 407.

Johnson, Donovan A., and Charles Lund. *Bulletin Board Displays for Mathematics*. Belmont, California: Dickenson Publishing Company, Inc., 1967.

Krulik, S., and I. Kaufman, *The Overhead Projector in Mathematics Education*. Washington, D.C.: The National Council of Teachers of Mathematics, 1966.

Landin, Leslie. *Living Blackboards*. Palo Alto, Calif.: Fearon Publishers, Inc., 1956.

McCurdy, Sylvia E. "Colored Chalk Techniques for Basic Mathematics." *Mathematics Teacher,* XLVIII, 8 (December 1948), 369–371.

Osborne, Alan R. "Using the Overhead Projector in an Algebra Class." *Mathematics Teacher,* LV, 2 (February 1962), 135–139.

Raab, Joseph A., *et al.* "Reviews of Films." *Mathematics Teacher,* LVI, 8 (December 1963), 578–605.

Vollman, William D., and Philip Peak. *How to Use Films and Filmstrips in Mathematics Classes.* Washington, D.C.: National Council of Teachers of Mathematics, 1960.

Chapter 18. The Role of the Textbook

Forbes, Jack. "Programmed Instructional Materials: Past, Present and Future." *Mathematics Teacher,* LVI, 4 (April 1963), 224–227.

May, Kenneth D. "Programming and Automation." *Mathematics Teacher,* LIX, 5 (May 1966), 444–454.

National Council of Teachers of Mathematics, Committee on Criteria for the Analysis of Instructional Materials. *Aids for Evaluators of Mathematics Textbooks.* Washington, D.C.: The Council, 1965.

Chapter 19. The Role of Computers

Adler, Irving. *Thinking Machines.* New York: John Day Co., 1961.

Biddle, John C. "Resource Unit in Computer Programming for Junior High School." *School Science and Mathematics,* LXVI, 6 (June 1966), 539–550.

Bolt, A. B. *We Built Our Own Computers.* New York: Cambridge University Press, 1966.

Davis, Gordon B. *An Introduction to Electronic Computers.* New York: McGraw-Hill Book Company, Inc., 1965.

Forsythe, Alexandra. "Mathematics and Computing in High School: A Betrothal." *Mathematics Teacher,* LVII, 1 (January 1964), 2–7.

Gutterser, Granville. "A Computer for Every Classroom." *Mathematics Teacher,* LIX, 4 (April 1966), 356–357.

Hausner, Melvin. "On an Easy Construction of a Computing Machine." *Mathematics Teacher,* LIX, 4 (April 1966), 351–355.

Hesse, Allen R. "Iterative Methods in High School Algebra." *Mathematics Teacher,* LVII, 1 (January 1964), 16–17.

Hoffman, Walter, *et al.* "Computers for School Mathematics." *Mathematics Teacher,* LVIII, 5 (May 1965), 393–401.

Horton, George W. "A Boolean Switchboard." *Mathematics Teacher,* LVIII, 3 (March 1965), 211–220. See also, "Enata." *Mathematics Teacher,* LVIII, 6 (October 1965), 513.

Indelicato, Brother Arthur. "Evaluation of Polynomials Using a Computer." *School Science and Mathematics,* LXV, 9 (December 1965), 768–769.

Leake, Lowell. "An Iterative Application of Elementary Algebra." *Mathematics Teacher,* LVII, 1 (January 1964), 12–15.

National Science Teachers Association. *Computers—Theory and Use.* Washington, D.C.: National Science Teachers Association, 1964.

Nygaard, P. H. "Iteration Solution Method." *Mathematics Teacher,* LVII, 1 (January 1964), 8–11.

Organick, Elliott. "SMSG and Computers." *American Mathematical Monthly,* LXXII, 2 (February 1965), 176–177.

Pierson, Elliot. "Junior High Mathematics and the Computer." *Mathematics Teacher,* LVI, 5 (May 1963), 298–301.

School Mathematics Study Group. *Algorithms, Computation and Mathematics.* Stanford, Calif.: School Mathematics Study Group, 1966.

Scientific American. *Information.* San Francisco: W. H. Freeman and Co., 1966.

Tillitt, Harley E., *et al. Computer Oriented Mathematics, An Introduction for Teachers.* Washington, D.C.: National Council of Teachers of Mathematics, 1963.

Vorwald, Alan, and Frank Clark. *Computers from Sand Table to Electronic Brain.* New York: McGraw-Hill Book Company, Inc., 1961.

Chapter 20. Planning, Equipping, and Using the Mathematics Department Facilities

Archer, Allene. *How to Use Your Library in Mathematics.* Washington, D.C.: National Council of Teachers of Mathematics, 1958.

Bartnick, L. P. *A Design for the Mathematics Classroom.* Washington, D.C.: National Council of Teachers of Mathematics, 1957.

Berger, Emil J., and Donovan A. Johnson. *A Guide to the Use and Procurement of Teaching Aids for Mathematics.* Washington, D.C.: National Council of Teachers of Mathematics, 1959.

Frame, J. S. "Facilities for Secondary School Mathematics." *Mathematics Teacher,* LVII, 6 (October 1964), 379–391.

Johnson, Donovan A. "A Design for a Modern Mathematics Classroom." *The Bulletin of the National Association of Secondary School Principals,* XXXVIII, 203 (May 1954), 151–159.

Kenna, L. C. *Understanding Mathematics with Visual Aids.* Paterson, N.J.: Littlefield, Adams Co., 1962.

Woodby, L. G., L. P. Bartneck, and A. W. Calvert. "Planning the Mathematics Classroom." *American School Board Journal,* 144, 5 (May 1962), 37–40.

Chapter 21. Field Trips and Excursions in Indirect Measurement

Boeckmann, Hermann. "Surveying for High School Students." *School Science and Mathematics,* LXIV, 5 (May 1964), 347–352.

Hamilton, W. W. "Field Work Modifies Our Work in Arithmetic." *School Science and Mathematics,* LI, 7 (October 1951), 527–531.

Johnson, Donovan A., and William H. Glenn. *The World of Measurement.* New York: McGraw-Hill Book Company, Inc., 1961.

Kidd, Kenneth P. "Measuring the Speed of a Baseball." *School Science and Mathematics,* LXVI, 4 (April 1966), 360–364.

Ransom, William R. "Some Mirror Trigonometry." *School Science and Mathematics,* LV, 8 (November 1955), 599–600.

Shuster, Carl N., and Fred A. Bedford. *Field Work in Mathematics.* East Palestine, Ohio: Yoder Instruments, 1953.

Chapter 22. Laboratory Lessons

Berger, Emil. "Devices for a Mathematics Laboratory." *Mathematics Teacher,* monthly section October 1950 through June 1954.

————. *Principles Guiding the Use of Teacher- and Pupil-Made Learning Aids,* 22nd Yearbook. Washington, D.C.: National Council of Teachers of Mathematics, 1954. Pp. 158–172.

Bruce, Matthew H. "Using the Cathode Ray Oscilloscope in the High School Trigonometry Class." *School Science and Mathematics,* LX, 8 (November 1960), 593–602.

Bruyr, Donald L. *Geometrical Models.* Portland, Maine: Walch Publishing Co., 1963.

Cameron, A. J. *Mathematical Enterprises for Schools.* New York: Pergamon Press, 1966.

Cundy, H. M., and A. P. Rollett. *Mathematical Models.* Oxford: Clarendon Press, 1951.

Dunn-Rankin, Peter, and Raymond Sweet. "Enrichment: A Geometry Laboratory." *Mathematics Teacher,* LVI, 3 (March 1963), 134–140.

Frame, J. Sutherland. "Facilities for Secondary School Mathematics." *Mathematics Teacher,* LVII, 6 (October 1964), 379–391.

Haddock, Glen, and Donald W. Hight. "Geometric Techniques for Graphing." *Mathematics Teacher,* LIX, 1 (January 1966), 2–5.

Hess, Adrien L. *Mathematics Projects Handbook.* Boston: D. C. Heath & Company, 1962.

Hochstein, A. E. "Trisection of an Angle by Optical Means." *Mathematics Teacher,* LVI, 7 (November 1963), 522–524.

Johnson, Donovan A., *et al. Exploring Mathematics on Your Own.* St. Louis: Webster, 1960. A pamphlet series.

Johnson, Donovan A., *Paper Folding for Mathematics Class.* Washington, D.C.: National Council of Teachers of Mathematics, 1957.

Johnson, Larry K. "The Mathematics Laboratory in Today's Schools." *School Science and Mathematics,* LXII, 8 (November 1962), 586–592.

Kluttz, Marguerite. "The Mathematics Laboratory: A Meaningful Approach to Mathematics Instruction." *Mathematics Teacher,* LVI, 3 (March 1963), 141–145.

Linn, Charles. *Probability and Statistics.* Columbus, Ohio: American Education Publications, 1964.

Maris, Sister M. "The Hypsometer—A Trigonometry Aid." *School Science and Mathematics,* LXVI, 1 (January 1966), 6–12.

Perham, Father Arnold. "An Exercise for the Mathematics Laboratory." *Mathematics Teacher,* LVIII, 2 (February 1965), 114–117.

Phillips, Harry L. "The Mathematics Laboratory." *American Education,* March 1965.

Spencer, Richard V. "Discovery of Basic Inversion Theory by Construction." *Mathematics Teacher,* LVII, 5 (May 1964), 303–306.

Turner, Billie L. *Devices You Can Make for Geometry.* Portland, Maine: Walch Publishing Company, 1958.

Wenninger, Reverend Magnus. "Mathematics of a Combination Sundial and Shadow Calendar." *School Science and Mathematics,* LXIII, 8 (November 1963), 623–633.

Chapter 23. Evaluation of Achievement

Anastasi, Anne. *Testing Problems in Perspective.* Washington, D.C.: American Council on Education, 1966.

Brownell, W. A. *et al. The Measurement of Understanding.* Forty-fifth Yearbook, National Society for the Study of Education, Part I. Chicago: University of Chicago Press, 1946.

Burlow, Elsa H. "Tips on Testing." *School Science and Mathematics,* LXIV, 8 (November 1964), 709–714.

Dutton, W. H. *Evaluating Pupils' Understanding of Arithmetic.* Englewood Cliffs, N.J.: Prentice-Hall, Inc., 1964.

Hanna, Gerald S. "A Summary of the Literature of Geometry Prediction With Emphasis Upon Methodology and Theory." *School Science and Mathematics,* LXVI, 8 (November 1966), 723–728.

Hedges, William D. *Testing and Evaluation for the Sciences.* Belmont, Calif.: Wadsworth Publishing Co., Inc., 1966.

Myers, Sheldon S., and Marion G. Epstein. "Mathematical Reform and the College Board Mathematics Examinations." *American Mathematical Monthly,* LXX, 6 (June–July 1963), 665–667.

Myers, Sheldon S. *Mathematics Tests Available in the United States.* Washington, D.C.: National Council of Teachers of Mathematics, 1959.

National Council of Teachers of Mathematics. *Evaluation in Mathematics,* 26th Yearbook. Washington, D.C.: The Council, 1961.

Chapter 24. Classroom Management

Albrecht, Mary E. "A Teacher Plans Her Day." *Arithmetic Teacher,* III, 4 (October 1956), 151–152.

Brannon, M. J. "Individual Mathematics Study Plan." *Mathematics Teacher,* LV, 1 (January 1962), 52–56.

Clark, John R., and Fehr, Howard F. "Learning, Theory and the Improvement of Instruction." *The Learning of Mathematics, Its Theory and Practice.* Twenty-first Yearbook. Washington, D.C.: National Council of Teachers of Mathematics, 1953.

Dodes, Irving Allen. "Planned Instruction." *The Learning of Mathematics, Its Theory and Practice,* 21st Yearbook, Washington, D.C.: National Council of Teachers of Mathematics, pp. 303–334, 1953.

Evans, Robley, *et al. You and Your Students.* Cambridge, Mass.: Massachusetts Institute of Technology, 1964.

Hankin, Aaron. *Meaningful Mathematics Teaching.* Valley Stream, N.Y.: Teachers Practical Press, 1961.

Hartung, Maurice L. "Motivation for Education in Mathematics." *The Learning of Mathematics, Its Theory and Practice.* Twenty-first Yearbook. Washington, D.C.: National Council of Teachers of Mathematics, 1953.

Kinney, Lucien B., and C. Richard Purdy. *Teaching Mathematics in the Secondary School.* New York: Holt, Rinehart and Winston, Inc., 1952.

Papy, G. "Methods and Techniques of Explaining New Mathematical Concepts in the Lower Forms of Secondary Schools," *Mathematics Teacher,* Part 1, LVIII, 4 (April 1965), 345–352. Part 2, LVIII, 5 (May 1965), 448–452.

Swineford, Edwin J. "Ninety Suggestions on the Teaching Mathematics in the Junior High School." *Mathematics Teacher,* LIV, 3 (March 1961), 145–148.

Wernick, William. "A List of Standard Corrections." *Mathematics Teacher,* LVII, 2 (February 1964), 107.

Chapter 25. Evaluation of Teacher Effectiveness

Butler, Charles H., and F. Lynwood Wren. *The Teaching of Secondary Mathematics.* Chapters 8, 9, 10. New York: McGraw-Hill Book Co., Inc., 1965.

DeVault, M. Vere. *Improving Mathematics Programs.* Columbus, Ohio: Charles E. Merrill Books, Inc., 1961.

Johnson, David C., and Donovan A. Johnson. "Evaluating a School Mathematics Program." *The North Central Association Quarterly,* XLI, 2 (Fall 1966), 184–191.

Polya, George. "On Learning, Teaching, and Learning Teaching." *American Mathematical Monthly*, LXX, 6 (June–July 1963), 605–618.

Ryans, David G. *Characteristics of Teachers*. Washington, D.C.: American Council on Education, 1960.

Wright, E. Muriel J. "A Rationale for Direct Observation of Behaviors in the Classroom." *Research Problems in Mathematics Education*. Washington, D.C.: U.S. Department of Health, Education and Welfare, 1960.

Chapter 26. A Look into the Future

Allendoerfer, Carl B. "The Second Revolution in Mathematics." *Mathematics Teacher*, LVIII, 8 (November 1965), 690–695.

Begle, E. G. "Open Letter to the Mathematical Community." *Mathematics Teacher*, LIX, 4 (April 1966), 341, 393.

Cambridge Conference. *Goals for School Mathematics*. Boston: Houghton Mifflin Co., 1963.

Fawcett, Harold P. "Reflections of a Retiring Mathematics Teacher." *Arithmetic Teacher*, LVII, 7 (November 1964), 450–456.

Fehr, Howard F. "A Unified Mathematics Program for Grades Seven through Twelve." *Mathematics Teacher*, LIX, 5 (May 1966), 463.

Johnson, Donovan A. "Next Steps in Mathematics." *Arithmetic Teacher*, XV, 3 (March 1967), 185–189.

appendix a:
exhibits and displays

The topics listed below are suitable for reports, exhibits, or projects. Those books referred to by author and title are listed in Appendix C. Exhibits are usually judged on the following criteria: originality, completeness, clarity, interest value, craftmanship, and mathematical thought. In order to organize an exhibit that is a success the following suggestions may be helpful:

1. *Select a topic that has interest potential.* The topics listed below suggest some of the many possibilities.

2. *Find as much information about the topic as possible.* Check bibliographies, such as those by Schaaf in *Recreational Mathematics* and in *The Mathematics Teacher.* Check *Reader's Guide* and *Education Index* as well as encyclopedias. The four-volume *The World of Mathematics,* edited by James R. Newman, published by Simon and Schuster, is a gold mine of ideas and material. Other important source books are *Mathematics and the Imagination, Mathematics in Western Culture, Mathematics, Its Magic and Mastery,* and *Fundamentals of Mathematics.* From these sources collect information, ideas, materials.

3. *Prepare and organize your material into a concise, interesting report.* Include drawings in color, pictures, applications, examples that will get the readers' attention and add meaning to your exhibit. Build models, mock-ups, or devices that add interest and understanding of the topics.

4. *Build an exhibit that will tell the story of your topic.* Use models, applications, charts that lend variety. If possible, prepare materials that viewers can manipulate. Give your exhibit a catchy, descriptive title. Label everything with brief captions or legends so that viewers will understand the principles involved. Make the display simple, but also attractive and dramatic. Use color for emphasis. Write captions in a unique way, such as with rope, pipe cleaners, plastic tubing, or yarn. Show craftsmanship, creativeness, diligence in arranging the exhibit. Have a brief summary of the basic ideas, plans, and references for your topic available for distribution.

5. *Be able to demonstrate the topic of your exhibit.* Speak clearly and correctly. Be well informed so that you can answer questions.

Sidelights on Mathematics

Ancient Computing Methods

How do you multiply with roman numerals? What is the scratch system, the doubling system, the lattice method of computations? What changes in our methods of long multiplication and long division are being suggested in recent arithmetic textbooks? How is the abacus used for computation? How are Napier's bones used for multiplication? How did the old computing machines work? How were logarithms invented? Who invented the slide rule?

Exhibit suggestions: Charts of sample computations by ancient methods. Ancient number representations such as pebbles, tally sticks, tally marks in sand, roman number computations, abaci, Napier's bones, old computing devices.

References:

Hogben. *Wonderful World of Mathematics.*

Larsen, Harold D., and H. Glenn Ludlow. *Arithmetic for Colleges* (New York: The Macmillan Company, 1958).

Kokomoor. *Mathematics and Human Affairs* (Englewood Cliffs, N.J.: Prentice-Hall, Inc., 1942).

Cryptography, Codes and Ciphers

How are codes made? What is the difference between codes and ciphers? How are machines used to make codes and to decipher codes?

Exhibit suggestions: Devices or charts for writing and deciphering codes. Code messages. Illustrations of famous codes of the past.

References:

Andree. "Cryptography as a Branch of Mathematics" (*Mathematics Teacher.* November 1952).

Bakst. *Mathematics, Its Magic and Mystery.* Chapter 6.

Laffin, J. *Codes and Cyphers* (New York: Abelard-Schuman, Ltd., 1964).

Peck. *Secret Codes.*

Schaaf. *Recreational Mathematics.* Pp. 107–112.

Smith. *Cryptography* (New York: Dover Publications, Inc., 1943).

Curves and Curve Drawing

What are conic sections, cycloids, spirals, cateraries, cardioids? What are the equations of these curves? How are these curves drawn? Where do these curves occur? How are these curves represented in polar coordinates? What are curves of constant breadth?

Exhibit suggestions: Devices for drawing curves. Models representing these curves. Applications of curves. Curves formed by curve stitching. Graphs and curves in rectangular coordinates, logarithmic coordinates, or polar coordinates. Models of three-dimensional curved surfaces. Designs graphed with sets of equations.

References:

Bakst. *Mathematics, Its Magic and Mystery.* Chapter 24.

Baravalle. "Geometric Drawing," *Multi-Sensory Aids in the Teaching of Mathematics*. Pp. 64–81.

Johnson. *Curves in Space*.

Kline. *Mathematics and Western Culture*. Chapter 12.

Kramer. *The Mainstream of Mathematics*. Chapter 7.

Lockwood. *A Book of Curves* (New York: Cambridge University Press, 1961).

Ogilvy. *Through the Mathescope*.

Curve Stitching

How can curves be formed by straight lines? What is the envelope of a curve? What is a pencil of lines? What curves can be formed by stitching? How can mathematical curves be combined to form beautiful models?

Exhibit suggestions: Stitch a variety of curves with brightly colored yarn or string in two or three dimensions.

References:

Cundy and Rollett. *Mathematical Models*. P. 38.

Johnson. *Curves in Space*.

McCamman, Carol V. "Curve Stitching in Geometry," *Multi-Sensory Aids in Teaching of Mathematics*. Pp. 82–85.

Graphing

What are the different kinds of graphs and graph paper? How do you make three-dimensional graphs? How is graph paper used in designing, enlarging drawings, planning cheering section designs, solving verbal problems, representing numbers, making slide rules? What is a nomograph? Stereograph? How can graphs be used in finding slopes, lengths, areas, perimeters? How do we graph inequalities?

Exhibit suggestions: Types of graphs, types of graph paper, graphs of equations. Graphing on acoustical tile or pegboard with elastic thread for graph lines. Models of stereographs or object graphs. Designs based on graphs of equations or the use of graph paper. Graphs of the common solutions of linear and quadratic graphs.

References:

Bristol. *Graphing Relations and Functions*.

Hogben. *Mathematics for the Millions*. Chapter 9.

Huff. *How to Lie with Statistics*.

Oystein. *Graphs and Their Uses*.

Reynolds. *Shape, Size and Place*.

Shelov. *How to Construct Graphs*.

Magic Squares

What is a magic square? Where and how did magic squares originate? How are magic squares made? How can you make magic squares with algebraic expressions? What games can be played with the principle of the magic square? What are the different kinds of magic squares? How can you make a magic cube?

Exhibit suggestions: Sample magic squares of varied numbers of cells. Illustrations of magic square construction with variations.

References:

Friend. *Numbers, Fun and Fact.*

Kraitchik. *Mathematical Recreations.* Pp. 142–92.

Meyer. *Fun with Mathematics.*

Schaaf. *Recreational Mathematics.* Pp. 68–79.

Mathematical Forms in Nature

What forms in nature represent the graphs of formulas? What shapes in nature are geometric and/or symmetric? What activities in nature illustrate mathematical functions?

Exhibit suggestions: Samples of spiral shells, crystals, ellipsoidal stones or eggs, spiralling sunflower seed pods, branch distributions illustrating Fibonacci series, snowflake patterns, body bones acting as levers, ratio of food consumed to size.

References:

Boys, Charles. *Soap Bubbles* (New York: Dover Publications, Inc., 1959).

Holde, A., and P. Singer. *Crystals and Crystal Growing* (New York: Doubleday & Company, Inc., 1960).

Newman. *World of Mathematics.* "Crystals and the Future of Physics," pp. 871–881; "The Soap Bubble," pp. 891–900; "On Being the Right Size," pp. 925–927; "On Magnitude," pp. 1001–1046.

Thompson. *On Growth and Forms* (New York: Cambridge University Press, 1952).

Wenninger. *Polyhedron Models.*

Measurement and Approximations

How are units of measure invented? What is the difference between accuracy and precision? What special rules must be followed when computing with measurements? Why is progress in science so very dependent on precise measurement?

Exhibit suggestions: Samples of a variety of units of measure, for example, square yard, cubic foot, cubit, furlong, Canadian gallon, grain. Examples of daily measurements, such as shoe size, hats, nails, stockings, calories, board foot. Models of odd measuring devices, such as pedometer, Geiger counter.

References:

Bakst. *Mathematics, Its Magic and Mastery.* Chapter 7.

Bendick. *How Much and How Many.*

Johnson. *The World of Measurement.*

Kokomoor. *Mathematics and Human Affairs.* Chapter 2.

Larsen. *Arithmetic for Colleges.* Chapter 11.

Shuster and Bedford, *Field Work in Mathematics* (East Palestine, Ohio: Yoder Instrument Company).

Number Curiosities

What are prime numbers? Perfect numbers? Amicable numbers? What are some unusual number relations? What are imaginary numbers? Irrational numbers? Complex numbers? Invent a number system that needs three coordinates to express its value. How have numbers been related to superstitions and magic? How have numbers been related to religion? Are there any references in the Bible to the use of mathematical ideas?

Exhibit suggestions: Charts of number relations. Proof that 2 is a prime number. Graphs of complex numbers. Illustrate the size of billion. Illustrate how rapidly a quantity grows by doubling.

References:

Bakst. *Mathematics, Its Magic and Mastery.*

Beiler. *Recreation in the Theory of Numbers.*

Friend. *Numbers, Fun and Facts.*

Gamow. *One, Two, Three, Infinity.*

Hunter. *Fun with Figures.*

Johnson and Glenn. *Number Patterns.*

Kasner and Newman. *Mathematics and the Imagination.* Chapters 1 and 2.

Schaaf. *Recreational Mathematics.* Pp. 27–43.

Optical Illusions

What are some optical illusions? Why do these patterns cause illusions? Are these illusions still apparent with three-dimensional representations? What tricks depend on these illusions? How are these illusions used in advertising, dress designing, and architecture?

Exhibit suggestions: Charts, models, ads, pictures of illusions.

References:

Bakst. *Mathematics, Its Magic and Mastery.* Pp. 469–478.

Beeler and Branley. *Experiments in Optical Illusions.*

Schaaf. *Recreational Mathematics.* Pp. 46–47.

Paper Folding

How can all the constructions of euclidean geometry be done by folding paper? What assumptions are made when paper folding is used to construct geometric figures? What polygons and polyhedrons can be formed by folding paper? What is a hexaflexagon? How can conic sections be formed by folding paper? What puzzles and tricks are based on paper folding?

Exhibit suggestions: Models, geometric constructions, polyhedrons, conic sections, puzzles formed by paper folding.

References:

Cundy and Rollett. *Mathematical Modes.*

Johnson. *Paper Folding for the Mathematics Class.*

Row, Sandara. *Geometrical Exercises in Paper Folding.*

Wenninger. *Polyhedron Models.*

Paradoxes and Fallacies

What fallacies result when an expression is divided by zero? What fallacies occur from incorrect constructions in geometry? What fallacies can be explained by limits? What fallacies depend on false probabilities?

Exhibit suggestions: Charts and illustrations of famous paradoxes. Experiments with coins or dice to illustrate false probabilities.

References:

Bakst. *Mathematics, Its Magic and Mastery.*

Dunn. *Mathematical Bafflers.*

Friend. *Numbers, Fun and Facts.* Pp. 69–96.

Kasner and Newman. *Mathematics and the Imagination.* Chapter 6.

Kendall and Thomas. *Mathematical Puzzles for the Connoisseur.*

Kline. *Mathematics and Western Culture.* Chapter 20.

Meyer. *Fun with Mathematics.* Pp. 155–161.

Northrop. *Riddles in Mathematics.*

Pi, i, e

What are several ways of obtaining the value of pi—measurement, limit of series, empirical probability, polygon perimeter? What are applications of *i?* What are the sources of the constant *e?* What formula expresses the relationship of π, *i*, and *e.* What series are used in obtaining values for π and *e?*

Exhibit suggestions: Experiments for the determination of π. Graphical representation of *i*. Development of the formula connecting π, *i, e.* Applications of π, *i, e.*

References:

Bakst, Aaron. "Mathematical Recreations" (*Mathematics Teacher.* October 1952).

Bakst. *Mathematical Puzzles and Pastimes.* Pp. 110–116.

Baravalle, H. Von. "The Number π" (*Mathematics Teacher.* February 1953).

Kasner and Newman. *Mathematics and the Imagination.* Chapter 3.

Meyer. *Fun with Mathematics.* Pp. 82–98.

Ogilvy. *Through the Mathescope.* Chapter 10.

Contemporary Mathematics

Numeration Systems

What were the numeration systems of ancient man? Where did our number symbols come from? What are the different ways of building a numeration system, for example, using words, letters, repetition of symbols, or place value? What are different ways of representing numbers, such as tally marks, rope knots, or standard notations. What are different number bases that have been used? Why are different bases used and what are the advantages of each base? What puzzles or tricks can be performed with different number bases? Can you invent a new numeration system with new symbols? Can you build a computing device for a number base other than our decimal system?

Exhibit suggestions: Charts or number symbols, numeration systems, and computations in each system. Computing devices for various number bases, such as abacus, Napier's bones, electric binary abacus, binary computer. Pamphlets and books on numeration systems.

References:

Bakst. *Mathematics, Its Magic and Mastery.*

Friend. *Numbers, Fun and Fact.*

Hogben. *Wonderful World of Mathematics.*

Johnson and Glenn. *Exploring Mathematics on Your Own.*

Kramer. *The Mainstream of Mathematics.*

Newman. *The World of Mathematics.* Volume I, Part 3.

Reid. *From Zero to Infinity.*

Mathematics, What Is It?

Mathematics is a science, a language, a system of logic. The fields of mathematics are many and are constantly increasing. Mathematics is not an old, dead subject; rather it is very much alive, with new discoveries and new inventions occuring constantly.

References:

Courant and Robbins. *What Is Mathematics?*

Johnson and Glenn. *Invitation to Mathematics.*

Kasner and Newman. *Mathematics and the Imagination.* Pp. 357–362.

Kline. *Mathematics and Western Culture.* Chapters 1–3.

Newman. *World of Mathematics.* Volume III, Parts 11 and 12.

Rappaport and Wright. *Mathematics.*

Stein. *Mathematics, the Man Made Universe.*

Topology

Why is topology called rubber-sheet geometry? How can a strip of paper or a bottle have only one surface? What is the famous Königsberg bridge problem? What is the four-color problem in mapping? How has topology used networks to build a mathematical structure? What are some new applications of topology? What are some stunts, tricks, and puzzles based on topology?

Exhibit Suggestions: Königsberg bridge problem, four-color mapping problem, puzzles, Möbius strips. Klein bottle, network analysis, proofs.

References:

Barr. *Experiments in Topology.*

Courant and Robbins. *What Is Mathematics?* Pp. 235–271.

Fadiman. *Fantasia Mathematica.*

Gamow. *One, Two, Three, Infinity.* Chapter III.

Gardner. *Mathematical Puzzles and Diversion.*

Johnson and Glenn. *Topology the Rubber Sheet Geometry.*

Jones. *Elementary Concepts of Mathematics.* Chapter 9.

Kasner and Newman. *Mathematics and the Imagination.* Pp. 265–298.

Newman. *World of Mathematics.* Volume 1, pp. 573–599.

Sets and the Logic of Algebra

How are sets used in logic, electric networks, and probability? What is the union and intersection of sets? What are the commutative, associative, distributive laws for sets?

Exhibit Suggestions: Analysis of statements with Venn diagrams. Electric circuits representing the relationships of sets.

References:

Allendoerfer and Oakley. *Principles of Mathematics.* Chapter 5.

Bailey. *Sets and Logic.*

Johnson and Glenn. *Sets, Sentences and Operations.*

Kemeny, Snell, Thompson. *Finite Mathematics.* Chapters 2 and 3.

Montague and Montgomery. *The Significance of Mathematics.*

Swain, R. L., and E. D. Nichols. *Understanding Arithmetic* (New York: Holt, Rinehart and Winston, Inc.), 1957. Chapter 2.

The Pythagorean Theorem

What are some unusual proofs of the Pythagorean theorem? What are some of the unusual relationships that exist between Pythagorean numbers? What models can be made to visualize and prove the relationship? How can this relationship be used in indirect measurement?

Exhibit Suggestions: Models using cardboard, marbles, BB shot, plastic to show the Pythagorean relationship. Designs in tile, cloth, wallpaper, which are based on this relationship. Charts of unusual proofs. Historical sidelights. Mock-ups of applications in indirect measurement.

References:

Berger. "A Model for Visualizing the Pythagorean Theorem" (*Mathematics Teacher*. April 1953).

Glenn and Johnson. *The Pythagorean Theorem.*

Hart. "Pythagorean Numbers" (*Mathematics Teacher*. January 1955).

Schaaf. "The Theorem of Pythagoras" (*Mathematics Teacher*. December 1951).

Valens. *The Number of Things.*

Statistics

How can statistics be summarized? What are the measures of central tendency? What are measures of variation? How is the relationship between sets of measures determined? What is a normal curve? What is quality control? How is the accuracy of a sample measured? How are statistics used to draw conclusions?

Exhibit Suggestions: Sample distributions of original data, with analysis and graphs. Examples of statistics found in advertisements and newspapers. Examples of misuses of statistics. Models of random sampling devices and Gauss probability board.

References:

Adler. *Probability and Statistics for Everyman.*

Allendoerfer and Oakley. *Principles of Mathematics.* Chapter 13.

Huff. *How to Lie with Statistics.*

Huff. *How to Take a Chance.*

Johnson and Glenn. *The World of Statistics.*

Kline. *Mathematics and Western Culture.* Chapter 12.

Mosteller, F., and others. *Probability and Statistics* (Reading, Mass.: Addison-Wesley Publishing Company, Inc.) 1961.

Newman. *World of Mathematics.* Volume III, Part 8.

Wallis and Roberts. *The Nature of Statistics* (New York: The Macmillan Company, 1962).

Probability and Chance

What is probability? What is the risk involved in driving a car? What are the chances you will die this year? What are the odds of winning a lottery? What is the mathematical expectancy in a carnival game? Why doesn't gambling pay? How is the law of disorder related to nuclear fission? How is probability used to derive new facts?

Exhibit Suggestions: Illustrate with toys or models the probability of accidents, crop damage from storms, winning bridge hands, slot machine odds, coin tosses, dice totals, contest winnings, lock combinations, multiple births.

References:

Adler. *Probability and Statistics for Everyman.*

Fehr, Bunt, and Grossman. *An Introduction to Sets, Probability and Hypothesis Testing* (Boston: D. C. Heath & Company, 1964).

Huff. *How to Take a Chance.*

Kemeny, Snell, Thompson. *Finite Mathematics.* Chapter 4.

Kline. *Mathematics and Western Culture.* Chapter 23.

Newman. *The World of Mathematics.* Volume II, Part 7.

Schaaf. "Probability, Gambling, and Game Strategy" (*Mathematics Teacher.* April 1954).

Fourth Dimension and Relativity

What is the fourth dimension? How is the fourth dimension related to time? How is the speed of light related to relativity? Could you live a thousand years if you travelled at the speed of light? What formulas are used in relativity? How can you use mathematics to represent any dimension—fourth, fifth, or n-th?

Exhibit Suggestions: Illustrate the meanings of the fourth dimension with tesseracts or superprisms. Models to illustrate the relativity of motion.

References:

Abbott. *Flatland.*

Bakst. *Mathematics, Its Magic and Mastery.* Chapters 22–23.

Gamow. *One, Two, Three, Infinity.* Chapter 4.

Kasner and Newman. *Mathematics and the Imagination.* Chapter 4.

Kline. *Mathematics and Western Culture.* Chapter 27.

Kramer. *Mainstream of Mathematics.* Chapter 12.

Lieber and Lieber. *The Education of T. C. Mits.* Pp. 187–211.

Newman. *The World of Mathematics.* Volume II, pp. 1107–1145.

Zippin. *Uses of Infinity.*

Game Theory

What kind of games are the basis for game theory? What definitions, assumptions, axioms are used in game theory? How can game theory be applied to recreational games? How is game theory related to linear programming for electronic computers?

Exhibit Suggestions: Charts outlining basic principles of game theory. Simple analysis of two by two games and matrix games. Simple models or circuits for programming games.

References:

Barson. *What Is Linear Programming?*

Bristol. *An Introduction to Linear Programming.*

Newman. *World of Mathematics.* Pp. 1285–1293.

Richardson. *Fundamentals of Mathematics.* Pp. 390–401.

Venttsel. *An Introduction to the Theory of Games.*

Williams, John D. *The Compleat Strategyst* (New York: McGraw-Hill Book Company, Inc., 1954).

Groups and Fields

What are groups and fields? How do groups and fields illustrate a mathematical structure? How are theorems and problems solved involving groups or fields? Examples and theorems.

References:

Allendoerfer and Oakley. *Principles of Mathematics*. Chapters 3 and 4.

Richardson. *Fundamentals of Mathematics*. Chapter 17.

Sawyer. *Prelude to Mathematics*. Chapter 7.

Stabler. *Introduction to Mathematical Thought* (Reading, Mass.: Addison-Wesley Publishing Company, Inc.) 1953. Chapters 4, 8, and 9.

Finite Geometry

What kind of figures do you get when the number of points and lines in space is restricted? What relationships or theorems can be found to be true? What kind of constructions are possible?

References:

Lieber and Lieber. *The Education of T. C. Mits.*

Norton. *Finite Mathematical Systems.*

Sawyer. *Prelude to Mathematics*. Chapter 13.

Stabler. *An Introduction to Mathematical Thought*. Chapter 7.

Yarnelle. *Finite Mathematical Structure.*

Infinity

What is infinity? Is one infinity more than another? Can you compute with infinite quantities?

Exhibit Suggestions: Illustrations and comparison of infinite amounts. Paradoxes of the infinite.

References:

Gamow. *One, Two, Three, Infinity*. Chapter 1.

Gardner. *Relativity for the Layman.*

Kasner and Newman. *Mathematics and the Imagination*. Chapter 7.

Kline. *Mathematics and Western Culture*. Chapter 25.

Lieber, Lillian R. *Infinity* (New York: Holt, Rinehart and Winston, Inc., 1953).

Newman. *World of Mathematics*. Volume 3, Part X.

Northrop. *Riddles in Mathematics*. Chapter 7.

Peter. *Playing with Infinity.*

Schaaf. "Science, Mathematics and Religion" (*Mathematics Teacher*. January 1954).

Thomas. *Limits.*

Zippin. *Uses of Infinity.*

Logarithms

What are logarithms? How were they discovered? How are the tables of logarithms computed? What is most useful about logarithms? How are logarithms used to build a slide rule?

Exhibit Suggestions: How to compute with logarithms. Graphs of exponential equations on logarithmic graph paper. Slide rule made from logarithmic graph paper. Problems solved with logarithms.

References:

Bakst. *Mathematics, Its Magic and Mastery*. Chapter 18.

Hogben. *Mathematics for the Millions*. Chapter 10.

Kokomoor. *Mathematics in Human Affairs*. Chapter 10.

Meyer. *Fun with Mathematics*. Pp. 90–98.

Ransom, William R. "Elementary Calculation of Logarithms" (*Mathematics Teacher.* February 1954).

Shuster, Carl N. "The Calculation of Logarithms in High School" (*Mathematics Teacher.* May 1955).

Logic

What are the laws of logic? What symbols are used in logical analysis? What are truth tables? What is syllogism? What are different methods of proof? What are Venn diagrams? What is Boolean algebra? How are electric circuits related to the analysis of statements? How do logic machines work?

Exhibit Suggestions: Logic machine which analyzes syllogisms. Unusual problems, puzzles, or proofs using logic. Truth analysis of a statement. Electric circuits which give truth table analyses.

References:

Adler. *Logic for Beginners.*

Allendoerfer and Oakley. *Principles of Mathematics.* Chapter 1.

Gardner. *Logic Machines.*

Jones. *Elementary Concepts of Mathematics.* Chapter 1.

Kemeny, Snell, Thompson. *Introduction to Finite Mathematics.* Chapter 1.

Kline. *Mathematics and Western Culture.*

Lieber. *Mits, Wits, and Logic.* Chapters 17–24.

Newman. *World of Mathematics.* Volume III, Part 13.

Pfeiffer, John. "Symbolic Logic" (*Scientific American.* December 1950).

Richardson. *Fundamentals of Mathematics.* Chapters 2 and 17.

Stabler. *Introduction to Mathematical Thought.* Chapters 1–4.

Non-euclidean Geometry

What is the basis for non-euclidean geometry? What is a pseudosphere? How do the geometries of Lobachevsky and Riemann differ? What are the proofs of some non-euclidean theorems?

Exhibit Suggestions: Models of sphere and pseudosphere, with geometric figures drawn on the surfaces. Charts comparing theorems in different geometries.

References:

Kasner and Newman. *Mathematics and the Imagination.* Pp. 135–153.

Kline. *Mathematics and Western Culture.* Chapter 26.

Lieber and Lieber. *The Education of T. C. Mits.* Pp. 138–153.

Lieber and Lieber. *Mits, Wits, and Logic.*

Lieber and Lieber. *Non-euclidean Geometry.*

Newman. *The World of Mathematics.* Volume 3.

Richardson. *Fundamentals of Mathematics.* Chapter 16.

Sawyer. *Prelude to Mathematics.* Chapter 6.

Wolfe, H. E. *Introduction to Non-euclidean Geometry* (New York: Holt, Rinehart and Winston, Inc., 1945).

Encyclopedia Titles:
  1. Nicholas Lobachevsky
  2. Johann Bolyai
  3. George Riemann
  4. Non-euclidean geometry

Number Theory

What is a number? What definition, axioms, and propositions are used to build a mathematical structure about numbers? What are different kinds of numbers, such as complex numbers? What is a modulus number system?

Exhibit Suggestions: Number tree. Proofs of theorems. Device to show how to obtain the value of irrational numbers. Computing device in a modulus system.

References:

Allendoerfer and Oakley. *Principles of Mathematics.* Chapter 2.

Courant and Robbins. *What Is Mathematics?* Chapters 1 and 2.

Dantzig. *Numbers, The Language of Science.*

Jones. *Elementary Concepts of Mathematics.*

Ogilvy. *Through the Mathescope.* Chapter 2.

Richardson. *Fundamentals of Mathematics.* Chapters 3, 4, and 15.

Permutations and Combinations

How can you compute the number of ways in which objects can be arranged? How can you find out the number of different ways dice may fall or coins turn up heads and tails? How many different hands of bridge can be dealt? How many different committees can be formed from a certain number of boys and girls? How many different four letter code words can be made from the letters of your name? How many different basketball teams can be formed from ten players?

Exhibit Suggestions: Contrast permutations and combinations with letters, digits, or models. Show the analysis of a variety of conditions where permutations or combinations are involved with charts and objects. Show how permutations are used by detectives, politicians, statisticians, engineers, scientists.

References:

Bakst. *Mathematics, Its Magic and Mastery.* Chapter 21.

Johnson. *Probability and Chance.*

Jones. *Elementary Concepts of Mathematics.* Chapter 6.

Mott-Smith. *Mathematical Puzzles for Beginners.* Chapter 10.

Perspective, Projective Geometry, and Transformations

How are three-dimensional objects represented on two dimensions? What are different ways of projecting lines or surfaces on a plane?

Exhibit Suggestions: Models of perspective. Analysis of pictures showing perspective.

References:

Courant and Robbins. *What Is Mathematics?* Chapter 4.

Ivins, William M. *Art and Geometry* (New York: Dover Publications, Inc., 1964).

Kline. *Mathematics and Western Culture.* Chapters 10 and 11.

Kline. "Projective Geometry" (*Scientific American.* January 1955).

Yaglom. *Geometric Transformations.*

Progressions

What is an infinite series? How can we find the sum of an infinite series? What are Fibonacci numbers? What are some applications of progressions in nature, industry, science?

Exhibit Suggestions: Illustrate progressions with models, such as a super ball bouncing in a plastic tube, pyramid box display, branches on a plant, an ancestral tree, a ball rolling down an incline. Unusual problems, such as doubling wages or compound interest.

References:

Bakst. *Mathematics, Its Magic and Mastery*. Chapter 17.

Kokomoor. *Mathematics and Human Affairs*. Chapter 12.

Kramer. *Mainstream of Mathematics*. Chapter 9.

Valens. *The Number of Things*.

Nomographs

How are nomographs made? What kind of problems can be solved with nomographs? How are nomographs related to computing devices?

Exhibit Suggestions: Examples of a variety of nomographs including the simple one for the addition of directed numbers. Charts showing how nomographs are constructed and used.

References:

Adams. "The Preparation and Use of Nomographic Charts in High School Mathematics" (*Multi-Sensory Aids for Teachers of Mathematics.* Pp. 164–81).

Meyer. *Fun with Mathematics*.

Meyer. *More Fun with Mathematics*.

Vectors and Matrices

What are vectors? How do we compute with vectors? How are vectors related to the solution of equations?

Exhibit Suggestions: Charts and devices to demonstrate applications and solutions.

References:

Kemeny, Snell, Thompson. *Finite Mathematics*. Chapter 5.

Mathews. *Matrices I and II*.

Norton. *Basic Concept of Vectors*.

Sawyer. *Prelude to Mathematics*. Chapter 8.

Schuster, Seymour. *Elementary Vector Geometry* (New York: John Wiley & Sons, Inc., 1962).

Applications of Mathematics

Space Travel and Ballistics

What is the trajectory of a bullet? How is the orbit of a satellite determined? How can man navigate in space where directions are no longer east-north-south-west? What formulas, equations, fields of mathematics are used in planning space travel?

Exhibit Suggestions: Models, pictures, charts of space missiles, with analysis of the trajectories or orbits. Formulas, graphs, computations involved in space travel. Automatic pilots in space. Problems of gravitation, pressure, friction, radio communication.

References:

Ahrendt, Myrl H. *The Mathematics of Space* (New York: Holt, Rinehart and Winston, Inc., 1960).

Bakst. *Mathematics, Its Magic and Mastery.* Chapter 36.

Hooke and Shaffer. *Math and Aftermath.*

Kline. *Mathematics, A Cultural Approach.*

Newman. *World of Mathematics.* Volume I, Part 4.

Art and Mathematics

Perspective, symmetry, balance are all mathematical ideas connected with painting. Reflections, rotations, constructions, similarity, and proportionality are also involved in painting.

References:

Kline. *Mathematics, A Cultural Approach.*

Kline. *Mathematics and Western Culture.* Chapters 9 and 11.

Newman. *World of Mathematics.* "Mathematics of Aesthetics," pp. 2182–2197; "Mathematics as an Art," pp. 2012–2023.

Schaaf. *Our Mathematical Heritage.* Pp. 3–54.

Valens. *The Number of Things.*

Weyl. *Symmetry* (Princeton, N.J.: Princeton University Press, 1952).

Ethics, Philosophy, Religion, and Mathematics

The logic of mathematics has frequently been the basis for philosophical thought.

References:

Kline. *Mathematics and Western Culture.*

Lieber and Lieber. *Human Values and Science, Art and Mathematics.*

Newman. *World of Mathematics.* "A Mathematical Approach to Ethics," pp. 2198–2290; "Mathematics and Metaphysicians," pp. 1576–1590; "Meaning of Numbers," pp. 2312–2347; "The Locus of Mathematical Reality: An Anthropological Footnote," pp. 2348–2365.

Schaaf. "Science, Mathematics, and Religion" (*Mathematics Teacher.* January 1954).

Literature with Mathematical Overtones

Mathematics is frequently the basis for essays, fiction, poems, and plays. The proof of guilt in a trial may follow a logical pattern. The intrigue of a mystery may be analyzed like a mathematical problem. The etherial aspect of mathematics may lend beauty to a poem.

References:

Fadiman. *Fantasia Mathematica.*

Gardner, Martin, ed. *The Annotated Alice* (New York: Clarkson N. Potter, Inc. Publisher, 1960).

Newman. *World of Mathematics.* "Cycloid Pudding," pp. 2214–2220; "Young Archimedes," pp. 2221–2249; "Geometry in the South Pacific," pp. 2250–2260; "Inflexible Logic," pp. 2261–2267; "The Law," pp. 2268–2273; "Mathematics for Golfers," pp. 2456–2459; "Common Sense and the Universe," pp. 2460–2470.

O'Brian. "Detective Story" (*Mathematics Teacher.* March 1954).

Plotz. *Imagination's Other Place.*

Music and Mathematics

Even Pythagoras set up ratios for a musical scale. Someone has said music is rhythmic counting. Music's symbolism and pleasing qualities have many other relationships to mathematics. A composer must learn the mathematics of music.

References:

Kline. *Mathematics and Western Culture*. Chapter 19.

Newman. *World of Mathematics*. "Mathematics of Music," pp. 2274–2311.

Ridout. "Sebastian and the 'Wolf' " (*Mathematics Teacher*. February 1955).

Science and Mathematics

Astronomers and physicists have always been dependent on mathematics for leadership in discoveries. A dramatic illustration of this is Einstein's mathematical discovery in 1905 of the formula for releasing energy by nuclear fission. Forty years later, August 1945, the terrible atomic bomb over Hiroshima announced the application of this formula. The discovery of Pluto, after its existence was proclaimed by mathematics, is another illustration of the use of mathematics in prediction. More recently, the law of disorder and the tools of statistics have aided research in many fields of science.

References:

Gamow. *One, Two, Three, Infinity*.

Hooke and Shafer. *Math and Aftermath*.

Kline. *Mathematics, A Cultural Approach*.

Kline. *Mathematics and Western Culture*. Chapters 13 and 14.

Kline. *Mathematics and the Physical World*.

Newman. *World of Mathematics*. Volume I, pp. 546–569; Volume II, Part 5.

Schaaf. *Our Mathematical Heritage*. Pp. 173–204.

Warfare and Mathematics

Mathematics has played an important role in modern warfare. Unfortunately, it is likely to play a greater role in future conflicts, if there are to be such. Radar, Loran, navigation, space missiles are a few recent applications of mathematics.

References:

Bakst. *Mathematics, Its Magic and Mastery*. Chapter 36.

Newman. *World of Mathematics*. "Mathematics in Warfare," pp. 2136–2157; "How to Hunt a Submarine," pp. 2158–2181; "Mathematics of War and Foreign Politics," pp. 1238–1253; "Statistics of Deadly Quarrels," pp. 1254–1263.

Map Projections and Cartography

What are ways of locating points on a plane, a sphere, in space? How can a spherical surface be projected to a plane surface? How can the distortions due to projection be reduced?

Exhibit Suggestions: Spherical projection device to project maps on plastic cylinder, cone, plane. Map samples. Analysis of projections and distortions.

References:

Chamberline and Riddiford. *The Round Earth on Flat Paper*.

Greenhood. *Down to Earth: Mapping for Everybody*.

Schaaf. "Map Projections and Cartography" (*Mathematics Teacher*. October 1953).

The Role of Mathematics in Western Civilization

What are significant events in the development of mathematics? Who are some of the famous persons contributing to mathematical knowledge? What are some of the amusing anecdotes from the lives of famous mathematicians? How has mathematics been involved in science, politics, military campaigns, architecture, transportation, philosophy, art, music, literature?

References:

Bell. *Men of Mathematics.*
Bergamine. *Mathematics.*
Hogben. *Wonderful World of Mathematics.*
Kline. *Mathematics and Western Culture.*
Kramer. *Mainstream of Mathematics.*
Newman. *World of Mathematics.* Volume I.
Ogilvy. *Tomorrow's Math.*
Turnball. *The Great Mathematicians.*

Suggested Bulletin Board Displays

What's My Name? Biographies of mathematicians for identification.
Curves for Swinging in Space. Spiral, cardioid, ellipsis, cyclical parabola, catenary.
The Magicians' Geometry. Topology.
What's the Trick about Magic Squares?
How to Confuse Your Friends. Paradoxes.
Why Take Chances? Probability.
There's a Formula in Your Future.
How Far from Here to There? Map projections.
Measuring Distances in Space. Indirect measurement.
How to Lose a Square. Fallacy, such as $64 = 65$.
Number Shapes. Triangular, square, and pentagonal numbers.
How Smart Are You? Puzzles.
Mathematics Predicts. Predictions of weather, eclipse, location of Pluto.
Mathematical Art. Curves, symmetrics, op art.
These Things Never End. Infinities, sequences.
Where Is the Fallacy? Proof that every triangle is isosceles.
One Way To Solve Problems. Flow charts and computer programs.
This Series Is Golden. Fibonacci Series.
Mysteries in Mathematics. Unsolved problems.
Say It with Formulas. Applications of mathematics in science.
Mathemagic. Tricks with numbers.
What's New in Mathematics? Linear programming.
The House that Math Built. A finite mathematical system.
Math Made Easy. Shortcuts.
Where Did the Bees Learn Mathematics? The mathematics of the honeycomb.

appendix b:
teaching aids

Commercial Projectuals for the Overhead Projector

The following companies have ready-made projectuals. Write to them for catalogs and complete information.

Admaster Prints, Inc., 425 Park Avenue, New York, N.Y. 10016.

Charles Beseler Co., East Orange, New Jersey.

Robert J. Brady Company, 3227 M St. NW, Washington, D.C. 20007.

John Colburn Associates, Inc., 1122 Central Avenue, Wilmette, Illinois 60091.

Creative Visuals, Inc., Box 310, Big Spring, Texas 79721.

DCA Educational Products, Inc., 4865 Stenton Avenue, Philadelphia, Pennsylvania 19144.

Encyclopedia Britannica Films, 1150 Wilmette Avenue, Wilmette, Illinois 60091.

John W. Gunther, Inc., P.O. Box G, San Mateo, California 94402.

C. S. Hammond and Company, 515 Valley Street, Maplewood, New Jersey 07040.

Hubbard Scientific Company, 2855 Shermer Road, Northbrook, Illinois 60062.

Instructo Products Company, 1635 North 55th Street, Philadelphia, Pennsylvania 19131.

Keuffel and Esser Company, 300 Adams Street, Hoboken, New Jersey 07030.

McGraw-Hill Book Company, Inc., 330 West 42 Street, New York, N.Y. 10036.

Minnesota Mining and Manufacturing Company, Visual Products, Box 3100, St. Paul, Minnesota 55101.

RCA Educational Services, Camden, New Jersey 08102.

Tecnifax Corporation, 195 Appleton Street, Holyoke, Massachusetts 01042.

Tweèdy Transparencies, 321 Central Avenue, Newark, New Jersey 07103.

United Transparencies, Inc., Box 888, Binghamton, New York 13902.

Visual Materials, Inc., 980 O'Brien Drive, Menlo Park, California 94025.

Companies Advertising Models and Equipment for Mathematics

Arithmetic Principles Association, 5848 NE 42 Ave., Portland, Oregon.

Arkay International, Inc., 2372 Linden Blvd., Brooklyn, N.Y.

Associated School Distributors, Inc., 220 West Madison St., Chicago, Ill.

Isay Balinkin, University of Cincinnati, Cincinnati, Ohio.

Berger Scientific, 37 Williams St., Boston, Mass.

Berkeley Enterprises, Inc., 815 Washington St., Newtonville, Mass.

Stanley Bowman, 12 Cleveland St., Valhalla, N.Y.

Milton Bradley Company, 74 Park St., Springfield, Mass.

Caddy-Imler Creations, 2517 W. 102 St., Inglewood, Calif.

Cambosco Scientific Company, 37 Antwerp St., Brighton Station, Boston, Mass.

Central Scientific Company, 1700 Irving Park Road, Chicago, Ill.

Charvos-Roos Corp., 50 Colfax Ave., Clifton, N.J.

Circline Ruler Company, 4609 Waveland Court, Des Moines, Iowa.

Corbett Blackboard Stencils, 548 Third Ave., North Pelham, N.Y.

C-Thru Ruler Company, 827 Windsor St., Hartford, Conn.

Cuisinaire Company of America, Inc., 12 Church Street, New Rochelle, N.Y.

Daintee Toys, Inc., 230 Steuben St., Brooklyn, N.Y.

Dana and Company, Inc., Box 201, Barrington, Rhode Island.

Denny Press, 1115 45th St., Des Moines, Iowa.

Denoyer-Geppert Company, 5235 Ravenswood Ave., Chicago, Ill.

Eugene Dietzgen Company, 2425 Sheffield Ave., Chicago, Ill.

Dinva Slide Rules, 688 South Remington Road, Columbus, Ohio.

Dyna-Slide Company, 600 South Michigan Ave., Chicago, Ill.

Educational Playthings, 1706 Hayes Ave., Sandusky, Ohio.

Educational Supply and Specialty Company, 2823 Gaye Ave., Huntington Park, Calif.

Engineering Instruments, Inc., P.O. Box 335, Peru, Ind.

Exton Aids, Box MT, Milbrook, N.Y.

Farquaher Transparent Globes, 3724 Irving St., Philadelphia, Pa.

Hans K. Freyer, Inc., Westwood, Mass.

Gamco Products, Box 305, Big Spring, Texas.

Ginn and Company, Statler Bldg., Boston, Mass.

Gould Scientific Company, Box 6743, Washington, D.C.

Graphicraft, Westport, Conn.

F. H. Hagnar, 1010 Navarro St., P.O. Box 361, San Antonio, Texas.

J. L. Hammett Company, Kendall Square, Cambridge, Mass.

Herbach and Rademan, Inc., 1204 Arch St., Philadelphia, Pa.

Houghton Mifflin Co., 2 Park St., Boston, Mass.

P. E. Huffman, Hutsonville, Ill.

Ideal School Supply, 8312 Birkhoff Ave., Chicago, Ill.

Industrial Research Laboratories, P.O. Box 471, Hempstead, N.Y.

Instructo Products Company, 1635 North 55th St., Philadelphia, Pa.

Jacronda Mfg. Company, 5449 Hunter St., Philadelphia, Pa.

Jameson Electronics Mfg. Co., 2233 University Ave., St. Paul, Minn.

Kendrey Company, P.O. Box 629, San Mateo, Calif. 94401.

Kenworthy Educational Service, 138 Allen St., Buffalo, N.Y.

Keuffel and Esser Company, 127 Fulton St., New York, N.Y.

Lano Company, 4741 W. Liberty St., Ann Arbor, Mich.

LaPine Scientific Company, 6001 South Knox Ave., Chicago, Ill.

The Learning Center, Inc., 53 Bank St., Princeton, N.J.

Lufkin Rule Company, 1730 Hess St., Saginaw, Mich.

Helberg Enterprises, Inc., 8327 North Lawndale Ave., Skokie, Ill.

Mathaids Company, 336 Kirk Ave., Syracuse, N.Y.

Mathatronics, Inc., 257 Crescent St., Waltham, Mass.

Math-Masters Labs, Inc., Box 310, Big Spring, Texas.

Math-U-Matic, Inc., 607 W. Sheridan, Oklahoma City, Okla.

Models of Industry, 2100 Fifth St., Berkeley, Calif.

John Morse and Sons, 142 W. Lake Road, Penn Yan, N.Y.

Nasco Science Materials, Fort Atkinson, Wisc.

National School Supply & Equipment, 27 East Monroe St., Chicago, Ill.

A. J. Nystrom and Company, 3333 Elston Ave., Chicago, Ill.

Owatonna Math Aids, Box 79, Owatonna, Minn.

F. A. Owen Publishing Co., Dansville, N.Y.

Palfreys School Supply Co., 7715 East Garvey Blvd., South San Gabriel, Calif.

Physics Research Laboratories, Inc., Box 555, Hempstead, N.Y.

Playball, Inc., 5–26 46th Ave., Long Island City, N.Y.

Playschool Mfg. Company, 1750 North Lawndale Ave., Chicago, Ill.

Frederick Post Company, 3650 North Avondale Ave., Chicago, Ill.

School Products Company, 330 E. 23 St., New York, N.Y.

School Service Company, 4233 Crenshaw Blvd., Los Angeles, Calif.

Science Research Associates, 259 E. Erie St., Chicago, Ill.

Scientific Development Corp., Watertown, Mass.

Scientific Educational Products, 30 E. 42 St., New York, N.Y.

Sifo Toy Company, 353 Rosabel, St. Paul, Minn.

Smith Brake Corporation, 1206 S. La Brea Ave., Inglewood, Calif.

Pickett and Eckell, Inc., 1109 S. Fremont Ave., Alhambra, Calif.

Speed-Up Geometry Ruler Co., Inc., 5100 Windsor Mill Road, Baltimore, Md.

L. S. Starrett Company, Athol, Mass.

The Stech Company, P.O. Box 16, Austin, Texas.

Howard Sutton Company, Inc., 17 Warren St., New York, N.Y.

Three M Company, 2501 Hudson Road, St. Paul, Minn.

Viking Importers, 113 South Edgemont St., Los Angeles, Calif.

Vis-X-Company, Box 107, Los Angeles, Calif.

Wabash Instruments and Specialties, Box 194, Wabash, Ind.

Walker Products, 1530 Campus Drive, Berkeley, Calif.

Weem System of Navigation, Annapolis, Md.

W. M. Welch Scientific Co., 1515 Sedgewick St., Chicago, Ill.

Whitman Publishing Co., 1220 Mound Ave., Racine, Wisc.

John C. Winston Company, 1010 Arch St., Philadelphia, Pa.

L. M. Wright Company, 686 Mariposa St., Altadena, Calif.

Yoder Instruments, East Palestine, Ohio.

Computer Kits or Trainers

All prices are approximate.

Analog Computer ($30.00). General Electric Company, Radio Receiver Dept. Utica, New York.

Arkay CT-650 Computer Trainer ($250). Arkay International, 2372 Linden Blvd., Brooklyn, New York 11208.

Bi-Tran Six ($6,000). Fabri-Tek, Minneapolis, Minnesota.

Binary Computer ($30). Welch Scientific Company, Chicago, Illinois.

Brainiac ($20). NASCO Science Material, Fort Atkinson, Wisconsin. Also, Math-Master Labs, Big Spring, Texas; and, Berkeley Enterprises, 36 W. 11 St. New York, New York.

Calculo: Analog Computer Kit ($15). Edmund Scientific Co. Barrington, New Jersey. NASCO Science Materials, Fort Atkinson, Wisconsin.

Compact Electronic Logic Demonstration ($40). Lano Company, Ann Arbor, Michigan.

Digi-Comp ($5). E. S. R. Inc. 350 Main Street, Orange, New Jersey.

Digiac 3010 ($800). Digital Electronics, Westbury, New York.

Minivac ($235). Scientific Educational Products Corp. New York, New York.

Computer Companies

Clary Corporation, 408 Juniper Street, San Gabriel, Calif.

Computer Control Company, Old Connecticut Path, Framingham, Mass.

Control Data Corporation, 8100 South 34th Ave., Minneapolis, Minn.

Digital Equipment Corporation, 146 Main Street, Maynard, Mass.

Frieden Inc., 2350 Washington Avenue, San Leandro, Calif.

General Electric Company, 13430 Black Canyon Highway, Phoenix, Ariz.

IBM, Data Processing Division, 112 East Post Road, White Plains, New York.

Honeywell, Minneapolis, Minnesota.

Mathatronics Inc., 257 Crescent St., Waltham, Mass.

National Cash Register, Main and K Street, Dayton, Ohio.

Radio Corporation of America (RCA), Electronic Data Processing, Cherry Hill, Camden, New Jersey.

UNIVAC Division, Sperry Rand Corporation, 1200 Avenue of the Americas, New York, New York.

Toys, Games, and Puzzles for Learning Mathematics

"Chinese Rings—Ancient Devils Needles." Cooperative Service, Inc., Delaware, Ohio.

"Craze." Progressive Enterprises, Inc., Indianapolis, Ind.

"Design Cubes." Creative Playthings, Herndon, Pa.

"Erector Set." A. C. Gilbert Company, New Haven, Conn.

"Fiddlestraws." Samuel Gabriel Sons and Company, New Haven, Conn.

"Fifteen Puzzle." William F. Drueke and Sons, Grand Rapids, Mich.

"Flexagons." Science Materials Center, New York, New York.

"Geodestix." Ge-O-Des-Stix, Spokane, Wash.

"Kaleidoscope." Creative Playthings, Herndon, Pa.

"Magic Designer." Northern Signal Company, Milwaukee, Wisc.

"Make-It-Toy." W. R. Benjamin, Granite City, Ill.

"Mek-N-Ettes." Judy Toy Company, Minneapolis, Minn.

"Pythagoras." Kohner Brothers, New York, New York.

"Rosie's Pyramid Puzzle." William F. Drueke and Sons, Grand Rapids, Mich.

"T-Puzzle." William F. Drueke and Sons, Grand Rapids, Mich.

"Teez." K. T. Games, Inc., Seaford, New York.

"Tinker-Toy." A. G. Spaulding and Sons, Evanston, Ill.

"Soma Wood Block Puzzle." Edmund Scientific Co., Barrington, N.J.

Commercial Games for Secondary Mathematics

"Equations" and "Wiff 'N Proof." Laymen E. Allen, Yale Law School, New Haven, Conn.

"Kalah." Kalah Game Co., 27 Maple Ave., Holbrook, Mass.

"Krypto." Krypto Corporation, 2 Pine St., San Francisco, Calif.

"Matrix, The Strategy Game." King Enterprises, New City, Rockland County, New York.

"Make One." Garrard Press, 510 North Hickory St., Champlain, Ill.

"Radix." James W. Lang, Box 224, Mound, Minn.

"Quinto." Minnesota Mining and Manufacturing Co., St. Paul, Minn.

Other Companies Producing Games

Are-Jay Game Co., Cleveland, Ohio.

Cadaco-Ellis, Inc. Merchandise Mart, Chicago, Ill.

Champion Publishing Co., 612 North Second St., St. Louis, Missouri.

Educational Cards, Detroit, Mich.

Exclusive Playing Card Company, Chicago, Ill.

Fortune Games, 1517 Levee St., Dallas, Texas.

Funway Games, Pellsoon, Mich.

Gangler-Gentry Company, Cantonsville, Maryland.

Hall and McCready Company, Chicago, Ill.

Imout, Box 1944, Cleveland, Ohio.

Kraeg Games, 4500 Shenandoah Ave., St. Louis, Mo.

Parker Brothers, Inc., Salem, Mass.

Schaper Manufacturing Co., Inc., Minneapolis, Minn.

School Service Company, 4510 West Pico Blvd., Los Angeles, Calif.

Science Research Associates, Chicago, Ill.

John C. Winston Company, 1010 Arch Street, Philadelphia, Pa.

appendix c:
publications

Mathematics Books for the Library

Titles marked with an asterick are recommended for junior high school students.

*Abbott, E. A. *Flatland*. New York: Dover Publications, Inc., 1932.

Adler, I. *Elementary Mathematics of the Atom*. New York: John Day Co., 1965.

*———. *The Giant Golden Book of Mathematics*. Wayne, N.J.: Golden Press Inc., 1960.

*———. *Logic for Beginners*. New York: John Day Co., 1964.

Adler, I. *A New Look at Geometrics*. New York: John Day Co., 1966.

———. *Probability and Statistics for Everyman*. New York: John Day Co., 1963.

———. *Thinking Machines*. New York: John Day Co., 1961.

Bakst, A. *Mathematical Puzzles and Pastimes*. Princeton, N.J.: D. Van Nostrand Company, Inc., 1954.

*———. *Mathematics: Its Magic and Mastery*. Princeton, N.J.: D. Van Nostrand Company, Inc., 1952.

*Barr, S. *Experiments in Topology*. New York: Thomas Y. Crowell Co., 1964.

Bell, E. T. *The Last Problem*. New York: Simon and Schuster, Inc., 1961.

———. *Men of Mathematics*. New York: Simon and Schuster, Inc., 1937.

*Bendick, J. *How Much and How Many*. New York: McGraw-Hill Book Company, Inc., 1947.

*——— J., and M. Levin. *Mathematics Illustrated Dictionary*. New York: McGraw-Hill Book Company, Inc., 1965.

*Bergamine, D. *Mathematics*. New York: Time, Inc., 1963.

Boehm, G. A. *The New World of Math*. New York: Dial Press, Inc., 1959.

*Bowers, H., and J. E. *Arithmetical Excursions*. New York: Dover Publications, Inc., 1961.

Brinton, H. *Measuring the Universe*. New York: Roy Publishers, 1962.

*Burger, D. *Sphereland*. New York: Thomas Y. Crowell Co., 1965.

Courant, R., and H. Robbins. *What Is Mathematics?* New York: Oxford University Press, Inc., 1941.

Court, N. A. *Mathematics in Fun and in Earnest*. New York: Dial Press, Inc., 1958.

*Degrazia, J. *Math Is Fun*. New York: Emerson Books, Inc., 1954.

*Diggins, J. *String, Straightedge, and Shadow*. New York: The Viking Press, Inc., 1965.

*Fadiman, C. *Fantasia Mathematica*. New York: Simon and Schuster, Inc., 1958.

Fadiman, C. *The Mathematical Magpie*. New York: Simon and Schuster, Inc., 1962.

*Friend, J. N. *More Numbers: Fun and Facts*. New York: Charles Scribner's Sons, 1961.

*————. *Numbers: Fun and Facts*. New York: Charles Scribner's Sons, 1954.

————. *Still More Numbers*. New York: Charles Scribner's Sons, 1964.

Gamow, G. *One, Two, Three, Infinity*. New York: The Viking Press, Inc., 1947.

Gardner, M. *Relativity for the Million*. New York: The Macmillan Company, 1962.

*Glenn, W. H., and D. A. Johnson. *Exploring Mathematics On Your Own*. New York: Doubleday & Company, Inc., 1961.

*————. *Invitation to Mathematics*. New York: Doubleday & Company, Inc., 1962.

Golomb, S. W. *Polyominoes*. New York: Charles Scribner's Sons, 1965.

Goodman, A. W. *The Pleasures of Math*. New York: The Macmillan Company, 1964.

Graham, L. A. *Ingenious Mathematical Problems and Methods*. New York: Dover Publications, Inc., 1959.

Greenblatt, M. H. *Mathematical Entertainments*. New York: Thomas Y. Crowell Co., 1965.

*Heath, R. V. *Mathemagic, Magic Puzzles, and Games With Numbers*. New York: Dover Publications, Inc., 1933.

Hogben, L. *Mathematics in the Making*. New York: Doubleday & Company, Inc., 1960.

*————. *Wonderful World of Mathematics*. New York: Random House, Inc., 1955.

Hooke, R., and D. Shaffer. *Math and Aftermath*. New York: Walker & Company, 1964.

*Huff, D. *How to Lie with Statistics*. New York: W. W. Norton & Co., Inc., 1934.

*————. *How To Take A Chance*. New York: W. W. Norton & Co., Inc., 1959.

Jacoby, O. *Mathematics for Pleasure*. New York: McGraw-Hill Book Company, Inc., 1962.

James, G., and R. C. James. *Mathematics Dictionary*. Princeton, N.J.: D. Van Nostrand Company, Inc., 1959.

Karush, W. *The Crescent Dictionary of Mathematics*. New York: The Macmillan Company, 1962.

*Kasner, E., and J. Newman. *Mathematics and the Imagination*. New York: Simon and Schuster, Inc., 1940.

Kline, M. *Mathematics: A Cultural Approach*. Reading, Mass.: Addison-Wesley Publishing Co., Inc., 1962.

————. *Mathematics and the Physical World*. New York: Thomas Y. Crowell Co., 1959.

————. *Mathematics in Western Culture*. New York: Oxford University Press, Inc., 1953.

Kraitchik, M. *Mathematical Recreations*. New York: Dover Publications, Inc., 1942.

Laffin, J. *Codes and Ciphers*. New York: Abelard-Schuman, Ltd., 1964.

Langman, H. *Play Mathematics*. New York: Hafner Publishing Co., 1962.

Lieber, L. *The Education of T. C. Mits*. New York: W. W. Norton & Co., Inc., 1954.

————., and G. Hugh. *Human Values and Science, Art and Mathematics*. New York: W. W. Norton & Co., Inc., 1961.

————. *Mits, Wits, and Logic*. New York: Institute Press, 1954.

*Madachy, J. S. *Mathematics on Vacation*. New York: Charles Scribner's Sons, 1966.

Marks, R. W. *The Growth of Mathematics*. New York: Bantam Books, 1964.

―――. *The New Mathematics Dictionary and Handbook*. New York: Bantam Books, 1964.

―――. *Space, Time and the New Mathematics*. New York: Bantam Books, 1964.

Maxwell, E. A. *Fallacies in Mathematics*. New York: Cambridge University Press, 1959.

Menninger, K. W. *Mathematics in Your World*. New York: The Viking Press, Inc., 1962.

*Meyer, J. S. *Fun with Mathematics*. New York: Dover Publications, Inc., 1952.

*―――. *More Fun with Mathematics*. Greenwich, Conn.: Fawcett Publications, Inc., 1963.

Muir, J. *Of Men and Numbers*. New York: Dodd, Mead & Company, Inc., 1961.

*Newman, J. R. *The World of Mathematics*. New York: Simon and Schuster, Inc., 1956.

*Northrup, E. *Riddles in Mathematics*. Princeton, N.J.: D. Van Nostrand Company, Inc., 1944.

*Ogilvy, C. S. *Through the Mathescope*. New York: Oxford University Press, Inc., 1956.

―――. *Tomorrow's Math*. New York: Oxford University Press, Inc., 1962.

Pedoe, D. *The Gentle Art of Mathematics*. New York: The Macmillan Company, 1958.

Peter, R. *Playing with Infinity*. New York: Simon and Schuster, Inc., 1962.

Plotz, H. *Imagination's Other Place*. New York: Thomas Y. Crowell Co., 1955.

Rappaport, S., and H. Wright. *Mathematics*. New York: New York University Press, 1964.

*Ravielli, A. *An Adventure in Geometry*. New York: The Viking Press, Inc., 1957.

Reid, C. *A Long Way from Euclid*. New York: Thomas Y. Crowell Co., 1963.

*―――. *From Zero to Infinity*. New York: Thomas Y. Crowell Co., 1955.

Rogers, J. *The Pantheon Story of Mathematics for Young People*. New York: Random House, Inc., 1966.

Sanford, V. *Short History of Mathematics*. Boston: Houghton Mifflin Company, 1940.

Schaaf, W. L., ed. *Our Mathematical Heritage*. New York: Collier Books, 1954.

Shaw, A., and K. Fuge. *The Story of Mathematics*. New York: St. Martin's Press, Inc., 1963.

*Shuster, C. N., and D. L. Bedford. *Field Work in Mathematics*. East Palestine, Ohio: Yoder Instruments Co., 1937.

*Simon, W. *Mathematical Magic*. New York: Charles Scribner's Sons, 1964.

Smeltzer, D. *Man and Number*. New York: Collier Books, 1962.

Smith, D. E. *History of Mathematics*, Vol. 1 and 2. New York: Dover Publications, Inc., 1925.

Smith, G. O. *Mathematics: The Language of Science*. New York: G. P. Putnam's Sons, 1961.

Struick, D. J. *A Concise History of Mathematics*. New York: Dover Publications, Inc., 1948.

Terry, L. *The Mathmen*. New York: McGraw-Hill Book Company, Inc., 1964.

Tocquet, R. *The Magic of Numbers*. Greenwich, Conn.: Fawcett Publications, Inc., 1957.

Trumbull, H. *The Great Mathematicians*. New York: New York University Press, 1961.

*Valens, E. G. *Number of Things: Pythagoras, Geometry and Humming Strings.* New York: E. P. Dutton & Co., 1964.

*Vergara, W. C. *Mathematics in Everyday Things.* New York: Harper & Row, Publishers, Inc., 1959.

Williams, J. D. *The Compleat Strategyst.* New York: McGraw-Hill Book Company, Inc., 1954.

Wolf, P. *Breakthroughs in Mathematics.* New York: Signet Books, 1963.

Zippin, L. *Uses of Infinity.* New York: Random House, Inc., 1962.

Mathematics Puzzle Books

Adler, I., and P. *The Adler Book of Puzzles and Riddles.* New York: John Day Co., 1962.

Ball, W. W. R. *Mathematical Recreations and Essays.* New York: The Macmillan Company, 1947.

Barnard, D. St. P. *50 Brain Twisters.* Princeton, N.J.: D. Van Nostrand Company, Inc., 1962.

Barr, S. *A Miscellany of Puzzles.* New York: Thomas Y. Crowell Co., 1965.

*Beiler, A. H. *Recreations in the Theory of Numbers.* New York: Dover Publications, Inc., 1964.

Carroll, L. *Pillow Problems and Tangled Tale.* New York: Dover Publications, Inc., 1958.

Domoryad, A. P. *Mathematical Games and Pastimes.* New York: The Macmillan Company, 1964.

*Dudney, C. *Amusements in Mathematics.* New York: Dover Publications, Inc., 1958.

————. *The Canterbury Puzzles.* New York: Dover Publications, Inc., 1958.

*Dunn, A. *Mathematical Bafflers.* New York: McGraw-Hill Book Company, Inc., 1964.

Filipiak, A. S. *Mathematical Puzzles, and Other Brain Twisters.* New York: A. S. Barnes & Co., 1964.

*Frolichstein, J. *Mathematical Fun, Games, and Puzzles.* New York: Dover Publications, Inc., 1962.

Gamow, G. and M. Stein. *Puzzle-Math.* New York: The Viking Press, Inc., 1958.

*Gardner, M. *Mathematical Puzzles.* New York: Thomas Y. Crowell Co., 1961.

————. *Mathematical Puzzles and Diversions.* New York: Simon and Schuster, Inc., 1959.

————. *Mathematical Puzzles of Sam Lloyd.* New York: Dover Publications, Inc., 1959.

*————. *Mathematics, Magic, and Mystery.* New York: Dover Publications, Inc., 1956.

*Heafford, P. *The Math Entertainer.* New York: Emerson Books, Inc., 1959.

*Hunter, J. A. H. *Figurets: More Fun with Figures.* New York: Oxford University Press, Inc., 1958.

*————. *Fun with Figures.* New York: Oxford University Press, Inc., 1956.

————. *Math Brain Teasers.* New York: Bantam Books, 1965.

*————., and J. S. Madacky. *Mathematical Diversions.* Princeton, N.J.: D. Van Nostrand Company, Inc., 1963.

Jacoby, O., and W. H. Benson. *Mathematics for Pleasure.* Greenwich, Conn.: Fawcett Publications, Inc., 1965.

Kaufman, G. L. *The Book of Modern Puzzles.* New York: Dover Publications, Inc., 1940.

*Kendall, P. M. H., and G. M. Thomas. *Mathematical Puzzles for the Connoisseur.* New York: Thomas Y. Crowell Co., 1964.

Kraitchik, M. *Mathematical Recreations.* New York: Dover Publications, Inc., 1953.

Lindgren, H. *Geometric Dissections.* Princeton, N.J.: D. Van Nostrand Company, Inc., 1964.

Longley-Cook, L. H. *Work This One Out.* Greenwich, Conn.: Fawcett Publications, Inc., 1960.

Merrill, A. A. *Mathematical Excursions.* New York: Dover Publications, Inc., 1933.

*Mott-Smith, C. *Mathematical Puzzles for Beginners and Enthusiasts.* New York: Dover Publications, Inc., 1954.

O'Beirne, T. H. *Puzzles and Paradoxes.* New York: Oxford University Press, 1965.

Phillips, H. *My Best Puzzles in Logic and Reasoning.* New York: Dover Publications, Inc., 1961.

————. *My Best Puzzles in Mathematics.* New York: Dover Publications, Inc., 1961.

Reichmann, W. J. *The Fascination of Numbers.* New York: Oxford University Press, Inc., 1963.

Reinfeld, D., and D. Rice. *101 Mathematical Puzzles and How To Solve Them.* New York: Sterling Publishing Co., Inc., 1960.

*Scripture, N. E. *50 Mathematical Puzzles and Oddities.* Princeton, N.J.: D. Van Nostrand Company, Inc., 1963.

Steinhaus, H. *One Hundred Problems in Elementary Mathematics.* New York: Basic Books, Inc., 1964.

Tielze, Heinrich. Famous Problems of Mathematics. Baltimore: Graylock Press, 1965.

Wylie, C. R. *101 Puzzles in Thought and Logic.* New York: Dover Publications, Inc., 1957.

Selected Professional Books for Mathematics Teachers

Association of Assistant Masters in Secondary Schools. *The Teaching of Mathematics.* New York: Cambridge University Press, 1957.

Association of Teachers of Mathematics. *Some Lessons in Mathematics.* New York: Cambridge University Press, 1964.

Brown, C. H. *The Teaching of Secondary Mathematics.* New York: Harper & Row, Publishers, Inc., 1953.

Bruner, J. S. *The Process of Education.* Cambridge, Mass.: Harvard University Press, 1960.

Brueckner, L. J., F. E. Grossnickle, and J. Reckzah. *Developing Mathematical Understandings in the Upper Grades.* New York: Holt, Rinehart and Winston, Inc., 1957.

Butler, C., and F. Wren. *The Teaching of Secondary Mathematics.* McGraw-Hill Book Company, Inc., 1965.

Cundy, H. M., and A. P. Rollett. *Mathematical Models.* New York: Oxford University Press, Inc., 1961.

Davis, D. R. *The Teaching of Mathematics.* Reading, Mass.: Addison-Wesley Publishing Company, Inc., 1951.

Dienes, Z. P. *Building Up Mathematics.* New York: Humanities Press, Inc., 1960.

Dubisch, R. *The Teaching of Mathematics.* New York: John Wiley & Sons, Inc., 1963.

Hadamard, J. *The Psychology of Invention in the Mathematical Field.* New York: Dover Publications, Inc., 1954.

Hedges, W. D. *Testing and Evaluation for the Sciences.* Belmont, Calif.: Wadsworth Publishing Co., Inc., 1966.

Johnson, Donovan, and Robert Rahtz. *The New Mathematics in Our Schools.* New York: The Macmillan Company, 1966.

Kenna, L. A. *Understanding Mathematics with Visual Aids.* Paterson, N.J.: Littlefield, Adams & Co., 1962.

Kinney, L. B., and C. R. Purdy. *Teaching Mathematics in the Secondary School.* New York: Holt, Rinehart and Winston, Inc., 1952.

Kinsella, J. J. *Secondary School Mathematics.* New York: Center for Applied Research in Education, 1965.

Land, F. W. *New Approaches to Mathematics Teaching.* The Macmillan Company, 1963.

Lovell, K. *The Growth of Basic Mathematical and Scientific Concepts in Children.* New York: Philosophical Library, Inc., 1961.

Organization for Economic Cooperation and Development. *Mathematics Today.* Washington, D.C., 1964.

Organization for Economic Cooperation and Development. *New Thinking in School Mathematics.* Washington, D.C., 1961.

Pemberton, J. E. *How to Find Out in Mathematics.* New York: The Macmillan Company, 1963.

Piaget, J. *Child's Conception of Number.* New York: W. W. Norton & Co., Inc., 1965.

Polya, G. *Mathematical Discovery,* Volumes I and II. New York: John Wiley & Sons, Inc., 1962.

Progressive Educational Association. *Mathematics in General Education.* New York: Appleton-Century-Crofts, Inc., 1941.

Reeve, W. D. *Mathematics for the Secondary School.* New York: Holt, Rinehart and Winston, Inc., 1954.

Sawyer, W. W., *Vision in Elementary Mathematics.* Baltimore: Penguin Books, Inc., 1964.

Westcott, Alvin M., and James A. Smith. *Creative Teaching of Mathematics in the Elementary School.* Boston: Allyn and Bacon, 1967.

Willoughby, S. S. *Contemporary Teaching of Secondary School Mathematics.* New York: John Wiley & Sons, Inc., 1967.

Selected Mathematics Texts for Mathematics Teachers

Adler, I. *The New Mathematics.* New York: John Day Co., 1958.

Allendoerfer, C. B., and C. O. Oakley. *Principles of Mathematics.* New York: McGraw-Hill Book Company, Inc., 1955.

Boehm, G. A. W. *The New World of Math.* New York: Dial Press, Inc., 1959.

Eves, H., and C. V. Newsom. *An Introduction to the Foundations and Fundamental Concepts of Mathematics.* New York: Holt, Rinehart and Winston, Inc., 1965.

Exner, R. M., and M. S. Rosskopf. *Logic in Elementary Mathematics.* New York: McGraw-Hill Book Company, Inc., 1959.

Harmon, F. L., and D. E. Dupree. *Fundamental Concepts of Mathematics.* Englewood Cliffs, N.J.: Prentice-Hall, Inc., 1964.

Jones, B. W. *Elementary Concepts of Mathematics.* New York: The Macmillan Company, 1963.

Kelley, J. L. *Introduction to Modern Algebra.* Princeton, N.J.: D. Van Nostrand Co., Inc., 1960.

Kemeny, J. G., J. L. Snell, and G. L. Thompson. *Introduction to Finite Mathematics.* Englewood Cliffs, N.J.: Prentice-Hall, Inc., 1957.

Kline, M. *Mathematics: A Cultural Approach.* Reading, Mass.: Addison-Wesley Publishing Company, Inc., 1962.

Kline, M. *Mathematics in Western Culture*. New York: Oxford University Press, Inc., 1953.

Meserve, B., and M. Sobel. *Mathematics for Secondary School Teachers*. Englewood Cliffs, N.J.: Prentice-Hall, Inc., 1962.

Moise, E. *Elementary Geometry from an Advanced Standpoint*. Reading, Mass.: Addison-Wesley Publishing Company, Inc., 1963.

Montague, H. F., and M. D. Montgomery. *The Significance of Mathematics*. Columbus, Ohio: Charles E. Merrill Books, Inc., 1961.

Reid, C. *Introduction to Higher Mathematics*. New York: William Morrow and Co., Inc., 1962.

Richardson, M. *Fundamentals of Mathematics*. New York: The Macmillan Company, 1958.

Stein, S. K. *Mathematics: The Man-Made Universe*. San Francisco: W. H. Freeman and Co., 1963.

Some Famous Mathematics Books

A'h-mosé, *Rhind Papyrus* (1700 B.C.).

Euclid, *Elements of Geometry* (300 B.C.).

Diophantus, *Arithmetica* (250).

al-Khwarizmi, *Kitab al jabr w'al-muqabala* (825).

Fibonacci, Leonardo (Leonardo of Pisa), *Liber Abaci* (1228).

Descartes, René, *La Géométrie* (1637).

Newton, Isaac, *The Mathematical Principles of Natural Philosophy* (1687).

Whitehead, A. N., and Bertrand Russell, *Principia Mathematica* (1910).

Hilbert, David, and Ernest Bernays, *Foundations of Mathematics* (1934).

John von Neumann, *Theory of Games* (1944).

Yearbooks: National Council of Teachers of Mathematics

1926—*A General Survey of Progress in the Last Twenty-Five Years.*
1927—*Curriculum Problems in Teaching Mathematics.*
1928—*Selected Topics in the Teaching of Mathematics.*
1929—*Significant Changes and Trends in the Teaching of Mathematics Throughout the World since 1910.*
1930—*The Teaching of Geometry.*
1931—*Mathematics in Modern Life.*
1932—*The Teaching of Algebra.*
1933—*Teaching of Mathematics.*
1934—*Functional Thinking.*
1935—*Teaching of Arithmetic.*
1936—*Mathematics in Modern Education.*
1937—*Approximate Computation.*
1938—*The Nature of Proof.*
1939—*Training of Mathematics Teachers.*
1940—*The Place of Mathematics in Secondary Education.*
1941—*Arithmetic in General Education.*
1942—*A Source Book of Mathematical Applications.*
1945—*Multi-Sensory Aids in the Teaching of Mathematics.*
1947—*Surveying Instruments: History and Classroom Use.*
1948—*The Metric System of Weights and Measures.*

1953—Learning of Mathematics: Its Theory and Practice.
1954—Emerging Practices in Mathematics Education.
1957—Insights into Modern Mathematics.
1959—The Growth of Mathematical Ideas, Grades K-12.
1960—Instruction in Arithmetic.
1961—Evaluation in Mathematics.
1962—Enrichment Mathematics for the Grades.
1963—Enrichment Mathematics for High School.
1964—Topics in Mathematics for Elementary School Teachers.
Note: Out-of-date yearbooks (1926–1948) are available from Ams Press, Inc., 56 E. 13 St., New York, New York 10003.

Principal Publishers of Mathematics Textbooks

Addison-Wesley Publishing Co., Inc., 524 South St., Reading, Mass. 01867.
Allyn & Bacon, Inc., 150 Tremont St., Boston, Mass. 02111.
American Book Co., 55 Fifth Ave., New York, New York 10003.
Appleton-Century-Crofts, 440 Park Ave. S., New York, New York 10016.
Barnes & Noble, Inc., 105 Fifth Ave., New York, New York 10003.
Blaisdell Publishing Co., 275 Wyman St., Waltham, Mass. 02154.
The Bobbs-Merrill Co., Inc., 4300 W. 62 St., Indianapolis, Ind. 46206.
Bruce Publishing Co., 400 N. Broadway, Milwaukee, Wis. 53201.
Cambridge University Press, 32 E. 57 St., New York, New York 10003.
Chelsea Publishing Co., 50 E. Fordham Rd., Bronx, New York 10468.
Thomas Y. Crowell Co., 201 Park Ave. S., New York, New York 10003.
The John Day Co., Inc., 62 W. 45 St., New York, New York 10036.
Doubleday & Company, Inc., 277 Park Ave., New York, New York 10017.
Dover Publications, Inc., 180 Varick St., New York, New York 10014.
Emerson Books, Inc., 251 W. 19 St., New York, New York 10011.
Encyclopedia Britannica Press, 425 N. Michigan Ave., Chicago, Ill. 60611.
W. H. Freeman & Co., Publishers, 660 Market St., San Francisco, Calif. 94104.
Ginn and Company, Statler Building, Boston, Mass. 02117.
Harcourt, Brace & World, Inc., 757 Third Ave., New York, New York 10017.
Harper & Row, Publishers, Inc., Elhi Division, 2500 Crawford Ave., Evanston, Ill. 60201.
D. C. Heath & Co., 285 Columbus Ave., Boston, Mass. 02116.
Holt, Rinehart and Winston, Inc., 383 Madison Ave., New York, New York 10017.
Houghton Mifflin Co., 2 Park St., Boston, Mass. 02107.
Laidlaw Brothers, Inc., Thatcher and Madison Sts., River Forest, Ill. 60305.
The Macmillan Company, 833 Third Ave., New York, New York 10022.
Charles E. Merrill Books, Inc., 1300 Alum Creek Drive, Columbus, Ohio 43216.
McCormack-Mathers Publishing Co., Inc., Box 2212, Wichita, Kansas 67201.
McGraw-Hill Book Co., 330 W. 42 St., New York, New York 10036.
Oxford University Press, 417 Fifth Ave., New York, New York 10016.
Pergamon Press, Inc., 122 E. 55 St., New York, New York 10022.
Prentice-Hall, Inc., Educational Books Division, Englewood Cliffs, New Jersey 01632.
Random House, Inc., 457 Madison Ave., New York, New York 10022.
Science Research Assoc., Inc., 259 E. Erie St., Chicago, Ill. 60611.
Scott, Foresman & Company, 1900 E. Lake Ave., Glenview, Ill. 60025.

Charles Scribner's Sons, 597 Fifth Ave., New York, New York 10017.

Silver Burdett Company, Park Avenue and Columbia Road, Morristown, New Jersey 07960.

The L. W. Singer Co., Inc., 249–59 West Erie Blvd., Syracuse, New York 13202.

D. Van Nostrand Co., Inc., 120 Alexander St., Princeton, New Jersey 08540.

Wadsworth Publishing Company, Inc., Belmont, Calif. 94002.

John Wiley & Sons, Inc., 605 Third Ave., New York, New York 10016.

Professional Periodicals and Pamphlets

Professional Journals

International Study Group for Mathematics Learning Bulletin. Professor Z. P. Dienes, University of Sherbrooke, Sherbrooke, Quebec, Canada.

Mathematical Gazette. The Mathematical Association, 22 Bloomsbury Square, London W.C. 1, England.

The Mathematics Teacher. National Council of Teachers of Mathematics, 1201 N.W. 16 Street, Washington, D.C. 20036.

The Arithmetic Teacher. National Council of Teachers of Mathematics, 1201 N.W. 16 Street, Washington, D.C. 20036.

School Science and Mathematics. Central Association of Science and Mathematics Teachers, P.O. Box 108, Bluffton, Ohio 45817.

Scientific American. 415 Madison Avenue, New York, New York 10017.

The American Mathematical Monthly. Mathematical Association of America, University of Buffalo, Buffalo, New York.

Mathematics Teaching. Association of Teachers of Mathematics, Vine Street Chambers, Nelson, Lancashire, England.

Mathematics Magazine. Mathematical Association of America, University of Buffalo, New York.

Scripta Mathematics. Yeshiva University, Amsterdam Avenue and W. 186 Street, New York, New York 10033.

Teaching Arithmetic. Pergamon Press, 44–01 21 Street, Long Island City, New York 11101.

Mathematics Student Journals

The Mathematics Student Journal. National Council of Teachers of Mathematics, 1201 N.W. 16 Street, Washington, D.C. 20036.

Mathematical Pie. 100 Burman Road, Shirley, Solihull, Warwick, England.

Newsletters

Science Education News. American Association for the Advancement of Science, 1515 Massachusetts Ave. NW, Washington, D.C. 20005.

School Mathematics Study Group Newsletter. School Mathematics Study Group, Cedar Hall, Stanford University, Stanford, California 94305.

Minnemath Center Report. University of Minnesota, Minneapolis, Minnesota 55455.

UICSM Newsletter. University of Illinois, Urbana, Illinois 61801.

Pamphlets

Pamphlets published by the National Council of Teachers of Mathematics, 1201 16 St. NW, Washington, D.C., 20036. All prices are approximate.

Administrative Responsibility for Improving Mathematics Programs ($.50).

Aids for Evaluators of Mathematics Textbooks ($.40).

An Analysis of New Mathematics Programs ($.50).

Careers in Mathematics ($.25).

Computer Oriented Mathematics ($1.50).

Continued Fractions ($.65).

Designing the Mathematics Classroom ($1.00).

Education in Mathematics for the Slow Learner ($.75).

Elementary and Junior High School Mathematics Library ($.35).

Five Little Stories ($.50).

Guide to Teaching Aids for Mathematics ($.75).

High School Mathematics Library ($.60).

How to Study Mathematics ($.50).

How to Use Field Trips ($.35).

How to Use Films and Filmstrips ($.50).

How to Use the Overhead Projector ($.50).

How to Use Your Bulletin Board ($.50).

How to Use Your Library ($.40).

Mathematical Challenges ($.80).

Mathematics Clubs ($.75).

Mathematics for the Academically Talented ($.60).

Mathematics Teaching as a Career (Free).

Mathematics Tests Available in the U.S. ($.50).

Numbers and Numerals ($.35).

Number Stories of Long Ago ($1.00).

The Number Story ($.85).

Paper Folding for the Mathematics Classroom ($.60).

Polyhedron Models for the Classroom ($.60).

Portrait of 2 ($.75).

Program Provisions for the Gifted ($.75).

Recreational Mathematics ($1.20).

Reviews of Films ($.40).

Revolution in School Mathematics ($.50).

The Secondary Mathematics Curriculum ($.50).

Secret Codes ($.60).

Some Ideas About Number Theory ($.60).

The Supervisor of Mathematics ($.15).

Twelfth-Grade Pre-College Mathematics Program ($.50).

Vectors in Three Dimensional Geometry ($.60).

Pamphlets available from The Department of Health, Education, and Welfare, U.S. Office of Education, Instructional Resources Branch, Washington, D.C. 20202. All prices are approximate.

Modern Mathematics and Your Child (OE—29047, $.20).

Elementary School Mathematics, New Directions (OE—29042, $.50).

Emerging Twelfth Grade Mathematics Programs (OE—29042, $.50).

In-Service Education of High School Mathematics Teachers (OE—29022, $.50).

The Leadership Role of State Supervisors of Mathematics (OE—29032, $.35).

Learning about Learning (OE—12019).

Pamphlets available from J. Weston Walch, Box 1075, Portland, Maine. Send to publisher for prices.

Walch, J. Weston, and Christobel M. Codell. *Colorful Teaching of Mathematics.*
Johnson, Donovan A. *Games for Learning Mathematics.*
Bruyer, Donald. *Geometric Models and Demonstrations.*
Turney, Billy L. *Geometry Teaching Aids You Can Make.*
Cordell, C. M. *Dramatizing Mathematics.*
Ransom, W. R., and E. A. Kelley. *Mathematics in Life.*
O'Brien, Katherine, *Successful Devices in Teaching Geometry.*
Brandes, L. G. *Math Can Be Fun.*
Brandes, L. G. *The Math Wizard.*
Ransom, W. R. *Algebra Can Be Fun.*

Enrichment Pamphlets and Monographs

"New Mathematics Library." Random House, Inc., 457 Madison Avenue, New York, New York 10022, or, The L. W. Singer Co., 249–259 W. Erie Blvd., Syracuse, N.Y. 13202.

Numbers: Rational and Irrational.
What Is Calculus About?
Introduction to Inequalities.
Geometric Inequalities.
The Contest Problem Book.
The Lore of Large Numbers.
Uses of Infinity.
Geometric Transformations.
Continued Fractions.
Graphs and their Uses.
Hungarian Problem Book I.
Hungarian Problem Book II.
Episodes from the Early History of Mathematics.
Groups and their Graphs.
Mathematics of Choice.
From Pythagoras to Einstein.

"Exploring Mathematics on Your Own." McGraw-Hill Publishing Co., Webster Division, 1154 Reco Avenue, St. Louis, Missouri 63126.

Sets.
Pythagorean Theorem.
Topology.
Numeration Systems.
Fun with Mathematics.
Number Patterns.
Invitation to Mathematics.
World of Statistics.
Shortcuts in Computing.
Computing Devices.
World of Measurement.

Adventures in Graphing.
Finite Math Systems.
Logic and Reasoning.
Basic Concepts of Vectors.
Probability and Chance.
Geometric Constructions.
Curves in Space.

"Thinking With Mathematics Series." D. C. Heath Co., 285 Columbus Ave., Boston, Mass. 02116.

Mathematics Projects Handbook.
The Concept of a Function.
Graphing Relations and Functions.
An Introduction to Linear Programming.
The Natural Numbers.
The Integers.
The Rational Numbers.
The Real Numbers.
The Complex Numbers.
Finite Mathematical Structures.
An Introduction to Transfinite Mathematics.
Congruence and Motion in Geometry.
An Introduction to Sets and the Structure of Algebra.

"Topics in Modern Mathematics." Ginn & Co., Back Bay P.O. 191, Boston, Mass. 02117.

Limits and Limit Concepts.
Random Numbers—Mathematical Induction—Geometric Numbers.
Digital Computers and Related Mathematics.
The Nature of the Regular Polyhedra—Infinity and Beyond—Introduction to Groups.
Pythagorean Numbers—Congruences, A Finite Arithmetic—Geometry in the Number.
An Introduction to Sets and the Structure of Algebra.
Introduction to Logic and Sets.
Principles and Patterns of Numeration Systems.

"Popular Lectures in Mathematics Series." Blaisdell Publishing Co., 275 Wyman St., Waltham, Mass. 02154.

The Method of Mathematical Induction.
Fibonacci Numbers.
Some Applications of Mechanics to Mathematics.
Geometrical Constructions Using Compasses Only.
The Ruler in Geometrical Constructions.
Inequalities.

"Topics In Mathematics" (translations from the Russian). D. C. Heath & Co., 285 Columbus Ave., Boston, Mass. 02116.

Configuration Theorems.
What Is Linear Programming?
Equivalent and Equidecomposable Figures.

Mistakes in Geometric Proofs.
Proof in Geometry.
Induction in Geometry.
Computation of Areas of Oriented Figures.
Areas and Logarithms.
Summation of Infinitely Small Quantities.
Hyberbolic Functions.
How to Construct Graphs and Simplest Maxima and Minima Problems.
The Method of Mathematical Induction.
Algorithms and Automatic Computation Machines.
An Introduction to the Theory of Games.
The Fibonacci Numbers.
Convex Figures and Polyhedra.
Eight Lectures in Mathematical Analysis.
Geometric Constructions in the Plane.
Geometry of the Straightedge and Geometry of the Compass.
Infinite Sets.
Isoperimetry.
Multicolor Problems.
Probability and Information.
Problems in the Theory of Numbers.
Random Walks.

"S.M.S.G. Enrichment Series." A. C. Vroman, Inc., 367 South Pasadena Ave., Pasadena, California 91105.

The Structure of Algebra.
Prime Numbers and Perfect Numbers.
What Is Contemporary Mathematics?
Absolute Value.
Mathematical Theory of the Struggle for Life.
Functions
  Circular Functions.
  Complex Number Systems.
  System of Vectors.
  Non-Metric Geometry.
  Plane Coordinate Geometry.
  Inequalities.
  Numeration.
  Algebraic Structures.
  Factors and Primes.
  Mathematical Systems.
  Systems of First Degree Equations in Three Variables.
  Radioactive Decay.

"Programmed Junior High Enrichment Units." The Macmillan Company, 866 Third Ave., New York, N.Y. 10022.

Sets, Operations and Circuits.
Bases and Numerals.
What Are the Chances?
Modular Systems.
Clear Thinking.

Points, Lines, and Planes.
Points, Lines, and Space.
Number Sentences.
Factors and Primes.
From the Naturals to the Reals.

"Mathematics Enrichment Programs, A-E." George C. Spooner, *et al.* Harcourt, Brace & World, Inc., 757 Third Ave., New York, N.Y. 10017.

Pamphlets on Careers in Mathematics

Can I Be a Mathematician? Educational Relations Section, Public Relations Staff, General Motors, Inc., Detroit, Michigan, 48202. 1964. 14 pp.

Careers in Mathematics. The Institute for Research, 537 Dearborn Street, Chicago, Illinois, 60605. 1960. 24 pp.

Careers in Mathematics. National Council of Teachers of Mathematics, 1201 16 Street, NW, Washington, D.C. 20036. 1961. 32 pp.

Employment Outlook for Mathematicians, Statisticians and Actuaries. U.S. Government Printing Office, Washington, D.C. 20402. 1964. 12 pp.

Is Math in the Stars for You? Women's Bureau, U.S. Department of Labor, Washington, D.C. 20025. 1957. 6 pp.

Mathematics Teaching as a Career. National Council of Teachers of Mathematics, 1201 16 Street, NW, Washington, D.C. 20036. 1964. 8 pp.

Mathematics and Your Career. U.S. Department of Labor, Bureau of Labor Statistics, Washington, D.C. 20402. 1964. 8 pp.

Professional Opportunities in Mathematics. The Mathematical Association of America, University of Buffalo, New York 14214. 1964. 32 pp.

Should You Be a Mathematician? Career Information Service, New York Life Insurance Company, Box 51, Madison Square Station, New York, N.Y. 10010. 1958. 15 pp.

You Will Need Math. Mathematics Association of America, State University of New York, Buffalo, New York 14214. 1967.

Sources of Free or Inexpensive Materials

The following companies have provided pamphlets and charts for mathematics teachers. Write to them for information regarding materials that are currently available and for possible costs.

American Automobile Association, 1712 G St., NW, Washington, D.C. 20036. (*Minimum Stopping Distance; Facts for Math; Automobiles—Facts and Figures.*)

American Bankers Association, Banking Education Committee, 12 E. 36 St., New York, New York 10016. (*Banking from the Stone Age to the Atomic Age; Money and Banking for Everyday Living.*)

Association for Computing Machinery, 211 E. 43 St., New York, New York 10017. (Computopics.)

Bell Telephone Laboratories, 463 West St., New York, New York 10014. (*Mathematics Research in Industry.*)

Boy Scouts of America, National Council, New Brunswick, New Jersey. (*Mechanical Drawing; Surveying.*)

Chase Manhattan Bank Museum of Moneys of the World, 1254 Avenue of the Americas, New York, New York 10020. (*Moneys of the World.*)

Laura E. Christman, Yorkville, Ill. (Mathematics calendar.)

Chrysler Corporation, Public Relations Division, Community Affairs Dept., Box 1919, Detroit, Michigan 48231. (*Mathematics Problems from Industry.*)

The Conference Board, 460 Park Ave., New York, New York 10022. (*Road Maps of Industry.*)

Consolidated Edison Company of New York,'4 Irving Place, New York, New York 10003. (*Easy Arithmetic.*)

C.U.P.M. Central Office, Box 1024, Berkeley, California 94701. (*Basic Library List.*)

The Duodecimal Society of America, 20 Carlton Place, Staten Island, New York 10304. (*Excursion in Numbers.*)

Ford Motor Company, Education Affairs Department, Dearborn, Michigan. (*How Long Is a Rod?; On the Art of Problem Solving; A History of Measurement,* chart.)

General Electric Company, Educational Relations, Department MWH, Schenectady, New York. (*Why Study Math?; You and the Computer.*)

General Motors Corporation, Educational Relations Section, General Motors Technical Center, Warren, Michigan. (*Precision, a Measure of Progress, Mathematics at Work.*)

Hamilton Watch Company, Public Relations Department, Lancaster, Penn. (*Time Telling.*)

Household Finance Corporation, Money Management Institute, Prudential Plaza Chicago, Ill. (*Money Management Library.*)

International Business Machines, 590 Madison Avenue, New York, New York 10022.

Institute of Life Insurance, Educational Division, 488 Madison Ave., New York, New York 10022. (*Sets, Probability and Statistics; Mathematics in Action.*)

Internal Revenue Service, Public Information Division, Washington, D.C. (*Income Tax Teaching Kit.*)

Keuffel and Esser Company, 300 Adams St., Hoboken, N.J. 07030. (Slide Rule catalog).

Litton Industries, Inc., Beverly Hills, California. (*Problematical Recreations; Mostly Greeks.*)

Marchant Calculating Machine, Oakland, California. (*From Og to Googal.*)

Martin Publishing Company, Box 251, North Hollywood, California. (*Mathematics.*)

A. A. Merrill, 25 Commodore Road, Chappaqua, New York 10514. (*Perpetual Calendar.*)

Merrill, Lynch, Pierce, Fenner and Smith, 70 Pine St., New York, New York 10005. (*How to Buy Stocks.*)

Monroe Calculating Machine Co., 555 Mitchell St., Orange, N.J. 07050.

Mu Alpha Theta, Box 117, University of Oklahoma, Norman, Oklahoma 73069. (*Mathematical Book List; Chips from Mathematical Logs.*)

Museum of Science and Industry, Jackson Park, Chicago, Ill. (*You Will Like Geometry.*)

National Aerospace Education Council, 1025 Connecticut Ave. NW, Washington, D.C. 20036. (*You and Space.*)

National Better Business Bureau, Chrysler Building, New York, New York 10017. (*Accident and Health Insurance; Life Insurance.*)

National Education Association, 1201 16 St. NW, Washington, D.C. 20036. (Curriculum materials.)

New York Life Insurance Co., Box 51, Madison Square Station, New York, New York 10010. (*Should You Be a Mathematician?*)

New York State Petroleum Council, 220 Delaware Ave., Buffalo, New York 11202. (*Mathematics in the Petroleum Industry.*)

Manager, School and College Relations, New York Stock Exchange, 11 Wall St., New York, New York 10005. (*Understanding the New York Stock Exchange; You and the Investment World.*)

Ohaus Scale Cooperation, 1050 Commerce Ave., Union City, New Jersey 07083. (*Manual for Measurement Science.*)

Savings Bank Association of New York State, 110 E. 42 St., New York, New York 10017. (*Quick Credit Cost Computer.*)

Scripta Mathematics, Yeshiva University, Amsterdam Ave. and 186 St., New York, New York 10033. (*Portraits of Mathematicians.*)

Sperry Gyroscope Co., Great Neck, New York 11020. (*Gyroscope through the Ages.*)

L. S. Starett Co., Athol, Mass. 01331. (Decimal equivalent charts.)

United Aircraft Corporation, 400 Main St., East Hartford, Conn. 06103. (*Age of Flight.*)

U.S. Department of Agriculture, Forest Service, Washington D.C. (*Ranger 'Rithmetic.*)

Superintendent of Documents, Government Printing Office, Washington, D.C. 92502. (*Household Weights and Measures; Metric System of Measurement; Units and Systems of Weights and Measures; Selected List of U.S. Government Publications; Sources of Information on Educational Media.*)

U.S. Secret Service, Treasury Department, Washington, D.C. (*Know Your Money.*)

Yoder Instruments, East Palestine, Ohio 45352. (*Computation with Approximate Data.*)

Wesleyan University Press, Education Center, Columbus, Ohio. (*Mathematics Clubs; Mathematics through Pictures.*)

Wesleyan University, Department of School Services and Publications, 100 Middleview Ctr., Middletown, Conn. 06457. (*Bibliography of Mathematics for Secondary School Libraries.*)

Publishers of Mathematics Tests

Bureau of Educational Measurements, Kansas State Teachers College, Emporia, Kansas 66801.

Bureau of Educational Research and Service, State University of Iowa, Iowa City, Iowa 52240.

California Test Bureau, 5916 Hollywood Boulevard, Los Angeles, Calif. 90028.

C. A. Gregory Company, 345 Calhoun Street, Cincinnati, Ohio 45221.

Educational Test Bureau, 720 Washington Ave., S.E. Minneapolis, Minn. 55414.

Educational Testing Service, 20 Nassau Street, Princeton, New Jersey 08540.

Public School Publishing Company, 345 Calhoun Street, Cincinnati, Ohio 45221.

Science Research Associates, 57 West Grand Avenue, Chicago, Ill. 60610.

World Book Company, Yonkers-on-Hudson, New York; Beacon Street 6, Boston, Mass. 02108.

index